APPETITE
FOR RISK

APPETITE FOR RISK

JACK LEAVERS

The Book Guild Ltd

First published in Great Britain in 2019 by
The Book Guild Ltd
9 Priory Business Park
Wistow Road, Kibworth
Leicestershire, LE8 0RX
Freephone: 0800 999 2982
www.bookguild.co.uk
Email: info@bookguild.co.uk
Twitter: @bookguild

Typeset in 12pt Bembo Std

Printed on FSC accredited paper
Printed and bound in Great Britain by 4edge Limited

ISBN 978 1912881 505

British Library Cataloguing in Publication Data.
A catalogue record for this book is available from the British Library.

To my girls — the real stars of the show — and our black Lab, Layla, my trusty writing sidekick.

And to the friends who journeyed alongside me, and the strangers who became friends.

CHAPTER 1

BASRA, IRAQ – NOVEMBER 2004

'Alpha Victor Two-One-Alpha: static vehicle right, six hundred metres, over.'

'Two-One-Bravo: roger static vehicle right, out.'

I peered over the driver's shoulder and spotted the car ahead through the heat shimmer rising from the tarmac. It sat alone at the agreed location: parked on the verge along a stretch of empty desert road between two shallow berms.

Our Land Rover approached with caution and rolled to a halt ten metres short of a black BMW saloon; the vehicle description and plate number matched my notes. The Two-One-Bravo Land Rover stopped twenty metres behind us and three soldiers emerged to scan the car and surrounding area through the magnified sights on their SA80 rifles.

We'd left the sanctuary of the large military base at Basra Airport a few minutes earlier, nipping out just before an inbound armoured patrol would have delayed our exit. This spot was out of sight from the base, but still close enough to sense an invisible cloak of protection from the resident British forces. Apart from the black car there were no other signs of life, and only the rhythmic rattle of the Land Rovers' diesel engines disturbed the silence of the bleak desert landscape.

I waited until one of the BMW's rear doors opened and a familiar figure appeared. He held up his hand in greeting and shielded his eyes from the sun's glare.

'Okay, here goes,' I said through the headrests to the patrol commander up front, my long-time friend, Ian.

He turned to me with concern etched on his tanned face. 'We'll see you at Khor Az Zubayr this afternoon. Call me if you run into any issues. Be careful, John.'

'Any issues' might mean bad news for me, but Ian's army officer career would also be at risk if his unofficial support for my activities was revealed, especially if the revelation came courtesy of my being kidnapped, shot, or otherwise compromised in downtown Basra.

Judging by the banter over the last week, his men thought it likely I was a spook of some kind. Ian's last, familiar comment sparked interested glances in my direction.

'Roger that mate, thanks.'

I nodded to the other guys, clambered over the tailgate, and dropped onto the road. When I neared the car, my eyes roved across the rough ground for any sign of IEDs before I stepped off the tarmac.

Clear.

A bead of sweat trickled past my left eye before I caught it with my sleeve. Admittedly I was apprehensive about the impending meeting, but it must have been over eighty degrees in old money, despite being November.

Ian's young translator, Hassan, stood by the open door of the BMW wearing his usual smile. A slim, friendly graduate in his early twenties, he was dressed in polished shoes, black trousers, and a white shirt without a tie. Business casual – like me.

'Morning, Hassan. Are we all set?'

'All set, Mr John.'

'Good. Let's get this show on the road.'

After tossing a wave towards the two departing Land Rovers, I removed my sunglasses and slid into the BMW, taking a moment to adjust from the searing sunlight to the darker interior.

'Gentlemen. John Pierce, good to meet you.'

Hassan climbed in and shut the door. The central locking clicked and an unexpected silence engulfed the car, putting me on edge and causing the smile to drop from Hassan's face.

'Are you a spy for the Israelis?'

Where the hell did that come from?

The dust cloud kicked up by Ian's patrol grew smaller ahead as they raced off along the stark, black thread of road; my link with safety slipping away. Little sign of the invisible cloak of protection now. A shock of alarm pulsed deep inside.

Hassan on my right, a large stony-faced guy on my left. If this was an abduction, I needed to force my way out of the car, as fast as possible and as violently as necessary.

The fuse lit by the question burned.

Stolen glances round the car detected no obvious weapons, but impossible these guys were unarmed – no-one was in these parts. Not the friendliest-looking bunch I'd met either. I doubted they were unfamiliar with the sight of bloodshed or the use of violence. Useful if they were on my side, not so good if they weren't.

The Land Rovers dropped out of sight once they passed the sandy berm. I tried to hold on to a composure wanting to disappear with them and focused on the forty-something questioner glaring from the front passenger seat. With a dodgy suit, shiny black hair, thick moustache, surly expression, and personal hygiene enhanced by a strong cologne, he was rocking the same look as stony face on my left and what I had seen of the driver.

A former bootneck, or Royal Marines Commando, I'd been around a bit myself, although accusations of spying were a first. Time to roll the dice: stay put or make a run for it?

Images fast-forwarded through my head: orange boiler suit, sharp knives, unwanted TV stardom – switching to a violent struggle, haring down the main drag, locals asking, 'Why did the crazy Brit attack us?' – switching again to questions, answers: 'We're so sorry, Mr John, but we had to ask.' Hassan apologetic on their behalf.

The last option worked for me. 'Stay put' it was then. Best the old bootneck charm worked its magic.

With the silent tension needing to be punctured, I blurted out, 'No.'

Not much charm there, not much composure either.

It was a simple escort to a business meeting in Basra city; no different to the way I'd moved around the area for the last week. These guys should be on my side, my protection. Hassan needed to sort this shit out, but he sat motionless on my right, panic written all over his face. No help coming from that direction.

Then another question, this time from the big guy on my left, complete with a warm blast of smoker's breath.

'You spy for the Americans?'

Was he kidding me? They'd all watched British Army vehicles drop me off down the road from the British base and heard my cheery greeting in the Queen's English. And surely they knew Hassan was the translator for a British Army officer.

'No.' Another weak-sounding reply. I needed to get a grip to avoid this being taken to a level I didn't want to visit.

'So, you're a spy for the British?'

Okay, so they got there in the end. Mind you, hopelessly off target. A derisive snort before I answered, 'They wouldn't pay enough.' Not that I really knew.

At last Hassan snapped into action and quick-fire Arabic barked between him and the others. When they all started smiling and shaking hands, I assumed the mini-inquisition was over.

'Assalamu alaikum, Mr John. Welcome, welcome. Sorry.' Laughter and pointing between them and me.

Yeah, good one. I almost smashed my metal pen into your face you grinning idiot.

That was it: from looming disaster to best buddies in a heartbeat. A ripple of perspiration moistened my shirt despite the fierce air conditioning. Hassan nodded as his eyes flicked over to mine although his smile wasn't convincing. By the looks of it, he'd enjoyed the exchange about as much as I had, but at least he wasn't sadly shaking his head.

The manner of my arrival and our location might have encouraged suspicion, but I wasn't a spy for anyone and had never been involved with any intelligence services.

I could point to a fair amount of experience in investigations and surveillance over the years, just never for the government – ours or anyone else's. And I did sometimes mix in circles that included special forces types and spooks. Not in any form of operational capacity though. No, instead I was here scrabbling to find business opportunities to get me out of my latest financial mess.

However, as those three questions had been fired at me, I'd been painfully aware of the tracking device strapped down my right thigh; a body search would have livened up the encounter no end. It wasn't Japanese micro-technology, or a James Bond-style gadget designed by Q and disguised as a button. Instead, it was British military style: chunky, soldier-proof, and unproven.

An ex-bootneck friend and communications expert, Jim, had jumped at the opportunity to have his prototype tracking kit tested as I roamed southern Iraq. The data was his primary interest, but he promised to keep an eye on my progress as and when he could. The built-in panic alarm provided an unexpected feeling of added security, despite the limited monitoring. Fingers crossed he'd be standing by if things went to ratshit, so he could let people know I was in trouble and where, before it was too late.

★

The BMW traversed the pot-holed Basra roads smoothly as we made our way into the city; the driver far superior to the other locals whose driving I'd endured over the last few days. The experience of travelling in local vehicles was very different compared to being with Ian and his soldiers. My vulnerability if we ran into the wrong crowd made it nerve-racking at times. An air of near normality could switch to apprehension in an instant if a checkpoint or police patrol loomed up ahead, let alone if we encountered anything more suspicious.

The high-profile military vehicles faced an escalating threat of attack, but returning to the bosom of Brit Mil's support and firepower always put a smile on my face. Unfortunately needs must, so I had to hope my low profile in the BMW would be enough to keep me out of trouble.

The car slipped unnoticed through the traffic as we sped towards my meeting with the Basra Trade Chamber. The afternoon might prove useful in terms of business, but first and foremost it provided an opportunity to meet Sheikh Mustafa, the organisation's deputy president. I needed to hand-deliver an important private message to him in the form of a sealed white envelope addressed in handwritten Arabic – old-school confidential communications.

Entrusted to me by business contacts in Dubai, I'd made sure it stayed secure by carrying it close ever since. I wasn't privy to the message contents, but they regarded it as crucial to their future business operations in southern Iraq.

My new business associates had paid $5,000 for an assessment of the ports and logistics in the Basra area, plus $2,000 for expenses. But I'd been left in no doubt they considered successful delivery of the confidential message a vital element of the task. There was also an opportunity to earn another grand if I received a reply to courier back to them.

Setting up a meeting with the Sheikh hadn't proved easy. Despite my efforts over the last week, this chance had only slotted into place in the last twenty-four hours. I'd completed the assessment of the ports, so delivering the letter was the last item on my 'to do' list.

We pulled up outside a large, white, three-storey building. My new back-seat buddy clambered out and motioned to stay put with a small movement of his hand. Everyone else got out of the vehicle and made an exaggerated show of checking the surroundings for any threats to my safety.

Good to see these chaps were looking out for me, but not something I'd be relying on. If I hadn't been there, I imagine they would have rolled from the car into the building in a big gaggle, trading witty repartee in loud Arabic. From inside the vehicle I scanned a full 360 degrees for any signs of danger. Of the few people in the vicinity, none showed unhealthy interest in our arrival.

★

'Most of the Trade Chamber are the problem. They're the ones behind all the violence and I wouldn't trust any of them in the slightest.'

Last night the commanding officer's translator had dispensed his pearls of wisdom and then spun round and sauntered out the door. I was grateful for his help to arrange the meeting, but that parting comment wasn't welcome news.

His words repeated in my mind as I mentally prepared to encounter the people he'd been talking about, with no clue how many would be present and what percentage might see me as a walking dollar sign.

Recently, a British journalist had checked into a local hotel and been kidnapped within fifteen minutes. Lucky for him he hadn't been sold on to the insurgents, so it hadn't turned into an orange jumpsuit and sharp knife scenario. Instead, he'd been released the following day although it was plenty enough to convince me to veto Ian's plan that I stay at a supposedly secure farmhouse owned by one of Hassan's relatives.

Instead I was staying in Ian's cabin at the British base, sleeping on the top bunk and trying to avoid detection. I expect a procedure existed to allow me to stay on the base officially, but we adopted the 'easier to ask forgiveness than it is to get permission' approach.

★

Hassan waved me out of the car. 'Mr John, everything is clear. Follow please.'

I grabbed my daysack and joined him on the shabby street.

'Thanks. Keep close when we get inside.'

We crossed the cracked road and weed-strewn pavement and passed through a narrow gate into a surprisingly lush and colourful garden. The contrast was even greater than expected because Basra was filled with heaps of rubble, twisted metal, and ramshackle buildings, all coated in a layer of fine dust. It was a dump, even compared to Baghdad. But this garden could have graced an English country manor.

A suited guard with an AK-47 stood by a large, ornate wooden door. He appeared smarter and more alert than your usual 'twelve hours on, twelve hours off' door sentry. As we approached, he murmured a greeting to the leader of our little group and rapped on the door behind him. It opened immediately and we entered a bright, cool hallway adorned with vases full of colourful flowers.

I stopped to fish the local Nokia phone out of my pocket and send an SMS to Ian.

At Alpha. Will advise > RV.

Once the meeting finished, we had a rendezvous (RV) planned at the port of Khor Az Zubayr, part of Ian's Area of Responsibility. I'd been there two days earlier, noting and appreciating the small British military detachment that oversaw security.

'This way, Mr John.' The leader of our little posse, Karim something or other, was now the perfect host compared to his earlier stint as an interrogator.

He gestured for me to enter through a doorway on the right. Inside it opened into a spectacular and spacious room, its brightly painted walls and high ceiling immaculately decorated with numerous gold flourishes. A covered table with hot drinks, juice, water, fruit, and snacks stood at one end and a large conference table dominated the centre.

Matching mahogany furniture and a highly polished floor gave the room a luxurious feel. Several display cases along the walls contained thickly bound books and ancient-looking trinkets. The purring air conditioners produced a pleasant, cool temperature.

It was encouraging to see only five men present, all sat at the conference table. The room had a closed door at the far end, but no sign of weapons or other threats. If this meeting remained a small, intimate affair, I could keep a closer eye on the participants and maintain a semblance of control. Much better than the rowdy band of warlord chieftains I'd half expected. Provided one of those present was the Sheikh, the afternoon should go okay.

I entered the room and all five rose smartly. Hassan caught up with me as they approached from both sides of the table.

'Okay, I want you to translate word for word, yes? I want to understand everything and not just bits of what's going on.'

'Don't worry, Mr John. I do the same things for Lieutenant Ian all the time.'

We'd see about that. In the past I'd often had translators forgetting their job and rambling off on their own conversational paths while I stood there like a chump, left out of the loop. Not for long mind you. A sharp word reminding them who paid the bills usually brought things back on track.

Compared to the squalid state of the city outside, these guys sported a range of snappy suits. They fitted the impressive surroundings better than my chinos, Timberland boots, button-down shirt, and lightweight canvas jacket. Although I reckoned my look wasn't a million miles from the archetypal 'East of Suez' English adventurer of a bygone era. If anyone thought I was underdressed for the meeting, they didn't show it.

Hassan slipped into translator mode: the speech firm and confident compared to his usual softer voice. My name featured in his opening sentence, but he didn't stop there and instead a flood of indecipherable Arabic followed. So much for the earlier pep talk.

I tried to catch his eye to stop, but he was in full flow. Then Karim and the others from the car joined in and the conversation washed back and forth between everyone in the room except me; my fault for not speaking the language. I occasionally nodded on recognising the odd word and smiled when everyone else did.

I've been told my behaviour sometimes gets noticed during these situations. Those present suspecting my claims of 'not speaking a word' are merely the devious machinations of yet another cunning Englishman. The idea of 'Perfidious Albion' lingered on in this part of the world and many believed the British still pulled all the important strings. Who knows, maybe they were right. But if somebody was pulling the strings, they were causing an almighty snarl which didn't seem to help anyone, us Brits included.

Finally, the conversation ebbed and Hassan introduced the tallest of the hosts. 'Mr John, this is Sheikh Mustafa, the Deputy President of the Basra Trade Chamber.'

Bingo! This was my man. I stuck out a hand.

'John Pierce. I'm very pleased to meet you.'

CHAPTER 2

The immaculately groomed Sheikh wore a perfect fitting navy blue suit and exuded an air of authority and confidence. As we shook hands, he held my gaze, smiled, then surprised me with almost flawless English in a deep, crisp voice.

'Mr Pierce, it is our pleasure to welcome you to the Basra Trade Chamber. We are honoured by your visit and look forward to working with the British to rebuild our city.'

'Thank you, Sheikh. I am looking forward to bringing British expertise and know-how to help rebuild Basra as a modern, twenty-first century port city.'

My knowledge of building a port or a city was negligible, but I'd put on my best 'big business' voice and the small audience lapped it up. I'm sure the Sheikh and the others here had shares in companies destined to get the pick of the contracts. Fine by me. Once I found out which contracts were funded and identified the best local partners, I could try to bring in suitable international outfits for management and oversight. If only it was as easy as it sounded.

After being introduced to the Sheikh's four smartly dressed companions, one of them, the organisation's secretary, regarded me solemnly.

'It is very regrettable that our president cannot attend the meeting today due to business travel. However, he asked me to invite you to a lunch in your honour at his home outside the city on Friday.'

A lunch in my honour. Not an everyday occurrence. The president must be worried his company would miss out on the contracting action.

'Please tell the president thank you for the invitation. I am very honoured. But I don't know if my tight schedule will allow me to attend on Friday. My movements are often influenced by matters outside my control. However, I will get back to you and confirm one way or the other.' Code for thanks, but no thanks.

It kept my options open though, in case an overwhelming reason to attend cropped up. That reason would need to be something very special. A social engagement with this mob somewhere outside the city in a week's time wasn't on my bucket list. I wanted to be long gone by then.

Weak smiles all round, me included. I don't think anyone cared much about my snubbing the president's invitation.

The ensuing discussion ranged over the various sectors that needed prioritisation. High on the list was the power sector, dredging the ports, repairing the roads, and building hotels to accommodate all the international businessmen expected to fly into a brand-new airport. The world loves optimists.

Everyone in the room assumed I worked for the British Government in some capacity; some devious capacity judging by the questions in the car earlier. At least nobody mentioned spying or the Israelis again. They wanted details of specific projects and the level of allocated funds. Seeking, no doubt, to get an inside advantage and jump the queue of local companies desperate to start earning decent money again after the war the previous year.

I made positive noises about future projects, which primarily consisted of educated guesses, and inferred I knew more than I could let on. It didn't hurt if they thought I was linked to Brit Gov.

Unfortunately, I knew nothing about the reconstruction plans, how much money was available, or where the cash would be spent first. I was hoping they'd tell me. My week in Basra so far had been spent at the military base with Ian and the guys, or in snatched meetings around the city and ports as I compiled my report and searched for lucrative business opportunities.

Although insurgent activity had only recently begun to escalate in Basra, the lack of secure hotels and scarcity of safe havens resulted in greater vulnerability than the comparative chaos of Baghdad. This was compounded by the lack of trusted locals to watch my back, unlike the friendly faces I had up in the capital.

I judged it time to take centre stage and get these guys eating out of my hand. See if they did know anything.

'Gentlemen. One area I need to understand is the availability of suitably experienced and capable local companies. I'm here with you, members and officials of the Basra Trade Chamber, to assess which companies are qualified to work with international contractors on key civil infrastructure work. Do you have any advice or guidance?'

With that, a flurry of hands reached into briefcases and bags all over the room. A stack of company profiles appeared on the table. All blurry photos, terrible English, and questionably large dollar values for previous projects. I tried to look suitably impressed as I began flicking through them whilst nodding my head.

The Sheikh had taken his time and presented a wedge of folders across the table.

'These three companies have my personal recommendation. They are amongst the best contractors in Iraq.' Big claims indeed.

Nobody disputed him, but the faces round the table were set to neutral rather than enthusiastic agreement. The Sheikh almost certainly owned or part-owned the three companies he'd recommended, and each of the others had produced one or more profiles, including the guys from the car. I half expected Hassan to pull one out of the hat.

Although I hadn't been able to provide any concrete information about contracts and funding, the room filled with energetic chat as we took a break for chai, juice, and nibbles.

Out of politeness, I took a bite from a sticky-looking pastry offered across on a tray. No wonder many of the male population were overweight and had bad teeth if they ate this stuff. The heavy sweet stuck to my teeth as my blood sugar levels took a rollercoaster ride.

Time was getting on. Now seemed as good a moment as any to collar the Sheikh and get shot of the envelope. A check to make sure it hadn't inexplicably disappeared from my slim leather folder, then I walked over and interrupted his conversation.

'Sheikh, can I speak to you a moment?'

'Of course.' He excused himself and took a step towards me. The hooded eyes of his dismissed colleague beamed contempt in my direction. Since the drama of the car inquisition everyone had been friendly enough, apart from this guy. It usually pays to trust your instincts with these things, and I just didn't like him.

I engineered a turn to face away from the rest of the room and opened the folder to reveal the white envelope with its Arabic inscription. 'I've been asked to give you this important message.'

The Sheikh regarded me with raised eyebrows and indicated with his hand.

'Yes, please take it.'

He plucked the envelope out of my folder. 'Should I read it now?'

That was difficult to answer because I had no idea what message the envelope contained. 'I… yes, I suppose that would be okay. In fact, yes it's probably a good idea.'

If I encouraged him to dash off a quick reply, then the $1,000 on offer to courier it back to Dubai would be coming my way. Perhaps the message even included something else that might be financially beneficial. Much better for the Sheikh and I to discuss it here and now rather than have to arrange another meeting before my journey home. I relied on Ian for any escort in and out of the military base, so there were no guarantees of being able to move around whenever I wanted.

Most of the room were engrossed in small group conversations as Sheikh Mustafa took a seat and deftly opened the envelope. He extracted three sheets of paper and started to read. Within ten seconds a frown creased his brow and he flashed me a quizzical look, which soon morphed into something more akin to disbelief and then anger.

I'd seen that 'what the fuck?' look many times before and an emptiness opened in my gut.

My mind raced as the Sheikh put down the papers and rubbed his neatly bearded chin, his face now set hard with a penetrating stare that alternated between the outspread pages, me, and the ceiling. Not the reaction I'd expected. What the hell had they written to piss the guy off this much? I'd be having strong words if I made it back to Dubai and they could forget employing me as a postman again.

After a tense minute, he gathered the pages with a heavy sigh and began to reread them. At a distance the text appeared to be written in Arabic. Not much point tackling me about its contents then.

I considered my vulnerability if the Sheikh held me responsible for the clearly unwelcome message and went all medieval. Apart from Ian, no-one in authority at the military base knew about me or my location. Even he'd be none the wiser if anything bad happened right now, not until watching it on Al Jazeera or CNN like everyone else. By the time it became clear there was a serious problem, I might not get an opportunity to transmit a warning before they confiscated my phones.

There was the tracking device strapped to my leg though. I calculated the time back in the UK. Jim might be monitoring my location in real time. Three hours behind in the UK on a weekday morning in November he'd be at work, so maybe, if I was lucky.

I caught the suit with the hooded eyes staring at me. No way he could read the document in the Sheikh's hands from his position, but it didn't take a genius to see I'd thrown a grenade into the proceedings. Made his day I'm sure. He broke eye contact, stood up, and left the room by the far door.

Did I need to call Ian and ask him to come and get me? A change to the original plan, but he was on the ground with his team already and might be able to alter the pickup time and location. A key problem with this option being I wasn't here in any official capacity and Ian would need authorisation from the military operations room to enter Basra city centre.

My activity complemented the Coalition goals to rebuild the place, but I was in southern Iraq on private business and staying at the British military base only because Ian was covertly escorting me through the main entry control point (ECP) in his team's vehicles. Even his soldiers didn't know I was just a mate from back home doing my own thing. He may have confided in his platoon sergeant though. Either that or the sergeant guessed something wasn't quite right, judging by his occasional comments.

Dropping me off to disappear for hours on end, the rest of the team apparently assumed I was either 'them' (British Special Forces – SAS/SBS), or a spook, or a 'wannabe twat' from the Foreign Office. Ian said each time I made it back the odds shortened on the first two and lengthened on the third.

A call to Ian would be premature. No point getting him spun up without a very good reason. Instead I opted for Plan B and headed out to call Jim on the sat phone. The security guard didn't like it when I opened the door and stepped outside to get a signal, but I pointed at the antenna on the phone and cracked on regardless. It took ninety seconds before the phone locked on to the satellites and I could make the call.

Jim answered immediately. 'Yes mate?' He must have recognised the Thuraya number.

'Listen, Jim. Everything good here, but I'm concerned things could go noisy. Are you able to keep an eye out for the alarm, just in case?'

'You're joking? Are we talking imminent threat?'

'Not really, mate, but I'm in some unknown company who might not be taking kindly to something that's just happened.'

'Understood. No problem with keeping eyes on the tracker. Actions on the alarm unchanged? I'm still to call this guy Ian on the numbers you gave me?'

'Roger that. And if you can't reach him, then you'll just have to go for the nuclear option and call the Basra Ops Room numbers on the list I sent. Tell them I'm at the Basra Trade Chamber building with one friendly, Hassan Al Ajeen. All being well, we're due to leave shortly for the next RV as per my email last night. Roger so far?'

'Roger so far,' Jim fired back.

I gave him my coordinates. 'Current location: Grid 38R QU 708x795x. Repeat back to me.'

Jim read the grid reference back and, after providing Hassan's cell phone number as an additional point of contact, I cut the call.

I returned inside and took my seat at the table. As I sat down, my hooded-eyed friend came back into the room through the far door with his phone in hand. When our eyes met, he stuffed it back into his pocket. Might be meaningless, but the timing bothered me.

Fifteen minutes later and we'd finally wrapped things up with promises of brotherhood and everlasting cooperation. I'd been trying to get moving ASAP, but these guys spent as long on their goodbyes as they did on their everlasting hellos.

Karim stepped back to let me go through the door first and out into the winter sunshine.

I smiled. 'No, after you.'

He smiled back and gestured again, but my reluctance had nothing to do with politeness. For security reasons I had no intention of being the first outside through that door. I'd already popped out once to call Jim and anyone watching might be waiting for me to appear again.

'No mate, after you.'

His smile dropped as he recognised the hard edge in my voice compared to the politeness I'd shown since we met – my turn to dominate the situation.

He shrugged his shoulders and stepped through the door, a couple of the others right behind him. No sound of any drama outside, so I gave Hassan the nod and we followed them into the garden.

The 'switched-on' guard had been joined by another alert-looking colleague, which inspired confidence our move to the car would have half-decent security cover. The new guy was positioned at the gate, with a view overlooking the vehicles parked outside, including the BMW we had arrived in.

Good. Under-car booby traps, or sticky bombs, were a pet concern of mine and prevalent in much of the country. It only took a moment to slip a magnetic device under a car. It would be high on my list of options if I wanted to take someone out.

Although we needed to get going, there was another round of hugs, kisses, and goodbyes first.

'Mr Pierce, your visit has been very interesting. Inshallah, you shall stay safe in your travels and I hope to see you for lunch at the weekend.' Sheikh Mustafa's demeanour was more formal and warier than before he'd read the letter, but his face showed no sign of anger or dark intent. Maybe that just wasn't his style.

As for lunch next Friday, *Good luck with that.* Call me paranoid, but the whole drama with the message had me firmly in the 'no can do' camp.

Unless…

I'd avoided bringing it up until now, but I had to mention the letter. My mind said, *Pitch for the thousand dollars.* My instinct said, *Don't get involved.* A draw, so I'd roll with the Sheikh's decision.

'Thank you, Sheikh. I'm sorry if the message I delivered from Dubai did not bring welcome news. As I think you realise, I have no knowledge of its contents. However, I was asked to be ready to relay your response. I can ensure confidentiality by hand-delivering any written reply if you prefer. Although I expect it will be easier for you to contact them than it was the other way round.'

His unblinking eyes locked on to mine with ominous intensity.

'My only response today is for you, Mr Pierce. I strongly advise you to be very careful with these people in Dubai. Iraq is experiencing difficult times and many things are not what they seem. Who to trust and who not to trust can be a life-or-death decision. I need time to consider the message with my advisors.'

It didn't sound promising for the extra $1,000 to take a reply to Dubai; not promising enough for me to stick around too long, anyway. The warning was a riddle. Without specifics it was impossible to say if there might be anything to it. Mercenary perhaps, but the seven grand paid up front by the Dubai chaps scored well for them so far in my book. After all, it was business not a social club. However, from now on I'd be on the lookout for anything suspicious.

'Thank you, Sheikh. I will bear your advice in mind.'

As we shook hands again, there was an urgent cry from my right from Hassan.

'GUNMAN!'

And then it all went Arabic, so I didn't know what was going on.

A scan of the buildings and the visible sliver of street revealed no indications of hostile activity. 'Where?' Louder: 'Hassan, where's the gunman?'

No answer. He stood in the gateway pointing towards an empty street corner fifty metres away and gabbled away in Arabic to Karim and the guard. I stepped back inside the building, pulled the phone out of my pocket, and got Ian's number ready so it only needed a single button press to call if required. Then I adjusted myself to ensure unimpeded access to the panic alarm switch inside my waistband. The other guard was close by, so there were at least two weapons ready to respond to any immediate danger that might appear, even if I wasn't 'carrying' myself.

When everyone else moved back inside the door, I followed the Sheikh into the meeting room. I needed space to rearrange my kit and take stock of the situation.

'It's probably unnecessary, but I suggest we remain here for at least a few minutes to make sure. Would you like another chai?' Sheikh Mustafa appeared calm and collected. That said, he might have been the biggest threat to my personal safety right then. You don't get to be a big wheel in the Basra business world by being a wallflower.

The rush from the gunman alarm made it a struggle, but I tried to match his calmness while remaining alert for danger.

'Thank you. A chai would be great, but please, not so much sugar.'

I indicated a small amount with my finger and thumb. If the sticky pastry had made my teeth feel like falling out, the tea they'd served earlier was so sweet it almost dissolved them on the spot. I drank tea and coffee without these days, but the energy boost from a little sugar could come in handy if things got feisty.

I eyed up the sticky pastries and grabbed a slack handful with a 'May I?' Almost laughing out loud as I imagined adding, 'I must get the recipe.' Idiot – I needed to stay switched on.

Two more bottles of still water went in the bag. My respectable businessman persona had slipped a little for this poor man's supermarket sweep, but you can get away with most things provided you throw in a smile and a thank you.

I rearranged the gear in my daysack. The business papers and CVs got relegated to the bottom, while the medical kit, GPS, knife, torch, and map were now readily accessible. The calorie-rich sticky pastries went in with the emergency rations in a side pouch.

I switched on the sat phone, extended the aerial, and prepared it ready to transmit location coordinates and a distress message to both Ian and Jim. That relied on having a connection when the send button was pressed, although I knew the earlier signal would have been lost inside the building and need to be reacquired. To provide a quicker alternative, I set up a similar arrangement with a simpler message from both my regular GSM phones.

Hassan appeared at the door and said, 'Saydee,' in a deferential acknowledgement to the Sheikh. He then addressed us both. 'Outside is clear. The man with the Kalashnikov has gone. Maybe he was a policeman or a soldier. I'm sorry.' His eyes flicked down to the floor before he added, 'We can go now.'

Not the most reassuring explanation.

'Perhaps it would be better if we had some of our security men escort you back to the airport?' Sheikh Mustafa might be genuine in his concern for my welfare, but then again, he might not.

He didn't know we weren't going straight back to the military base, but instead heading south down to Khor Az Zubayr for the RV with Ian and his team. At least, he didn't know until Hassan stuck his oar in. Whatever Hassan said, the port name was clearly audible.

Since he now knew our destination, his offer was worth considering. I was already driving about in a vehicle full of guys I hardly knew and with limited protection. My hooded-eyed friend studied me from across the room as I took a few seconds to decide.

I went for it.

'Thank you, Sheikh. If I could borrow these guards, do they have a car they can use?'

Sheikh Mustafa smiled and nodded. 'Excellent. I'm sure Karim would take good care of you, but it is prudent to travel with appropriate security. Especially in these increasingly dangerous times.'

He called out in Arabic and the secretary came over. After receiving a brief set of instructions, the secretary left the room.

I was confident taking up his offer was a good call. If these guys had a heinous plan, I was screwed anyway. If not, then his guards had been about the most switched-on local security I'd encountered so far, plus a second car gave us some redundancy if the BMW ran into problems. I hadn't seen any weapons with Karim and the guys from the car which meant they only had sidearms at best, but no longs like AK-47s. Not unless they had them stowed uselessly in the boot.

Mr Hooded Eyes had got wind of the plan and didn't seem to appreciate the turn of events, muttering in angry Arabic. Hassan had an indignant look on his face as he turned and fired a comment in his direction.

'What's the problem, Hassan?'

'Mr Sinan is complaining about the guards travelling with us.'

The hooded-eyed Mr Sinan looked pissed, but then he hadn't looked the happiest bunny all afternoon.

By this time, Sheikh Mustafa had walked over to Mr Sinan and they engaged in a brief, robust and one-sided conversation; the Sheikh doing the transmitting and Mr Sinan the receiving.

Hassan looked at me and nodded. 'We can go now. One of the guards will follow us in a car until we reach the port gates.'

Only one guard rather than two, but better than nothing. It was a pleasant surprise when he climbed into a smart-looking Toyota Land Cruiser and started the engine.

I tapped out >RV and pressed send.

CHAPTER 3

Khor Az Zubayr Port, thirty kilometres south of Basra city, was the final call for Ian's patrol that afternoon. As the platoon commander he could adjust timings and routes, which meant some flexibility if needed. It was secured by British troops, so if his patrol got delayed or worse, I'd be in a safe location. Stranded but safe. That made it a good RV location for us to link up before we made our way back to the airport base in time for dinner.

The traffic moved at a steady pace as we travelled along the main highway heading south west out of Basra, followed by the white Land Cruiser driven by the guard. The flat, sun-baked terrain ran along either side of the busy artery, sprinkled with rundown buildings, piles of mangled metal, and oceans of rubble. Nothing indicated whether this was a new post-apocalyptic hell or the pitiful reality from years of Saddam's oppression of the southern Shi'ites.

Fifteen minutes after setting off, we made the turn left onto Route 26 and mixed with lighter traffic for the twenty-kilometre straight road down to Khor Az Zubayr. The previous depressing vista and occasional listless inhabitants now replaced by largely empty scrub and sporadic foliage. Sat in the middle of the rear seat to have the best cover from outside view, I started to relax and shook my head as I reflected on the afternoon's events. Hassan on my right must have noticed. 'Is there a problem?' he asked.

'No mate. Fifteen more minutes, yes?'

'Yes, we're almost there.'

Hassan had done well today. Ian would be pleased his man hadn't let him down.

Ten minutes down the road, there was a build-up of traffic at the roundabout ahead. From my previous visits to the area, I knew the left-hand turning for the port was close. However, instead of being allowed to carry on straight ahead after the roundabout, all traffic was being directed to take the first exit right by two armed, balaclava-clad soldiers, with what appeared to be a minor accident spread across the road behind them. Not enough to warrant a diversion in my book.

'No, no, fuck that.' I leant forward to direct the driver. 'Carry on. Straight ahead.'

When he didn't react, I turned to Hassan.

'Tell him to go straight ahead. Go round these clowns.'

My spidey senses were twitching, but I wasn't unduly worried. It was natural to be apprehensive when you saw men in balaclavas wearing camouflage gear and toting weapons, although it wasn't uncommon in Iraq. Even though I'd encountered similar in Baghdad, the first time I'd run into them here a few days earlier I'd almost reached for the panic alarm. Now when I saw them, the usual thought that sprang to mind was, *It must be hot under there in the summer.*

Due to the congestion, the traffic slowed to a crawl as we approached the entrance to the roundabout. Our escort followed a few metres behind, closing when anyone tried to cut in between us. As our driver changed lanes to manoeuvre left round the scene of the accident, the nearest balaclava guy stepped across into our path and pointed one arm at us and one down the exit to our right. Something didn't feel right. Like we'd been singled out.

'Back. Go back. Tell him, Hassan.'

After the resultant blast of Arabic, the driver stamped on the brake before throwing the car into reverse. He'd reacted quickly this time but it was too late. Mr Balaclava had reached the driver's window and started shouting with his AK raised.

'For fuck's sake.' All we needed.

It still wasn't clear whether we had a bigger issue here, but I didn't want to get channelled off into the nearby town unless there was absolutely no choice. Ian had shared reports indicating several previous attacks had either occurred or originated there.

A flash of white as the Land Cruiser appeared on our left and skidded to a halt. The Trade Chamber guard jumped out with his AK-47 in hand and started yelling at the soldier who'd stopped us.

This could easily become a real mess. I turned to Hassan. 'Get out.'

'No...' he began to say, but changed his mind when he saw my face and instead opened the door.

I swept my daysack onto my back and led him around the rear of the car, intending to position myself by the Land Cruiser and be ready to jump in. If we could commandeer the larger SUV, then we could cut across the central reservation to go 'counter flow' down the wrong side of the road to bypass the clusterfuck this side of the roundabout.

As we cut behind the BMW I heard shouts. The second balaclava guy was running towards us and another two broke into a jog thirty metres behind him.

The first guy glanced over, and we locked eyes as I snaked past the back of the car. He shouted at me, prompting an angry response from our Land Cruiser guard. With all the shouting and running, things were escalating fast. In fact, this was going to ratshit. I needed to select the least worst option and run with it. A burst of AK fire from the approaching men focused my attention.

Little time to react if I was going to make a move, and this might still be a simple misunderstanding with real traffic cops, albeit one that was fast getting out of hand. A second volley of AK fire raked the bonnet of the BMW and made the decision for me. No chance of commandeering the Land Cruiser, so I kept it between me and the balaclavas and started to run towards the central reservation. My eyes darted left and right, checking the slowed and stopped cars for new threats.

'Come on, Hassan.'

He looked like he was shitting himself. I probably didn't look my best either. So close to safety as well – only five kilometres – which

I'd have happily run if I thought I could get past without being mown down by gunfire.

All our balaclava-clad friends had reached the two cars now and weapons were coming up on aim in our direction as they bellowed after us. We either needed to stop and put our hands up or start sprinting and hard targeting down the main drag back the way we'd come.

A sudden roar of engines erupted above the hubbub and two bursts of fire from an automatic weapon passed high overhead towards the four balaclava boys gathered round the BMW and Land Cruiser. My head snapped left. It didn't take a rocket scientist to spot the likely candidates: three black vehicles closing at speed from behind on the other carriageway, their 'top cover' troops with weapons pointing our way.

Back over at our vehicles, the Trade Chamber guard raised his weapon towards the original balaclava guy next to the driver's side of the BMW. That could get messy if these were real police. Fortunately, a third rattle of warning shots caused him to dive for cover behind the cars like everyone else.

It looked as though Mad Max had arrived on the scene. The three aggressive-looking black vehicles with prominent up-armouring came screaming to a halt on the opposite side of the road. They were running counter flow, heading the same direction we had been going, except using their immunity from traffic laws to try to avoid the bag of bollocks at the roundabout.

The guy on top cover in the first vehicle looked like an expat – thank Christ for that. Plenty of Anglo-Saxon language started pouring out of the new arrivals, loudly directed at the balaclava gang and everyone else in the vicinity. Two expat vehicle commanders hopped out bringing AK-47s up on aim, and the top cover guys looked like they were daring someone to have a go.

Then a burly figure emerged from the lead vehicle. No doubt about it, my luck was in. Not only was he an expat, but I knew him: Alec Gibbs, a Welsh ex-para. I didn't need a written invitation. I was on my toes and sprinting towards him yelling 'Follow me' back at Hassan.

The new arrivals were a game changer for the balaclava crew. As I glanced back, they were already retreating into the roundabout towards two unmarked SUVs parked on the verge of the exit road.

'Fuck me if it isn't Johnny Pierce.' A broad smile broke out on the big Welshman's face. 'Just what the hell are you doing pissing off the locals and upsetting everyone's afternoon? Typical Royal.'

'Alec. Am I glad to see you. I don't know what the fuck is going on here, but can you get me down to Khor Az Zubayr?' The relief in my voice made me sound like a giddy teenager.

'No problem. We're heading down to Umm Qasr to pick up a convoy, so it's on the way. Jump in and you can tell me what trouble you're getting yourself in these days. I take it he's with you?' He pointed at the doubled-over figure of Hassan trying to catch his breath.

Hassan and I jumped in the lead vehicle and Alec got on the radio to his team, telling them to mount up and advising everyone we'd be stopping at Khor Az Zubayr. Next, he informed his HQ the 'shots fired' report he'd sent had turned out to be a local disturbance.

A few minutes later, I wished good luck to Alec and his men as they prepared to leave after dropping us at the port. He made it clear I owed him a crate of beer and was highly dubious of my promise to deliver the goods. 'Yeah, right. I won't forget,' he said, waving a dismissive hand as he climbed back in his vehicle.

Alec and I had first met a few years before on a security job in the UK. Now he was working for Security Force International, known as SFI, a British security company running convoys all over Iraq.

'Get yourself down to Kuwait and talk to Big Steve,' he said before leaving.

I hadn't met Big Steve, but I knew he was the former rugby-playing company boss who worked out of a beachside hotel in Kuwait City. Alec had a good point: the money they paid security guys out here was like rock star wages for most ex-British soldiers. It sounded appealing compared to spending your own cash like muggins here was doing.

Since I'd arrived at the port early, I decided to make the most of it and take a wander round while I got my heart rate back under control following the afternoon's entertainment. Ian's patrol wasn't due to arrive for another two hours.

Khor Az Zubayr was managed by shipping giants Maersk. When I called at his office, the French manager, Georges, jumped at the chance to give the grand tour. As he guided me round, Georges outlined an ambitious expansion plan. My ears pricked up when he mentioned scrap metal. I had a German client interested in exporting the vast heaps littering much of the country.

He showed me an area of empty rough ground the size of a fat football pitch. 'This area here is zoned for scrap metal. HMS1 and HMS2 only.'

Previous research told me that meant scrap metal already prepared and cut to industry specifications and sizes.

'Really? This whole area?'

What a result. The Germans might be on to something.

'Yes. The capacity will be approximately 100,000 tonnes. The Governor is very interested in making money exporting the huge quantities left in the country after the war.'

It made sense. The stuff was everywhere.

'That's understandable. Do you know anything about the licensing side of that? Who will be able to use this place and how it will work?'

Georges took off his glasses and polished them on his shirt. He squinted at me in the dazzling sunlight. Despite us being alone, he moved closer and dropped his voice.

'I believe the Governor's son is responsible for that side. And he has a company who wants to export the scrap now the law allows for it.' He laughed. 'I think anyone else wanting to get involved will find it very difficult to get permission. If you know what I mean.'

'Ahh.' I knew exactly what he meant. Shit.

If the Basra Governor's son had designs on being the Mr Big of the scrap export industry, the Germans would either need to partner up with him or look for a new business angle. Both options sounded unlikely.

My chances of growing a revenue stream from exporting scrap metal might have dimmed, but that wasn't the only show in town.

Coalition forces provided security at the biggest ports, so a plan to set up an office in the secure environments at Khor Az Zubayr or Umm Qasr might be feasible. With the safety of Kuwait City less than two hours away by road, it could be a great location to grab a slice of the huge import/export market. The trade routes through the southern ports were critical to the Iraqi economy and would have to remain secured by the Coalition for the foreseeable future.

★

Later that evening back at the base, I sat alone in Ian's cabin and reflected on the afternoon's events. Should I have activated the panic alarm or sent a distress message? The panic alarm was the 'First IA' (Immediate Action) if I got into trouble, but it wasn't clear if the incident at the roundabout had been targeted at me or not.

Someone from the Basra Trade Chamber could have tried to organise something; not difficult to envisage my hooded-eyed friend Mr Sinan involved in a nefarious plot. But equally it could simply have been a genuine misunderstanding.

Perhaps I overreacted, although the AK-47 rounds into the bonnet of the BMW had been a huge red flag in my book. If Alec hadn't shown up, then who knows what might have happened? In the end there was no harm done, but I vowed to be more cautious in the future. There's only so many times you can rely on your luck before it runs out.

Ian returned from a briefing and closed the door behind him. We hadn't had a chance to talk privately since his patrol had picked me up.

'So, what do you think?' he asked. 'Any indications they were after you in particular?'

'Not really, mate. They could have been police or other ISF *(Iraqi Security Forces)*. Perhaps I jumped the gun a bit quick. But it definitely didn't feel right. It's easy to take it personally when some idiots let rip a couple of bursts of seven-six-two in your direction, but... who knows?'

Ian looked at the report paperwork on his desk. 'In that case, I think we should put it down to a local misunderstanding. I'm not going to include it in any report because the details are so unclear and, more importantly, none of our patrol witnessed it.'

'Makes sense. Alec Gibbs reported it to the SFI HQ as a local disturbance with shots heard. Nothing more.'

'That settles it. Without evidence anything sinister was afoot, we'll leave it as it is. The involvement of a PSC *(Private Security Company)* at the scene complicates things even further. We've got enough going on without getting involved in that sort of mess.'

While we agreed there was no evidence of foul play, it didn't alter the fact there could have been serious consequences for my safety and Ian's career. Having achieved everything I'd set out to accomplish in Basra, it was time to call it a day and head home before something bad did happen.

Ian had a patrol going down to Shaibah Logistics Base the following day, close to the Kuwaiti border. His guys were keen because it meant a visit to a bigger NAAFI. More importantly, it provided an ideal opportunity for me to be driven through the visa-exempt military lane and dropped off on the Kuwaiti side of the border where they'd picked me up eight days ago.

★

We passed through the border crossing the following morning without a second glance. I'd miss the soldiers' banter and the unexplainable buzz of the threat, but it was also a relief when I jumped out of the Land Rover and turned to say my goodbyes to Ian and his men.

I almost forgot our friendship wasn't public knowledge. 'Thanks for all this. I know you stuck your neck out for me and I'm really grateful.'

Okay, so I did forget. Ian's widened eyes jogged my memory.

I tried a regain. 'And you guys. Thanks for making my job easier. I'm sure running contractors like me about is a pain in the arse.' Smiles of acknowledgement broke out. 'Although it stops you being able to spend too much in the NAAFI.' A couple of ironic laughs. Enough to cover my opening faux pas with Ian? I thought so.

As the Land Rovers circled round and dived through the military lane, I strolled into the shade of the only shop that appeared to be open. Back to safety, job complete.

There was little sign of life apart from the sound of a truck engine revving in the distance. I needed transport down to the airport, but there were no cabs in sight and no lorries coming through the border to try thumbing a lift. I entered the empty shop. 'Taxi?' I asked, holding my thumb and little finger to my ear and mouth.

The guy behind the counter didn't seem to understand what I wanted or didn't care. I had a card for Khalid, the taxi driver who'd dropped me off over a week ago at the same location, so I called him up. It was over 100 kilometres to Kuwait City, but it might be a long wait otherwise.

'Khalid? It's John. You dropped me off at the Iraqi border a week ago.'

'Yes of course, Mr John. Hello. Are you back in Kuwait needing a taxi?'

'I am, yes. But I'm not in the city. I'm up at the border. Same place you dropped me off.'

'Okay. You want me to come to pick you up?'

'If you can that would be great.'

'I'm in my taxi and I'll be on my way now. One hour and fifteen minutes I'll be at the border.'

'Thanks, Khalid. That's great. See you soon.'

What a hoofing bloke. Throwing money about wasn't my style but Khalid deserved a decent tip, plus I'd make sure to keep his card for any time I returned to Kuwait.

★

On arrival at the airport I went straight to the British Airways desk and changed my ticket to a flight leaving for London within two hours. With that done, I took Khalid to a restaurant. When we'd both got a coffee, I gave him fifty dollars for his efforts and questioned him about the border. It turned out I knew more than he did, but it hadn't been time and money wasted. I now had a likeable and competent driver to call on anytime I travelled to Kuwait.

Once a happy Khalid had left, I had time to kill before my flight. A recent escapade in London had led to getting caught up in surveillance targeted at some associates. I'd known it was a stupid thing to get involved in, but a bit of peer pressure and I had the breaking strain of a KitKat.

Paranoia still lurked inside, so after scrutinising my dining companions I left the restaurant and moved through the airport trying to detect any suspicious activity. Unsurprisingly, my efforts were to no avail.

I laughed at myself for being ridiculous, wandered into the Build-A-Bear store, and browsed for a while before choosing a classic plain teddy for my youngest daughter, Becky. If anyone was watching, they could dig out.

CHAPTER 4

TEN MONTHS EARLIER

LONDON – EARLY JANUARY 2004

After leaving the Corps in 1998, I'd worked on the London close protection circuit, mainly providing security for a variety of Middle Eastern sheikhs and their families. Most of the work in the UK was low threat, mundane stuff, especially if you hadn't been a 'badged' special forces soldier.

While working regularly with one Middle Eastern family, I'd struck up a friendship with Mohammed, a British-Iraqi driver from Manchester who was born in Baghdad. I'm sure he preferred to be called a chauffeur, but to be honest he was a poor driver with a penchant for road rage, even with clients in the car. However, he was affable and funny, and we immediately hit it off.

He regularly spoke of Baghdad and normal life before the 1991 Gulf War and the sanctions that followed. How we should travel there when the sanctions were relaxed to experience his favourite fish dish called masgouf, cooked on charcoal by the banks of the Tigris. Before the 2003 Iraq War, the idea was laughable because Saddam Hussein enjoyed a position as international bogeyman and public enemy number one. The chances of me ever strutting my stuff in the souks of Baghdad were pretty much zero.

Mohammed seemed to travel backwards and forwards quite regularly though. Although his wife and kids lived in Manchester, it sounded like the rest of the family remained in Baghdad. I guessed they were probably Sunni Muslims like Saddam because his brother was high up in a ministry and that seemed unlikely if they followed the Sh'ia side of Islam. But apart from general grumbling, Mohammed never had much ' of substance to say, good or bad, about religion, Iraqi politics or Saddam.

When Mohammed called me up in early January 2004, he had recently returned from Baghdad and babbled on about contracts and business opportunities. While working together in London the previous summer, we'd discussed the idea of setting up business in Iraq if the right conditions evolved. Now he was reporting back with a positive assessment and encouraging me to go see for myself.

My business had a gaping hole in both the diary and the revenue column, so I told him I'd think about it. Give some thought to the how and, more importantly, the how much? It was a brush-off, but Mohammed didn't hear it like that. He would be in London later in the week, so where should we meet?

There was little to lose by agreeing to meet up for a chat and hear tales of Baghdad, occupation, business opportunities, and what appeared to be a growing insecurity problem. I wouldn't have called myself an expert on the situation in Iraq, but I monitored the news. The UN headquarters was blown up in 2003, prompting them to evacuate most of their staff from the country, and the media reported escalating attacks as the Coalition dropped the ball on the peace after winning the war.

★

I met Mohammed in the lobby of the Churchill Hotel in Portman Square, close to the Marble Arch end of London's Oxford Street. We'd both worked at the hotel regularly with Middle Eastern clients whilst they splashed their oil money around, but this would be my first time paying for drinks here. I expected an eye-watering bill.

At least Mohammed was unlikely to choose a beer or any other alcohol. Not for religious reasons – he drank – but he avoided drinking in places like this where he knew many of the staff. That meant the bill shouldn't be excessive. After all, how many soft drinks can two guys get through in an hour or two?

'John, I'm pleased to see you again. How are your family? Have you had lunch yet?'

Nice try.

'Yes thanks, I've eaten. It's good to see you. How was Baghdad?'

A flicker passed over his face. Either he'd realised he wouldn't be getting a free lunch, or he'd been intending to pay, and I'd just seen myself off. Whatever. I'd prefer a Subway or a Big Mac anyway.

'You wouldn't believe it. Those American bastards are so powerful, but they won't turn on the electricity for the city. Without air conditioning it's unbearably hot in the summer and now it's dark and cold in the winter. My family have had to go back to using oil heaters and candles. It's like we went back a hundred years. Those bastards could turn it on if they wanted.'

I would encounter this view time and again in Iraq. Mohammed and many of the locals in Baghdad had pro-Western leanings and were grateful for the overthrow of Saddam, but still thought the US and its partners chose not to provide the essential services.

Even without a hardcore of Baathists and Islamists taking potshots at the Coalition forces, the whole thing would probably still have been a total disaster. Our people were incompetent, lazy, and tied up with endless bureaucracy and shit management, just like everywhere else. There was no telling him that though.

'No, it's more than that. I tell you, they are deliberately punishing the people.'

'Well mate, what does that mean for us? You think there's a real chance of winning any decent contracts over there?'

It's arguable how much weight should be given to the opinion of a Manchester taxi driver regarding international investment, but there couldn't be too many business people in the UK with good contacts in Baghdad. I'd been mulling this over since Mohammed's phone call earlier in the week. With an office set-up in Baghdad and trusted local support, surely there would be a decent chance to grab a small slice of the big reconstruction pie. Bearing in mind my abysmal financial situation, this could be the opportunity of a lifetime.

'Inshallah, we will be very successful. Everything needs to be done. So many years of sanctions and then the war. They can't do it themselves. They need the international companies to come and do the work properly.'

I'd never heard him use the Arabic word for 'God willing' before. Clearly the recent trip to his homeland had included some holy inspiration.

Over soft drinks and a bill more reasonable than expected, we sat and chatted through the practicalities of travelling to Baghdad and assessing things for myself. Mohammed's reasons for not going with me weren't entirely convincing: he thought it better if I made my own mind up without interference from him. Plus, after his recent lengthy spell away from home, he wanted to spend time with his wife and kids up in Manchester.

The final clincher was cost; if both of us went, it would be doubled. Mohammed didn't have the money to fund another trip, and I couldn't afford his travel and costs on top of my own.

Instead, the idea on the table would see me travel to Baghdad alone and meet up with his brother on arrival. His ministry building had been destroyed by an American smart bomb, so he could be at my disposal for the duration of my stay. Mohammed said Walid grew up to be the smartest brother in the family and was a decent family man, married with a Westernised Shi'a wife and well connected with the movers and shakers still left in Baghdad. Hopefully his talents included being a better driver than Mohammed. But if I was going to seriously consider this jaunt, there was the small question of how I'd get to Baghdad.

CHAPTER 5

EPSOM, UK – LATE JANUARY 2004

My wife, Claire, was not taking the news of my imminent departure to Baghdad well. The limitations forced on my planning by our current financial situation weren't helping either.

When I'd left my corporate investigation job the previous summer to start my own risk management company, there had been a few immediate projects lined up, including a lucrative task in Moscow. For a short while we had more money than ever before, and things were looking rosy. But now, five months since the optimistic days of the business launch, the initial contracts had long been completed and replaced instead by a sickening scarcity of work.

In my relatively new entrepreneurial guise, the theoretical plan to fly to Jordan and drive to Baghdad had grown legs over the last couple of weeks without me consciously deciding to go ahead. But once I'd begun compiling a plan, working on contingencies, and researching options, it had developed a life of its own.

The arrangements for the flight to Jordan and the accommodation in Baghdad were straightforward. However, two big black holes still existed: one was the drive from Amman to Baghdad; the other what I would do once I arrived in the Iraqi capital. The business activities I was happy to leave fluid until I was on the ground, but the drive to Baghdad was a different matter. This was by far the most dangerous element of the journey and, as the trip loomed closer, my agreement to travel by taxi across western Iraq seemed like a case of misplaced bravado.

The overall objective in Baghdad was to establish if I agreed with Mohammed's positive assessment of the situation. If so, then I needed to identify the various options and costs of setting up shop.

I intended to provide consultancy services to international companies, using local support and knowledge to help them win a share of the reconstruction contracts. Iraq needed everything after the West had sanctioned and bombed it to a ruin over the previous decade. I wasn't a business mastermind, but I had spent the best part of four years running 'cover' companies in multiple sectors for intellectual property investigations.

I'd learnt a hell of a lot whilst developing business relationships between these cover companies and the corporate targets, all whilst gathering intelligence and evidence for clients. The work required plenty of due diligence on potential partners, suppliers, distributors, competitors, and anyone else the client wanted to check out – and I was good at it. I only had a few average O levels, but behind those meagre statistics lurked a pretty smart cookie; the minimal academic qualifications due to a lack of application rather than intelligence. That's what I told myself anyway.

After three enjoyable years at the investigation company, I'd started to get frustrated. Most of my colleagues were retired ex-policemen a fair few years older than me. Nearly all were great guys who became good friends but, only in my mid-thirties, the pace of life had cooled too much for my liking. My time in the Corps and various previous adventures had given me a wanderlust that wasn't satisfied, even with the occasional overseas investigation case. I became filled with a desire to go out and negotiate the great deals I was cutting with my cover companies, but for real.

In the late summer of 2003, this combined with a bitter argument over the firm's late invoice payments to one of my overseas agents and convinced me to hand in my notice and open my own company. An unexpected offer of a consultancy contract from a former boss provided a financial incentive and spurred me on further.

We'd bumped into each other outside the office as he left a meeting with our Corporate Division boys and voiced his annoyance with the way a technical glitch had ruined a critical surveillance task our guys had been running for him.

'You ever leave this lot mate and we could do a better job together at half the outrageous fees these idiots just charged me for a job they fucked up!'

Pete was right, but as we found out, it often didn't matter that you could do the job just as well for half the money; the reputation and accountability of the established players got them the work. It was a painful lesson for both of us. Only three months after we started, I had to agree with Pete that we weren't winning anywhere near enough work to justify my fixed monthly fees. The resulting cancellation of the contract dealt a tough blow that left a big hole in my financial plans.

So that was the extent of my business background as I looked to mix it in with my military and security experience to make my fortune in Iraq. The way I saw it, fate seemed to have dealt me a set of cards that pointed towards Baghdad, despite the risks. Claire clearly thought that hand of cards should be played differently.

'You're actually going to Baghdad?'

I don't think I'd ever heard Claire sound incredulous before.

'Seriously? Are you mad? Driving to Baghdad? What the hell are you thinking?' Then with a forlorn note, 'What about us... me... the girls?'

I looked at her, unsure what to say, but she hadn't finished, and the questions were rhetorical. Kind of anyway. She expected an answer but not yet. Her bewitching green eyes flashed with anger. No sign of their usual mischievous sparkle.

'What are you thinking... just... why would you?'

As well as the anger, Claire's face had dropped when I announced I'd be flying in only two days. I couldn't blame her either. It would be obvious it was a barking mad idea to anyone who stopped to consider it, which explained why I'd made a point to avoid doing just that.

Things had moved on autopilot at first, but now this course of action had developed into a workable plan. And with my limited funds, the plan provided my only viable option to get a piece of the reconstruction action in Iraq. No one else would pay for me to go to Baghdad and tout for work.

If pressed, I'd prefer to describe it as a 'ballsy move', but it was difficult to argue much with Claire's description that included 'stupid' and 'suicidal'.

'Sweetheart, things are all arranged on the Iraqi side. I'll be travelling low-profile with highly trusted escorts. Once I'm in Baghdad, I'll be able to piggyback off the Coalition and international press set-ups. It'll be okay and, more to the point, how many Westerners are in Baghdad right now with trusted Iraqi contacts? I swear to you, if I get out there and things look really dodgy, then I'll be the first one to bug the hell out. But this is a real chance to get in on the ground floor. Make some real money.'

Everything I'd said was true, although it relied on the best-case scenarios and taking Mohammed at his word for the arrangements at the Iraqi end. With so many unknowns, it was impossible to predict what would happen and how any of this would work out.

'One thing I do know is that it's time to put up or shut up. It's not like I'm looking forward to this trip, but if I'm going to do this, then I need to get on with it. I'm trying to make contingency plans for everything, but in the end it comes down to getting my arse on a plane and just doing it.'

I'd spoken on and off with Mohammed about business in Iraq since the end of hostilities nine months before in April 2003. By contrast, Claire had only become aware of the seriousness of my planning five minutes ago.

After his recent trip to Baghdad, Mohammed judged the time was right and everything would go well, so I tried to project the same confidence to Claire. I had my doubts of course. Was he blagging it as well? Probably. Was his confidence just an act for my benefit, and did he really think it was a massive, high-risk gamble? Almost definitely.

Claire must have seen the shadow of doubt pass across my face.

'You've got no life insurance, no support, nothing. How will I even know if anything happens to you? Tell me? How? How many days should I wait before I call someone? Who would I call? You haven't got a clue what it's like.' She turned away as the tears rolled down her cheeks.

Fortunately, she wasn't aware of the video tape I'd made earlier that morning for her, our teenager Natalie, and our one-year-old daughter Becky. It could best be described as a 'sorry I screwed up' tape, where I told Claire and the girls how much I loved them and tried being positive about how they should make the most of their lives, go to university, be happy, and all that sort of stuff. I'd left it in the filing cabinet next to my old service will.

Helpfully titled '*Play this if I'm Dead!!*', I'd almost shed a tear as it dawned on me how shitty it would be for the girls if I never came home. Funny how it wasn't the thought of dying that seemed to matter, but the effect it would have on those left behind.

I hadn't cried since Alan Shearer scored for England against Scotland in Euro '96 and tears leaked out in sheer joy and relief – and that was only the first goal of the match. Just like today, back then the emotion had swelled out of nowhere. Claire had been sitting next to me in our married quarters in Poole, watching with a bemused smile on her face and wondering what had happened to the rufty-tufty marine she'd married. My emotional register had certainly never included crying at sport before.

She said later she hadn't known whether to hug me or leave me to it. In the end she'd left me to it and gone into the kitchen shaking her head and making some quip about me being a 'new man', before laughing like a drain with our neighbour Karina, who was already in the kitchen grabbing another glass of wine.

'I'm sorry.' Not enough, but all I could muster.

Into the silence I added, 'I love you.'

That wasn't something I said very often and certainly not often enough. Perhaps that made it more special when I did say it, but I doubt Claire would have agreed.

We'd been married for fifteen years and experienced plenty of ups and downs, although nothing different from other service couples who spent long periods apart and never had enough disposable income. Claire had fallen pregnant at only nineteen and, being the chivalrous guy I no longer was, I'd asked her to marry me.

Natalie was now fifteen and finding her own feet. Not my little buddy like before she was a teenager, but she had grown up funny, pretty, and smart. Stubborn too, with a temper that could smoulder and burn with fiery intent. I knew who she got that from, so I couldn't really complain.

I put my arms round Claire's shoulders and tried to turn her towards me. She resisted at first, but soon softened and we kissed. That was something else we didn't do enough of lately. Although with a teenager and a one-year-old in the house, mixed with my new business and Claire's nursing job, that wasn't much of a surprise.

The anger had left Claire's eyes and instead she looked lost, like we were twenty years old again and being wrenched apart by the Corps. Her left alone with a young baby while I went off soldiering round the world. A normally hidden well of emotion started to stir. Christ, this was becoming a habit. I breathed deeply and forced it back down.

'It'll be okay, don't worry.' I forced myself to smile. 'This time next year, we'll be millionaires… honestly.'

She looked at me, shaking her head as a grudging smile crept onto her face. She sighed and said, 'I love you too,' before kissing me quickly on the lips and then pulling away, her hands remaining fixed on my hips.

'Sorry, I know how it is and I know you've mentioned this Baghdad thing before, but it's suddenly so real, so soon. I'm sorry.'

And then with an effort to sound brighter, 'Let's do something before you go. How about the zoo? Becky's never been before. What about London Zoo tomorrow?'

My flight to Amman was scheduled for Monday: two days' time. We knew from long experience it was better to stay busy and not think about the impending separation and danger.

'Yeah, the zoo is a great idea.'

Leaning in, we kissed and smiled at the same time. Things hadn't always been great between us in the last few years, but we always seemed to come out okay in the end.

CHAPTER 6

AMMAN, JORDAN – EARLY FEBRUARY 2004

It was gone midnight as I hauled my bag off the carousel at Jordan's Queen Alia International Airport in Amman.

The flight on Royal Jordanian had been empty enough to allow me to spread out comfortably. After reading for a while, a smile had crept across my face as I'd recalled the weekend with Claire and the girls. The trip to London Zoo had been great fun, helped by the dry weather and rare winter sun. We'd all ignored my imminent departure and concentrated on having a good time.

Although only twelve months old, Becky's sense of humour already shone through. A few times on our day out I caught myself appreciating her total innocence and wishing nothing bad would ever hurt her; that she wouldn't have to carry the burden her whole life of a father who left her before she was even old enough to remember him.

I wasn't religious but I kept an open mind to hedge my bets. One or two dodgy situations in the past had led to promises being offered up to the big guy in return for a slice of divine intervention. This time though I hadn't been praying, I'd been ordering myself to do everything possible to stay lucky and make sure I came home.

When I stretched out my tired leg muscles, an image of our black Labrador-cross, Taz, flashed into my head as the lights of a southern European city passed below. We'd run that morning on Epsom Downs as we did most days, and always on the days I flew abroad. I'm not superstitious, but it had become a good luck routine. Running up on the Downs in the early morning fresh air with the panorama of London spread out below us always relaxed me, until she saw another dog or a horse and decided to inject some chaos into the proceedings.

Taz had a resigned air when I left the house with my gear that morning for the waiting taxi. Probably recognised only too well the signs she'd be missing out on our runs for a while. Claire wasn't much of a dog person and she certainly wasn't much of a runner these days. She still had a tidy figure though, which prompted the memory of our frantic sex from the night before to pop up. My smile broadened.

Despite my dismissal of superstition, somewhat bizarrely I also had a plastic eyeball that always came with me on these trips as a good luck charm. Natalie had given it to me when she was tiny after pulling it out of a Christmas cracker. I'd taken it on my first tour to Northern Ireland and been very lucky during a touch-and-go incident. After that, the more times I got lucky, the more it was sure to be packed when I travelled. Only held together by black masking tape these days, it had caused the odd raised eyebrow amongst customs officers over the years.

Right up until the announcement to prepare for landing, I'd suppressed the growing sense of trepidation about this trip. With our imminent arrival in Amman it rose up again, but a couple of deep breaths before meeting the eye of a smiling, doe-eyed Royal Jordanian air hostess and those thoughts receded again.

Once I was on the ground, freshly stamped visa in my passport, I surveyed the surroundings on my first-ever visit to Jordan. Finally getting started always made everything easier. The worst time is always the run-up to a job like this and thinking about the 'what ifs'. Once you've rolled the dice, it's time to get on with it. Or as Julius Caesar put it slightly better back in the day: 'Alea jacta est' – *The die is cast.*

★

I'd tried to establish a firm protocol for my airport pickup.

'No, tell them not to write my name on a card at the airport,' I'd repeated. My attempt at explaining to Mohammed why it could compromise my identity wasn't getting through.

'Just get them to write GRC.'

Mohammed looked puzzled. 'What does that mean?'

'It means I'll be able to identify them and make an approach if I'm happy.'

Mohammed considered my answer. 'Why wouldn't you be happy?'

'Because I don't know these people. I know you say I'll be met by the brother of the trusted taxi driver who always drives you to Baghdad, but to be honest that doesn't fill me with absolute confidence. I just want the chance to make my own assessment and approach him in my own time once I'm comfortable with the situation.'

Mohammed nodded in acceptance. 'So, what is GRC?'

'It doesn't mean anything. They're simply three letters that I will recognise. Like a code. You understand?'

'Ah, okay, I understand now. A three-letter code. I'll speak to them and arrange it.'

★

As my eyes roamed across the last few people holding cards, it became clear the plan was not quite coming together as envisioned. I dismissed yet another porter trying to entice me to a waiting taxi and started to consider the options if my pickup didn't happen. With not much of a list to work with, the cheap hotel at the airport beckoned.

Despite repeated requests, Mohammed hadn't provided any contact numbers, addresses, or any other information about my transfer from Amman to Baghdad. I only knew the driver's name was Thamer and when I arrived he would be asleep in preparation for the 3.00am start. The airport pickup arrangements were therefore in the hands of Thamer's brother, Hamad.

I was now the last Westerner waiting in the area, apart from an overweight guy with glasses who was bellowing into a mobile phone and jabbing a finger in the air.

Out of the blue there was a crash to my right as a luggage trolley smashed into the farthest carousel, followed by shouts and then the wailing of a young kid. I guessed from his body position sprawled across the trolley that the kid had been riding it like a go-kart. An older-looking boy smirked from behind a nearby pillar.

As porters and uniformed guards gathered round the stricken trolley, raising their voices at each other and everyone else, a huge man with a big shock of black hair appeared by the pillar. He grabbed the older lad in his wake and scooped up the crying younger boy. *Bit late for young kids*, I thought as he strode purposely in my direction.

'You must be Mr John. I am Hamad, and these are my sons Jamal and Sirwan. Welcome to Amman.'

The big guy thrust out a huge hand and I shook it as I considered how best to politely ask him to prove his identity to make sure I wasn't being lured off somewhere.

'Do you have a sign with you?' I asked. It was doubtful criminals would come bounding along with young kids in tow, but it pays to be careful and follow the set procedure whenever you can.

'No. The boys were writing them but then argued which one was the best. In the end they both ended up ripped, so we threw them away. We didn't need them; we found you. Come on, the car is this way. Let me take your bag.'

So much for the security protocol. Giving myself an internal bollocking, I let Hamad take my small-wheeled grip while I kept my black, cabin-sized rucksack slung over one shoulder.

The guards eyed us suspiciously and the remaining porters were clearly disappointed a potential customer was being whisked out from their grasp at the last minute. The other Westerner stared over at us although the beep of a car horn from a sleek S-Class Merc soon caught his attention. He began wheeling his luggage towards the kerb while a chauffeur jumped out of the vehicle to assist.

An S-Class wouldn't be bad but looking at Hamad and his sons I had my doubts we would be travelling in quite the same luxury.

If I reckoned it unlikely that kidnappers would bring kids along, the sight of the car in front of me cemented my view I wasn't the victim of a criminal enterprise; not unless they intended to grab me and take me back to 1986 that is. As a beaming Hamad swept his hand in presentation, the car in front of me looked as though it had come straight off the set of the movie *Back to the Future*.

With its top-opening gull wings, it was either a DeLorean DMC-12 or a damn fine copy. I was lost for words. It was in great condition, I could give him that. A fine specimen no doubt of a somewhat cult car with a limited production run. However, to say it was unexpected was putting it mildly.

'But how are we going to fit...' As I spoke, a petite woman wearing a headscarf hopped out of an adjacent Honda and called to the boys in Arabic.

'Mr John, this is my wife, Mariam.'

Mariam walked towards me and held out her hand as she said in excellent English, 'Mr John, it is our pleasure to welcome you to Amman and our home.'

With the lightest and briefest of touches I shook her delicate hand and thanked her for coming to greet me at the airport. 'You really didn't need to go to all this trouble. If I had your address, I would have caught a taxi.'

'Nonsense,' Hamad said, as Mariam cajoled the boys into the Honda. 'You are our guest.'

I tried to imagine me, Claire, and the girls rocking up to Heathrow to greet a business traveller flying in at midnight, but it wouldn't have even crossed our minds. It wasn't the last time I would be touched by the welcoming nature and friendliness of people across the Middle East, even to those who they didn't know and might never meet again.

My watch showed almost 1.00am as we finally entered the door of the family apartment in downtown Amman. The two boys were still boisterous, but it didn't matter because it seemed most of the neighbours were still up and about.

'This is my brother Thamer, your driver for Iraq,' said Hamad, as a shorter, bearded man with similar features smiled back at me while we shook hands.

'As salaam alaikum,' Thamer offered in greeting. So much for getting his head down ready for our 3.00am start.

'Alaikum as salaam.' I almost sounded like a native. All downhill from there if my Arabic got tested much further though.

'Baghdad taxis are not allowed to Queen Alia Airport, which is why we picked you up,' said Hamad. Fair enough.

Back to English for me as well. 'Thamer, great to meet you. Are we still going to be good to go for three am?'

Thamer kept his smile up but glanced across at his bigger brother. I looked over to Hamad as well. His confused expression showed he hadn't quite caught what I'd asked either.

I simplified it. 'Are we leaving at three o'clock?'

'Yes, yes,' replied Hamad, before a quick exchange in Arabic with Thamer.

'My brother speaks English, but not so much,' explained Hamad.

That would prove to be an understatement although we were to make do without too many dramas. In some ways it was quite handy. I didn't particularly want to spend 800 kilometres with Iraq's version of a London cabbie in my ear the whole way.

Just in case, I had a small 'Pocket Comms' flip book designed to help people who didn't know the local lingo to communicate via images – a category that definitely applied to me.

'Okay. Does he need to sleep?' I brought my hands together and up to my face in the international sign for getting your head down.

'He's already slept. Don't worry, you will leave on time to get to the border and be there ready for it to open.'

CHAPTER 7

I've always been a light sleeper and an early riser, waking up when required without needing a shake. But less than two hours later my watch alarm had to pierce into deep sleep to rouse me. The display showed 02:30. I hoped Thamer felt chirpier than I did. We had a long way to go today and I wouldn't fancy driving it after less than ninety minutes' sleep.

I shit, showered, and shaved in ten minutes before joining a bright-eyed Thamer in the kitchen for breakfast. The sweetness of the tea probably doubled my blood sugar levels as I wolfed down eggs, bread, and cheese. Mariam fussed over us, ensuring we had enough to eat and our glasses stayed filled with the hot, sweet chai from the pot.

I stood up and rubbed my hands together as a prompt for Thamer. 'Time to get moving, big man.'

He gave me a blank look. Mariam spoke to him in Arabic and after his reply she said, 'One more glass of chai and you will go. Do you want anything else to eat?'

'No, thank you. I've eaten plenty. You really shouldn't have gone to all this trouble. Please pass on my thanks to Hamad as well.'

As I picked up my rucksack the kitchen door opened, and Hamad appeared in the doorway. He looked like shit which caused me to snort a laugh out loud. His wild hair, half-shut eyes, and slow gait gave off a zombie-like vibe. Our goodbyes at the apartment were mercifully swift, and we headed for the car on time. I expect Hamad's head hit the pillow again before we'd even reached the stairs.

If the Baghdad taxi wasn't permitted to the airport, I knew it couldn't be the car from the movies that was taking me to Iraq. As we crossed the car park, the sharpness of the early morning seeped through my jacket. I watched anxiously for Thamer to indicate our ride; some of the vehicles we passed would have disgraced a demolition derby.

When he stopped and opened the door of a red-and-white estate car, I was relieved. It wasn't the newest car on the block, but in the dark it appeared to be in pretty good nick. I later found out all the Baghdad taxis used this colour scheme. With my wheeled bag nestled in the large boot, I dropped into the rear seat and checked the contents of my daysack to be at the ready.

We had to drive over 300 kilometres to reach the Jordan-Iraq border where Mohammed had assured me an Iraqi visa would be issued on entry. Best he was right. If that failed, then I'd be back in London pretty smartish.

★

I woke with a start, lifted my head off the back seat, and glanced at the surroundings. Grey dawn light revealed a desert shanty town filled with trucks and small kiosks selling food, water, and other convenience wares. The taxi had hit a deep pothole as Thamer navigated gingerly around a stationary truck. We picked up speed until he must have sensed or heard me stirring.

He braked and asked, 'Water? Mai?'

'Err… the border, here?' I tried to spot any official-looking signs among the hotchpotch of shacks, parked lorries, ISO containers, and scattered rubbish. A glance at the brightening sky revealed it must have been getting on towards 6.00am, the time the border supposedly opened. I was loath to stop if we weren't close, in case it turned into a big effort to get him going again.

'Yes, yes. Border is very near.'

'Okay. Water, yes. Mai.' I knew a little basic Arabic like the word for water from working with Middle Eastern families over the previous few years. Our conversation wasn't exactly flowing but it seemed we could communicate effectively enough.

I stocked up on bottled water, a handful of chocolate bars, and two cans of warm Red Bull. With the little broken sleep I'd managed, the chocolate and Red Bull could be useful if I started to seriously flag later.

Thamer wandered off to get food from one of the steaming carts nearby. On his return we sat down at a small table for a glass of sweet chai, despite the tang of diesel in the air. A quick look at the toilets before we left revealed someone appeared to be staging a dirty protest, so I knocked that idea on the head. Hopefully there would be a Western toilet at the border post. Within ten minutes of stopping, we were back in the car and I felt energised as we passed a sign for the Karameh Border Crossing.

We passed through the Jordanian side easily, albeit with some puzzled looks. Then it was a short drive to the Iraqi Turaibil border post.

We parked up and went into a single storey, white, stone building, Thamer leading the way before he stopped and motioned for me to go to the counter marked 'Foreigners'. He scurried off to sort out his own documentation while I approached the counter. Just like the Jordanian officials, the Iraqis were very polite. They took my passport and one of the officials directed me to take a seat in the mostly empty room, telling me to wait for a 'short while'. Stares came my way from the few other guys sat in the room. Most looked like they had rocked up for a pirate movie casting session, although given it was 6.00am at the start of the dangerous road through the western deserts of Iraq, their bleary eyes, stubble, and wary nature could be expected.

My chief concern was being identified as a target of opportunity for kidnap or robbery. There weren't many people in the room, but it would only take one phone call to others along the 500 kilometre highway to Baghdad to cause some real problems.

My security on this part of the trip was always the most worrying aspect. Mohammed said he'd journeyed backwards and forwards numerous times with Thamer over recent years and never had any issues. He'd made the trip twice since the end of the war the previous year and was sure it would go smoothly. Of course, he wasn't a fair-haired, blue-eyed Westerner who stuck out like a dog's bollocks. I'm sure if I had swarthy Middle Eastern looks, lifelong Arabic, and a deep knowledge of the culture and religion, I too would have thought it was a piece of cake. Mohammed was suddenly conspicuous by his absence.

I did have a contingency plan of sorts. Ten years before, when I'd left the Corps for a three-year stint in civvy street before rejoining, I got mixed up in a project in Bosnia at the height of the Yugoslav Civil War. To this day I'm not sure who I worked with, but they provided me with press ID which included an address and phone number in London for an outfit called KR Media. Using that, I'd then obtained a Foreign Press Bureau ID Card from an office in the Croatian capital Zagreb to enable me to travel into the conflict areas. Both of those cards sat in my wallet. To augment them, I had recently applied for and received an ID card for the British Association of Journalists. It didn't have a photo, but it had PRESS in big letters on the front.

Armed with these credentials, I intended to use them if detained by anyone unfriendly. I pictured myself jumping out of a vehicle with: 'Ah finally, I've found you at last. John Pierce, reporter for KR Media. This is your chance to tell the other side of the story.'

Not a foolproof plan I'll admit, but a plan of sorts nonetheless.

'Mr John.'

It had only been a minute since handing over my passport, so I hoped this didn't indicate a problem. Once back at the counter they gave me a form to complete *sans* any writing implement. Fortunately, I carried a notebook, pencil, and pen – a habit drummed into us from day one of basic Royal Marines training at Lympstone. I quickly filled in the required details and handed it back. Less than five minutes after sitting down and trying to get comfortable in the hard chair, my name echoed out again.

'Mr John.'

The moment of truth.

'Welcome to Iraq and we wish you a pleasant stay in our country.'

The official handed over my passport complete with Iraqi entry visa stamp and smiled as though he frequently welcomed British travellers to this tourist haven. Who knows, perhaps he did. For all I knew, this could be an everyday occurrence. At least they hadn't sat me down and asked if I was out of my mind for even thinking of driving the road from here to Baghdad. Mind you, they probably pictured an armoured escort waiting outside, rather than the somewhat dusty Baghdad taxi that would now whisk me on my way.

When I strolled past the ranks of the waiting pirate audition, they didn't look thrilled the Westerner had jumped the queue. Some grumbling followed in my wake, but no-one appeared to take any malevolent interest or try to engage me in conversation. I exited stage left and headed for the car.

Back at the taxi there was no sign of Thamer. By now the sun had nudged above the horizon to reveal more traffic transiting the Jordanian side and heading this way. Despite the sunshine, the desert air remained cold from the night and caused me to shiver as I cursed him for disappearing when we should be setting off. A minute or so later he popped out from a nearby doorway, all smiles, and jumped in the driver's seat.

'We go now?' Like he'd been waiting for me.

I bit my tongue. 'Yep, let's go.'

My watch read 06:05, so bang on schedule. I returned to the back seat, donned my baseball cap, and settled down for the ride.

★

The empty three-lane highway stretched into the distance through the desert scrubland as we motored through the western reaches of Iraq's Anbar Province. Initially I peered forward through the headrests, constantly checking whether an illegal checkpoint or roadblock had been revealed in the distance. But there's only so long anyone can keep up that sort of vigilance.

Apart from passing two or three slow trucks early on, the only traffic we encountered was the occasional vehicle overtaking our relatively ponderous taxi. Usually they were new-looking SUVs like the Toyota Land Cruiser, a Middle Eastern favourite.

After about an hour, I began to relax and hope the remaining 400 kilometres to Baghdad would pass by as uneventfully. More vehicles started to appear travelling towards the border in the opposite direction, but there was a soothing tranquillity to the vast desert panorama which helped prevent getting spun up with tension every time a black dot emerged up ahead.

That was until a town appeared over to the right and Thamer took the ramp leading off the highway.

'Where are we going?'

'Family.'

'What do you mean? Are we stopping?' My curt reply reflected my annoyance. Thamer and his brother's family had been nothing but good to me till now, but this turn of events had raised my hackles. Control of the situation was slipping from my grasp.

'My family here.' Not the most complete explanation, although enough to get the gist.

Anyone who researched the security situation in Iraq knew its western Anbar Province was a stronghold for Sunni militants and not somewhere you wanted to be hanging around having a family day out. Not unless you were part of the in-crowd.

It was 7.15am and I wanted to get as much distance under our belts as possible before the roads started to fill up. Instead, within a couple of minutes we were slowing down at a T-junction on the outskirts of the town of Rutba, turning left into a more built-up area of stone buildings bleached in the sun.

There was little sign of life as we pulled up outside a pair of tall, yellowing gates. Thamer left the car and pressed a button, prompting an almost instant opening of the gates by a tall woman (I assumed), dressed head to toe in black. We must have been expected. Thamer jumped back into the car and eased it into the driveway. Our host closed and bolted the gates behind us.

Inside the stone-walled house the temperature was Baltic. The cold permeated my jacket, although the woman silently serving chai with aged hands was padding about with bare feet.

Thamer had said 'My mother's sister' as we entered. His aunt was a big unit as well, with feet like flippers. I guessed her genes more closely matched Thamer's bigger brother, Hamad. She and Thamer engaged in murmured conversation, but no other family members joined us. Perhaps she lived alone.

A dish of bread, tomatoes, and cheese appeared. I took the opportunity to grab another breakfast and hoped I wouldn't have to read the riot act to Thamer about getting back on the road. He'd already been driving for most of the last four hours, so a break and some more sustenance wasn't a bad idea. We still had a long way to travel and I'm a reasonable guy, but it was my money paying the bills and I wanted to get this drive to Baghdad done and dusted.

Before long, Thamer stood up and stretched, prompting me to gather my daysack and do the same. The goodbyes were thankfully short and included my liberal use of 'Shukran' to say thank you to our host.

The limited field of view through the gate restricted my attempt to check the lie of the land outside. From what I could see, it appeared the scene outside was the same peaceful morning we'd left on the way in. Holding still, I strained to detect the sound of footsteps or the murmur of voices but there was no sound of either people or vehicles. The only noise was Thamer filling the car with petrol from a jerrycan. Service stations might be rare or non-existent and stopping at any we did find would increase risk. Good thinking by Thamer to top up here, even if the fuel quality might be questionable.

I took up my position in the rear of the taxi and steeled myself for the next leg of the journey.

On arrival, Thamer had driven straight into the small driveway, so on leaving we'd have to reverse out once the gates were open. From a security perspective this sucked. Too late now but driving out forwards we'd be better able to react to any potential surprises. I made a rolling motion with my hands and mimed the car reversing and taking straight off at speed, hoping Thamer would understand not to dawdle once we left. It wouldn't have won me any prizes playing Boxing Day charades, but I think he got the message. At that moment I felt a long way from safety.

With the gates opened by his aunt, Thamer eased the taxi into the sunshine and backed onto the dusty road. Low in the seat, my eyes swept up and down the road and over the nearby houses, checking for any sign of hostile activity but only registering silence and calm.

We pulled away, seemingly only observed by a chicken strutting past the house. As we reached the highway with no vehicles following, I breathed easier. In comparison with the breakfast tour of Rutba, the main road was a tangible link with the rest of civilisation. We began eating up the miles again and the traffic didn't appear to be noticeably heavier. Hunkered down in the rear wearing my baseball cap, things were going pretty much to plan, although I remained nervous of any checkpoints or roadblocks we might encounter. There wasn't much point worrying about that eventuality now though. I'd just have to deal with it if and when it happened.

CHAPTER 8

For the second time that morning I woke from a half sleep as the car bumped along at walking pace. Instantly wide awake, I scanned outside to check why our speed had dropped so severely, expecting the worst. We were off at the side of the main highway in amongst a collection of shacks and a disused fuel station. There were a handful of cars, several lorries, and a few drivers and passengers nearby, none of whom appeared to take any notice of our arrival.

'What are we doing?'

As the taxi rolled to a halt, Thamer pointed towards a stone building with a side entrance as a man emerged shaking his hands. I couldn't begrudge the guy a toilet stop but I hoped he'd make it quick.

'Where are we?' I held my hands open to emphasise my question.

Pointing ahead to the right, Thamer made a swish of his hand and with a single word answer informed me 'Ramadi' was up ahead.

I needed to take a leak myself, but not if it meant leaving the vehicle unattended. Discreetly checking my rudimentary map once Thamer had disappeared inside the toilet block, I realised it was a long way to Baghdad with a full bladder.

Once he returned, I motioned for him to wait, paused to let a couple of guys pass the car, and then casually opened the rear door. I pulled up my jacket collar and adjusted the peak of my baseball cap down to shield my eyes as I made my way towards the toilet entrance.

Walking confidently like you know what you're doing and where you're going will get you a long way in most places. It helps if you can blend in physically, but I had to work with what I had. With my hands in my jacket pockets, holding the phone in one and a folding KA-BAR knife with a razor-sharp, black, four-inch blade in the other, I kept my pace slow to avoid arousing suspicion. It felt like eyes were studying me as I walked the fifty or so metres, but there were no shouts of recognition or cries of 'infidel'.

Turning into the doorway, I almost collided with a young guy on his way out. He stood back and apologised in Arabic as I grunted an indistinguishable reply. Realisation dawned on his face as our eyes briefly met.

'I'm sorry,' he said, in English this time.

'No problem,' came my automatic reply as I continued into the building. Bollocks. This needed to be the quickest piss in history.

Nature intervened against me and it felt like an eternity before I stood at the broken sink making an unsuccessful attempt to wash my hands due to the lack of water.

I took a deep breath, adjusted my collar and baseball cap in the cracked mirror, and set off back to the car. Again, just as in Rutba, I detected no obvious sign my presence had registered any special interest with anyone. The guy I'd bumped into was nowhere to be seen, but I remained concerned he might be watching to identify my vehicle and send the information on ahead.

While I'd been emptying my bladder, Thamer had bought more food, water, and fizzy drinks; so much for not leaving the car unattended. As I locked the door behind me, I turned down his offer of a can of Pepsi and pointed up the road. He shrugged his shoulders, devoured the rest of his oily sandwich-type snack, and set off again.

I still couldn't see any sign of my toilet doorway acquaintance as we merged back onto the highway. I monitored the wing mirrors for any suspicious following vehicles, but the only one in sight was an ancient and sluggish Mercedes truck pulling a forty-foot container. After a few hundred metres, I switched my focus to the road in front. Whether or not our stop had triggered any interest, there was no sign of any hot pursuit.

The emptiness of the desert gave way to surprisingly lush greenery and trees as we approached Falluja. We crossed a bridge over the Euphrates River not long after our toilet break. The presence of American military vehicles and soldiers on the road was a welcome sight. A chicane slowed the traffic and they scrutinised every passing vehicle. We weren't stopped so I didn't get a chance to interact with them, but that fleeting encounter was enough to sense a link to order and safety.

From Falluja it was only fifty kilometres to Baghdad. For the first time since starting out from the border, the end was in reach. Keep pushing on and we could make it without any issues.

You shouldn't relax and let your guard down as you approach the end of any dangerous task, but the sight of friendly forces for the first time since six o'clock that morning had given me a fresh boost of optimism, although the second can of Red Bull I'd just finished probably helped. It was just gone 1.00pm and I pictured checking into the hotel within the hour and grabbing some much-needed rest before meeting Walid, Mohammed's brother.

As we entered the outer reaches of Baghdad, I began to feel a whole lot more secure. It's far easier to hide amongst a crowd, provided you don't stick out. Cruising into town in a Baghdad taxi was like being in London in a black cab – they filled the roads everywhere. As a precaution, I slunk down and made sure I was well covered from easy view.

However, it soon became clear my initial feelings of reprieve were premature as we hit multiple lanes of stationary vehicles. Suddenly I felt very exposed and trapped if things were to go south. Sat in traffic, drivers and passengers tend to start taking in their surroundings and noticing things like a low-budget Englishman sitting in the car next door. Far from feeling safer in the city, I now longed to be back on the highway with speed as a weapon.

As the time ticked by, I had no idea how far we were from our hotel destination in the centre of the city. Every time I asked Thamer how far or how long he simply opened his hands and uttered a phrase that ended with 'Inshallah'. Not a promising sign.

None of the traffic lights worked and there were no police in sight. Cars drove on the wrong side of the road, along pavements, trying to pull U-turns, and anything else they could think of to gain an advantage. All despite both directions being at a virtual standstill. Total chaos and all against the backdrop of piled debris, run-down neighbourhoods, bombed-out buildings, and an overwhelming sense of decay.

Despite my frustration with our slow progress and dismay at this unexpected exposure, I kept my paranoia in check. Finally, Thamer turned off the gridlocked main road and into the side streets. He was a taxi driver, so perhaps he knew a shortcut.

We weaved slowly through the heavy traffic, but at least we were moving. After turning into a quiet residential road, we pulled up outside a house with a peeling white metal gate. I didn't know where we were, only that it wasn't the Palestine Hotel.

If he noticed it, Thamer ignored the resigned look on my face as he bounded out of the car and went to the gate, calling out a greeting. Next thing, a slender woman with long, dark hair opened the gate from inside and two small kids ran out shouting 'Baba' at Thamer. He scooped them up and then put them down one at a time before motioning for me to follow him towards the house.

Thamer's wife, Sara, spoke good English, as I discovered when she started chatting after bringing us chai, sliced fruit, mixed nuts, and a bowl of assorted sweets. Although I wasn't comfortable about the car being out on the road and not knowing where I was, soon Sara was pointing out our location on my map. She assured me it was a safe neighbourhood where everyone had known each other for years.

Thamer beamed as Sara translated how honoured he was to be my driver and to welcome me to his home. He also hoped I had enjoyed our journey and found his driving to my satisfaction. He might have felt less honoured if he knew I was flat broke and travelling on financial fumes, although the fact I was journeying unprotected across this dangerous route in his old Baghdad taxi should have been a clue.

They invited me to stay for dinner, but I convinced them I needed to reach the hotel and 'meet with my colleagues'. It was 3.30pm, so we'd made pretty good time despite the unexpected Baghdad traffic. Sara said it would take thirty minutes to drive to the hotel, but please could I try some of her cakes first. By 4.00pm we had said our goodbyes and set off again. My doubtful promises to join them one night for dinner seemed to have made everyone happy.

As we turned onto a main road, I was surprised by the electronic goods stacked high on the broken pavements. Boxes of televisions, fridges, and air conditioning units sat outside a multitude of colourful shopfronts bearing the same brand names and logos: LG, Panasonic, Samsung, and Hitachi. The imported products lined both sides of the road as we drove through this commercial district of the city.

Just under thirty minutes after leaving Thamer's house, I caught sight of the instantly recognisable building up ahead on our right. Recognisable, that is, to anyone who had watched TV news coverage of the Iraq War and its aftermath. With the hotel looming above us, Thamer pulled up on the right-hand side of the road near where a group of locals armed with AK-47s read news-sheets and smoked, some leaning against the nearest wall and others lounging on plastic chairs. Behind them lurked an opening between a concrete barrier topped with razor wire and the end unit of a parade of shops. Thamer turned and beamed a satisfied smile. 'Hotel guards.'

After flipping the boot open, Thamer wheeled my bag towards the guards and encouraged me to follow. A quick exchange of Arabic, followed by a glare in my direction, and they let us through. We walked down an empty road with the hotel on our left behind concrete barriers topped with razor wire and a line of two-storey dilapidated buildings to our right.

Two left turns and three minutes later we entered through the glass doors into the busy lobby of the hotel. The babble of English in various accents caught my attention. The many Western expats filling the lobby was quite a surreal sight after the epic and lonely drive across the desert. Almost like stepping into another world.

Still wheeling my bag behind him, Thamer strode over to the reception desk on the right and primed the smart-suited guy standing behind it in Arabic. The duty manager looked at me. 'Mr John, welcome to the Palestine Hotel.'

CHAPTER 9

BAGHDAD – FEBRUARY 2004

After checking into my room, I called Walid who answered within a couple of rings. He sounded relieved that Thamer had delivered me to Baghdad safely and tried to insist on coming straight over to see me. That wasn't happening; I needed a shower and a spot of Egyptian PT. We agreed to meet at 6.30pm for a quick hello and a chance to plan for the following day. Almost two hours – enough time for a power nap.

In early 2004, Baghdad had the feel of a wild frontier. A few Western expats still lived out in the city and many continued to zip around town without armed protection as they ate in restaurants, visited shops, and attended meetings. There was an air of insecurity, of uncertainty, but not yet the menacing feeling death stalked the streets with purpose.

The soundtrack to the city was punctuated by regular gunshots and bursts of automatic fire, mixed with the occasional explosion. It reminded me of Bosnia with UNPROFOR in '95. The constant reminder war was close by, even if you didn't actually see it very often. The way they celebrated weddings and just about everything else in this place, the sounds of a 'Lebanese unload' could be either violence or celebration. If you knew which, you were probably in the wrong place at the wrong time, whatever the answer.

The Palestine Hotel in the heart of the city was a melting pot of security contractors, military personnel, Iraqi businessmen, and Western executives. It was outside the Green Zone which sat on the other side of the river, so a useful location for someone like me who needed freedom of movement for easy access with my local contacts. There were no checkpoints to navigate or American troops to bypass.

An eighteen-storey hotel with a unique facade of concrete flower-type designs on most of the balconies, the Palestine was located on the east bank of the Tigris River by Firdos Square – the square where the huge statue of Saddam was torn down by Baghdad residents with the help of US forces. Now a different statue stood in its place: a modern art piece with a ball balancing on a crescent moon. I'd read it was meant to symbolise the unity of the three main branches of Iraqi society – Sunni, Sh'ia, and Kurds. Art isn't really my bag, but it looked as though they just threw up the first thing they found to fill the void from Saddam's previously imposing figure.

Also perched on Firdos Square was the next-door Sheraton Hotel. Compared to the tired brown and orange decor of the Palestine, you might expect the Sheraton to have been a picture of luxury. However, it had been a long time since the real Sheraton Hotels had managed it and, by comparison to my lodgings, it was a dark and dreary place which resembled a bunker on the ground floors. The one good thing about the Sheraton was that most of the gunfire, bombs, and rocket attacks seemed to be attracted that way instead of hitting the Palestine. Not so good if you lived in the Sheraton of course.

Many of the international press corps also based themselves out of the Palestine, including CNN on the floor directly above me or very close to it. How did I know? Because when CNN reported from Baghdad, the backdrop was identical to the view out of my window down across the square and over the blue-domed mosque visible in so many news reports. Unfortunately, we weren't the only ones to see that backdrop and the locals would pitch up to demonstrate their grievances in the knowledge it would all be shown on American TV.

In amongst the mix, a few entrepreneurs like myself flitted about. Guys representing small companies or their own interests, all searching for contracts to get a foothold in the melee of post-war Iraq. I didn't bump into anyone quite as 'seat of the pants' and low budget as my efforts, but they might simply have been good at blagging it, like me.

My room was basic but comfortable and the 'Welcome Home' card on the desk became my bookmark for several years. The water pressure wasn't stellar, and the temperature hardly luxurious, but in a city with many people struggling to survive it was plenty good enough. A balcony provided a view across the city, although I kept clear of it following a whispered warning given to me on the day I arrived.

Watch out for the snipers. They take potshots if they spot any Westerners.

I hadn't seen any reports along those lines, but better safe than sorry.

The other key advice for when you're staying in a country with fluctuating power supplies and ambivalent levels of maintenance: never use the lifts, always take the stairs.

The US military provided security to the hotel, including armoured vehicles and at least one M1 Abrams tank on permanent duty. Razor wire and concrete barriers surrounded the extended perimeter to restrict access to only one pedestrian entrance and a separate gate for authorised vehicles via the road adjacent to the river. As I'd seen on my arrival, local armed security personnel guarded the pedestrian entrance, positioned a few hundred yards from the hotel front doors and out of the line of sight. It opened onto the main road that ran between Firdos Square and the central Tahrir Square.

Only one entrance made access control easier, but it provided a simple opportunity for anyone to observe movements on foot to and from the hotel. The first couple of days it didn't bother me so much, but after that any surveillance of my movement pattern could quickly identify my vulnerability as I came and went without any security escort.

In my favour, it would probably be assumed I had a 'short', or sidearm, which might dissuade an attack in the immediate vicinity of the hotel. Plus, the Kalashnikov-wielding guards would be able to intervene in the event of an attack. How likely the guards would be to come to my rescue was debatable, but it meant the most likely threat upon leaving the hotel was being picked up by hostile surveillance.

★

Walid presented as the polar opposite to his brother Mohammed back in the UK. Where Mohammed was outspoken, brash, worldly-wise, and opinionated, Walid came across bookish, quiet, and intellectual. During our time together, Walid said that Mohammed could start a fight in an empty room – an apt description. For all their differences, they were each personable, possessed a great sense of humour, and spoke excellent English. It wasn't a surprise I found them both easy to get along with, but I did wonder how well they got on together.

As we sat having a 'Nescafe' coffee downstairs in the hotel, Walid confirmed his readiness and availability to assist for the duration of my stay. His ministry remained operational, but currently redundant because the mining sector wasn't on the immediate priority list. He might need to pop in during the odd morning to show his face. Apart from that he was at my service.

'What is it you need to do here in Baghdad?' he asked.

'Well, three things really. I need to understand the security situation and whether it's even feasible for me to operate here. Secondly, I need to try and identify business opportunities. And thirdly, I need to find local partners to support any contracts that might be won. Here at the hotel I'll be keeping my ear to the ground, but I'd like you to think about the best people for me to meet and any places I should visit. Potential partners, business offices, accommodation. That sort of thing.'

Walid sat back and fiddled with his glasses as he considered my requirements. 'I must say John that I don't know much about business. Especially not now, after the war. But I do know someone who might be able to help. My wife's cousin by marriage is a senior general in the Iraqi Army. He has been to England and speaks good English. I will try to talk with him tonight and arrange for us to meet tomorrow.'

'Okay, that sounds good. He's family so I assume we can trust him, yes?'

'Yes, completely. He is the cousin of my wife's sister-in-law, Dina. The two women are very close. The General has been to our house many times in the past.'

'Great.' I pulled $150 out of my wallet. 'Slightly different topic, but if I give you this can you try and get me a cheap mobile phone and some credit? I need a local number and it'll be the cheapest way for us to keep in touch.'

Walid took the money and counted it carefully. 'I will come to the hotel in the morning with the phone and the receipt. Ten o'clock?'

'I'll be down here at ten. But if you need time in the morning to arrange any meetings or buy the phone, then don't worry about being a bit late. Just call me or message me on my UK phone and let me know. Okay?'

'Okay. I'll go now and see you here in the morning. I don't expect to be late, but I will let you know if I am held up. The checkpoints can make it difficult getting over the river.'

'Thanks, Walid. Take care on your way home and I'll see you tomorrow.'

Walid's attitude to timekeeping was a good sign. As was honesty in what and who he knew. Far preferable to having someone promising loads and failing to deliver. I'd only just met the guy, but I had a good feeling he'd be the right man to help me make the best of this trip.

★

General Imad was an old school Iraqi officer; tall with grey hair, a ramrod straight back, and aristocratic features. Sandhurst-trained with impeccable English, the General bemoaned the waste of lives suffered by the military during Saddam's ill-fated wars with Iran and the West, and the catastrophe the Americans had inflicted on the country with their bungled attempts at managing the aftermath of the previous year's conflict.

As a senior general and a Sunni Muslim, it was safe to assume he had been a card-carrying member of the Baath party. Given the American priority to expunge the Baathists from all walks of life, it was unlikely a call to assume a senior position at the Iraqi Ministry of Defence was in the post. However, the General remained optimistic the Americans would see sense and bring back the military officers, civil servants, scientists, accountants, engineers, and managers who had run the country before the overthrow of Saddam, even though they'd had to become party members to get on.

As we sat drinking chai in the warm afternoon sunshine in his pretty garden in the centre of Baghdad, he searched for a glimmer of agreement from me that a new appointment to serve the country could be expected.

'So, when do you think the Americans will realise they need us to make Iraq work? They're not stupid people. They know they need to forget about the party and the old ways and concentrate on the future.'

'I really don't know, General. The administration in Washington seems to have de-Baathification as its main priority. I'm not working with the Coalition people here, so I don't have any insights.'

'But you must be able to see they are throwing away the chance to rebuild this country.'

'I can see it, yes. The press can see it. Even the people in the administration must be able to see it. But I don't know if that's going to be enough. They won't even acknowledge the mistake of dissolving the army.'

'I'm sure they'll change their minds. American soldiers are dying already and many more will follow if they allow these bandits to gain momentum and popular support. They need the experience of people like me at the Ministry of Defence. We can stop this.' His words might have been positive but the General's face broadcast dismay, probably because I thought his recall to service unlikely.

With the political discussion out of the way, I outlined my objectives in Baghdad. I told him I needed to identify business opportunities and how best to secure them, understand the bureaucratic steps to operate in Iraq, and assess the chances for success. I left out the part about having to then try and find money from somewhere to do anything about it; something neither he nor Walid needed to know.

With the General's military connections, he raised the topic of security services and equipment, but the competition in that sector was fierce and the costs prohibitive. Our conversation slowed as we considered alternatives in between drinking our tea.

After a lapse into silence, the General said, 'I do know some people involved in the reconstruction, although I don't know the details. I could introduce you to one man in particular, Faris. He worked in the old government and has lots of connections. He's moved into business now.'

It sounded like this could be an interesting guy to meet, but I was wary at the mention of his previous work for Saddam's mob.

'What did he do in the government?'

'He worked in state security.'

'Do you mean he was a spy?'

'Oh no, no. Nothing like that. State security here in Baghdad. Not spying.'

I wasn't convinced. It might depend on how you defined spying.

I turned to Walid. 'Do you know this Faris guy?'

'No, I don't think I've ever met him,' said Walid, 'not unless he was here at one of your gatherings?'

General Imad frowned in concentration. 'He may have been here once or twice, but I don't remember introducing you to him. In the old days, even people like me were careful with the state security men.'

It wasn't ideal, but anyone with any clout in this place was likely to have a chequered past.

'Okay. There's nothing to lose by meeting him. When can we set it up?'

★

Faris looked like he had been sent from central casting following a request for an Iraqi spy lookalike. Short, overweight, dark sunglasses, dressed in a smart dark suit, and with a polite but reserved manner, the man exuded a sense of clandestine activity and deals.

He spoke English well enough and smiled plenty, but my gut feeling pegged him as the calculating type, and I don't mean like an accountant. He was also business-like and claimed he knew a lot of influential people who could get things done in this city. I couldn't imagine hanging out with him grabbing a beer, watching football, and talking shit, but this was the type of contact I needed to make this venture work.

The small talk quota must have been reached as Faris finally turned to business. 'So, Mr Pierce, what are you doing in Baghdad?'

'I'm looking for contracts. Looking for business. Local business partners as well. I'm also checking if it's safe enough for us to operate here. I've known Walid's brother for a few years and now seems to be the right time to see if we can use our friendship to bring together Iraqi and Western companies and make some money.'

'And you're here alone? With no links to the Americans?'

'Well I've got Walid alongside me but yes, I travelled alone. I don't have any links with the Americans or the Coalition yet, although I'll soon change that.'

'They have the money,' he said simply.

'That they do. So Faris, what's your set-up? What are you guys involved in? Is it your company or are you working for someone else?'

Faris took a moment before answering. 'We have a number of businesses in different areas. Mainly trading and construction.'

'Any contracts with the Americans?'

'No, not yet.'

'Okay. Well maybe we could put our heads together and come up with a few ideas.'

Either I'd run ahead too fast or Faris was the naturally cautious type. He took his time before answering every question. I doubt he'd met many Western expats before, so a wily old Saddam-era state security guy was likely to be on his guard.

'I think we should meet again,' he said. 'Where is your office? In the Green Zone?'

'I don't have an office yet. That's part of why I'm here. Decide if it's safe enough and look for potential office space and a place to live. I'd be interested in your thoughts on the security situation.'

After the expected pause as his brain whirred through a few cycles: 'The Green Zone is the safest area for foreigners. Outside there are some areas safer than others. Near the embassies for instance. You will need guards and if there is a checkpoint close by it will be better.'

'I tell you what, let's meet up tomorrow and you can show me some of the safer areas outside the Green Zone. Without any American contacts yet, it might prove tricky to get somewhere in there.' I didn't mention I'd nearly fallen off my seat in the bar the previous night when a contractor had told me the rental costs of the villas in the Green Zone. Way out of my league.

It was General Imad who had arranged our meeting. He'd told me Faris wasn't his business partner or close friend, so I should make up my own mind about him without any pressure. Neither Walid nor Mohammed knew Faris at all, so his link to my Iraqi friends was tenuous. But the involvement of the General might just help prevent me getting fleeced, abducted, or otherwise screwed over. No guarantees of course, but there were never going to be any in this place.

★

Faris gave me the Makarov handgun the next morning when we met up. He didn't say anything, just produced it in his outstretched chubby hand and nodded his head. Normal safety procedures were to immediately check the weapon state. i.e. whether or not it's cocked and made ready with a round up the spout, ready to fire if you pull the trigger. On this occasion I opted to assume the Makarov was 'made ready' until I established otherwise. After confirming the safety catch was applied, I slipped it into my jacket pocket.

Removing the magazine and pulling back the slide to check for a round in the chamber was not de rigueur here in Iraq, so I intended to wait until back in the vehicle to do that. Better than attracting attention from everyone in the vicinity as they heard a weapon being cocked. If doing that ejected a round from the chamber, I'd need to catch it to avoid questions over my firearms competence as I scrabbled in the dirt to recover it. And if not already cocked, then they might think the Western idiot had made the weapon ready to fire for no obvious reason.

Although a former Royal Marine, I'd never actually used a Makarov before. AK-47s, or Kalashnikovs, had been the only Soviet weapons I'd got my hands on, usually when playing irregular enemy forces on exercise in the Corps. One of the units I'd served with had been widely used in the 'red team' or enemy role, and many times I'd worn jeans, jumper, and a balaclava whilst carrying an AK-47 as a 'terrorist'.

I recalled a lecture on the Makarov saying it had a small (eight round) magazine and a heavy trigger pull that tended to reduce first shot accuracy. Any targets over about thirty metres max and you were probably wasting your time. This would only be for cases when danger erupted up close and personal.

Once in the car, I cleared the weapon whilst holding it down low, out of sight. It had been loaded but not made ready. A magazine check revealed it held ten rounds rather than eight. Either my dodgy memory or an updated model. No spare magazines, so if things did get lively, I'd only have the ten rounds to work with. But the front seat passenger had an AK-47 in the footwell and I'd seen Faris had a sidearm on his belt. If I assumed at least one more AK-47 in Faris's vehicle, then we had a bit of firepower if it came to it. A lot more reassuring than me and Walid cutting around town in his rusty old Chevy with only our wits and sparkling personalities to protect us.

The next few days saw us visit a succession of properties with a view to identifying an office and accommodation. General Imad didn't join us for these trips round Baghdad, but Faris provided smart cars and a mixture of earnest male and female assistants. His business card showed only his name and telephone number, so it was unclear if he operated on behalf of a specific company or simply for himself. Walid didn't know and my attempts to probe into Faris's current status when we joined the General for dinner a couple of times didn't reveal much either.

Even though we were out in the 'Red Zone', some of the rents being asked were astronomical and none of the properties were in a realistic price bracket for me. We discussed scenarios with shared office space and associated costs although I doubted sharing with Faris would be a good idea. One key benefit arose from these viewings: mixed in with my meetings and lunches, they provided an opportunity to observe the regular pattern of Baghdad life in proximity to its residents.

The concept of setting up in Baghdad seemed tempting, even though the practicalities of running an operation, hiring staff, and ensuring security would be expensive. It was never my intention to make any decisions before sitting down and discussing it with Mohammed back in the UK, but that didn't stop Faris and his gang from showing me ever more salubrious properties. These places would have been great for the large international outfit they clearly thought I ran rather than the tiny limited company they were actually dealing with. My rudimentary efforts at designing a corporate website had clearly worked on this audience.

CHAPTER 10

SOUTH OF BAGHDAD

'Look at his face. Can you see his face? He hates you.' Mr Saleh had suddenly turned from an urbane, confident businessman into an excited Willy Wonka as we'd driven through the gates of his factory to the south of Baghdad. It made a striking change from the recent days spent with the cagey Faris and his crew.

General Imad had introduced the two of us over a phone call from his place the previous day and we'd met up that morning and spent the day together. Instead of focusing on the business set-up, it gave me a chance to spend time with a wealthy businessman and discuss discernible business opportunities.

Lunch had been delicious fish cooked over hot coals in a tented restaurant with an open fire pit by the banks of the Tigris. And Mohammed was right: masgouf was delicious. The place was hired for our exclusive use and his private goon squad sat in a car immediately outside, watching over us and the superbly maintained vintage black Mercedes we'd arrived in.

This wasn't just for my protection. Local kidnappings were rampant and anyone with money was fair game as were their families. During the war the previous year, most of the prison inmates had ended up free to roam the city and get back to business. With the economy shot to pieces and the scarcity of jobs, crime was about the only sector showing rocketing expansion. Mr Saleh wasn't taking any chances.

As I checked out the faces of the workers in the compound, I wasn't feeling the love from any of them. A good job the goon squad were following right behind us or this might have got unpleasant. An especially furious-looking individual with wild hair and wilder eyes stood out. If there was anyone looking angrier than this guy, then I probably needed to be drawing the Makarov.

'All his family were killed in an American air strike. He hates the Americans. He hates you. If I wasn't here, he'd try to kill you.'

Why this was said in such an enthusiastic manner I couldn't quite grasp.

'Well let's keep him at a distance. I don't think it will help productivity if I have to shoot him.'

Mr Saleh's head turned so fast I thought he had to have done himself an injury. 'Of course. You have nothing to worry about. I apologise. You are safe here.'

That remained to be seen.

We were about half an hour south of Baghdad at Mr Saleh's drinks factory. He was giving me the grand tour after I'd explained to him over lunch how I was looking to bring leading Western brands into Iraq and here on the search for suitable local partners.

'Bring me Coca Cola and all our dreams will be realised,' he'd told me.

As I inspected the dusty compound, run-down buildings, and forlorn production line, it was difficult to envisage the Coca-Cola quality control people ripping his hand off to sign on the dotted line.

I tried to introduce a diplomatic reality check. 'Coca-Cola is likely to already have partners here or in Jordan.' Drinks manufacturing was a sector I knew precious little about and, with no advance warning about the type of business he owned, I'd had zero time to conduct any background research.

Mr Saleh swept my negativity aside. 'I want you to find me a new production line in the UK or Germany. Send me some details and we can refurbish this factory and make it fit for the big companies. Anyway, we shall expand our water production and become the best brand in Iraq.'

He was thinking big. Provided he had the money, then this could be worth a closer look.

★

'He's outraged I brought you here.'

Mr Saleh reverted to being Willy Wonka as we headed back out through the gates. He drove the highly polished Mercedes himself with only me in the car alongside, the goon squad bringing up the rear in the other Merc. Not exactly low profile but the goons bristled with weapons and ammunition, ready for a fight rather than just for show.

The dirt road leading from the factory wound through some undulating terrain on its way to the main road. We rounded a sandy hillock to be confronted by a pickup truck manned by four armed balaclava-clad men bearing down on us. As it slewed to the right, I could see a fifth balaclava behind a large pintle-mounted anti-aircraft gun, a 12.7mm (.50 cal) DShK, or 'Dushka'. My eyes must have popped out of my head like something from a Looney Tunes cartoon.

I drew the Makarov and hoped they hadn't spotted me through the tinted windows. Mr Saleh put his arm across.

'No, Mr John. It's okay, these are security forces.'

He stopped the car and opened the window to shout a greeting to the vehicle commander as I tried to bring my heart rate back under control. I was going to need a drink tonight.

When I did get back to the hotel, Walid joined me in the gardens for a Nescafe. Caffeine would do for now, but as soon as he left I'd be hotfooting it to the bar for a beer. I squinted at my laptop in the late afternoon sun as Internet searches revealed a few used production lines available in Europe which might fit the bill for Mr Saleh's expansion plans. An agreement with Coca-Cola might be tricky to say the least but helping to source equipment and goods could be eminently doable.

★

After ten days that felt much longer, I'd accomplished most of what I had set out to do. I hadn't stumbled upon the holy grail of a big contract waiting for my signature, but the possibilities here were exciting and the Palestine Hotel attracted a lot of interesting people.

In the early evening all the American news crews from CNN and other stations were earning a crust transmitting live feeds from Baghdad to breakfast news in the US. I usually returned to the hotel by the time it started getting dark. So back by sixish. After finishing any admin and having a shower, I'd head for the restaurant to see what culinary delights awaited. With only an empty room upstairs waiting for me, I then tended to gravitate towards the downstairs bar.

General Order Number One for the US military included an alcohol ban for troops in Iraq, so no surprise soldiers were thin on the ground in there. The odd security contractor would pop in, but they were a busy bunch. Instead, I either chatted with the local bar staff while I wound down in the secure environment or mingled over a beer with reconstruction contractors. Most were engaged in telecommunications and engineering projects for the big American companies, but a few were smaller scale and on the lookout for business opportunities in a similar fashion to me. The reaction if I mentioned I worked alone with local contacts was always the same: don't do it; and if you do then be really, really careful.

The security situation was getting more precarious, leading to increasing numbers of expats moving out of relatively insecure villas and into secure hotels like the Palestine. My apprehension levels increased the more times I left the hotel for my daytime travels. I varied the timings as much as possible, but I had little choice other than to use the single pedestrian exit and entrance. And the more times I used it, the more concerned I became about attracting hostile attention. Those drinks in the bar at the end of most days took the edge off, but my unease grew each day. Now each morning when I woke up, it was with a sense I'd ridden my luck so far but today it might just run out. Time to review my options for travelling back to the UK.

Outside the immediate entrance to the hotel by the steps, a small informal 'Haji market' of traders had been established, selling knock-off DVDs, porn, local phone cards, dodgy-looking electronics, sweets, fizzy drinks, and souvenirs, including watches and other paraphernalia with 'uncle' Saddam's picture.

Saddam had been apprehended and reportedly had new secure digs at Baghdad Airport. None of the Iraqis I had met showed any affection or obvious allegiance to the former leader, so the phrase 'uncle' Saddam appeared to be more a way of poking fun at him than anything else. Poking fun at him and indirectly at the Americans as well; the subtext being things were now so bad under their stewardship that people could reminisce about the old days. I doubted any of the people using the phrase had spent time in his prisons or had family members disappear or be killed though.

Later I encountered the same use of 'uncle' Saddam when in Kurdistan. It seemed many Iraqis simply had a dark sense of humour. In similar fashion, it struck me that many of the Baghdad population had the kind of Blitz spirit which people in the UK think of as uniquely British. Despite the lack of power, jobs, and money; crumbling infrastructure; lengthy queues for fuel; and rampant insecurity, they mostly just got on with living their day-to-day lives as best they could.

I shifted into the late afternoon sunshine and called Claire to let her know I'd be heading home soon. My few phone calls to her had been short and sweet, partly from necessity because I didn't want to rack up outrageous call charges on the satellite phone. Jim had told me not to worry about it, but I didn't want to find the line out of credit or disconnected when I really needed it, all because I'd spent twenty minutes a day whispering sweet nothings back to Claire in the UK. That wasn't our style anyway. I remember the both of us running out of things to say during the weekly fifteen-minute phone calls during my deployment to Bosnia back in '95.

Claire was pleased I'd soon be home although expressed concern about the drive back across the desert to Jordan. She never made a big deal about these sorts of things, but it worried her. It worried me as well.

There was no Internet availability at the Palestine, so every day I set up my BGAN at a table in the hotel gardens and pointed it towards the satellite. It allowed me to keep up to date with the news, send emails, check flight availability, and research on the Internet. Like the sat phone, I didn't want to kick the arse out if it in case one day it disappeared because I'd run up charges the size of a small country's GDP.

To anyone observing, I would have looked like any another field executive out here making serious money with a large contractor. My business and personal bank accounts said otherwise though. Another reason for heading home was to keep the costs of the trip down. Every additional day cost me another 100 dollars including the hotel room. I needed to watch my money because this was a cash economy and there were no ATMs if you ran out.

CHAPTER 11

When I visited General Imad again on the afternoon before I was due to leave Baghdad, he asked if his son Ahmed could accompany me back to Amman. In his early twenties, Ahmed spoke great English and would be an asset to have alongside. He needed to travel to Amman for his own reasons, and I wasn't going to turn down the offer to go halves on the costs.

'If you need to go to Amman and can travel tomorrow morning, then it would be great to have you along. Thamer's English isn't great, and my Arabic is abysmal. It'll just be us though. We don't have any security. And we're going to be leaving early so we miss all the traffic.'

'That's fine. I want to be in Amman by mid-afternoon anyway. As for security, my father knows a lot of people.'

'You mean guards to travel with us?'

'No, I mean the tribes and the army. If there's any sign of terrorists along the road then he will be warned and can call to let me know. I will give him the taxi plate number, so he can pass it on if needed.'

It was a benefit I hadn't expected and anything that might increase the level of security for the journey was welcome news.

As we left his house, the General mentioned Faris had been trying to reach me, so back in the car I called him using my local phone.

'Faris, it's John. You've been trying to get hold of me?'

'Yes, Mr John. I have arranged a meeting tonight with an important businessman. I will pick you up at seven from your hotel. Just you, Mr John. Not your friend Walid.'

'That's very short notice. Who is this guy and what does he want to talk about?'

'Business. Lots of opportunities. He's a powerful man in Baghdad and he wants to meet you. I think it will be very good for you.'

The run back from the General's house to the Palestine was due to be my last Baghdad journey before boarding Thamer's taxi early the following morning for the long drive to Amman. I'd focused on these two tasks as the final hurdles to cross before being able to relax for my flight home. The idea of arranging an evening meeting with persons unknown wasn't something that appealed. Neither was the request from Faris that I go alone with him.

However, I couldn't turn it down. It would put a different complexion on everything if a highly promising business opportunity came into my hands. With a heavy sense of foreboding I agreed Faris should pick me up alone as suggested.

'Okay, seven pm. I'll be waiting near the gate. Call me as you arrive and I'll come out.'

Back at the hotel I said my warm goodbyes to Walid. After parking the car in the first available space about fifty metres from the access gate, he walked with me to the hotel and we moved into the gardens with a Diet Coke and a bottle of water each.

'Thanks, Walid. I'm really grateful for all your help these last couple of weeks. I know that working with me could be dangerous for you. And say sorry to your wife for me, for dragging you away nearly every day.'

'No need to thank me. It's been my pleasure. I hope I have helped you make good use of your time in Baghdad. I also hope we will soon see more British and Americans here to help us rebuild and not just the soldiers.'

He tried to insist on coming in the morning to wave me off in the taxi, but I torpedoed that idea. Come 6.00am I intended to be moving as quickly as possible out of the city to avoid the horrendous morning gridlock and get a head start for the border. I'd already ensured Thamer would pick up Ahmed before coming to the Palestine. I wanted a straight shot out of Baghdad once I was loaded in the car.

After spending most of the last ten days with the reassurance of the Makarov, I'd miss having a weapon when I had to return it before heading to Jordan; despite knowing that if we ran into an armed group on the highway, those ten rounds wouldn't be enough, and the presence of a firearm during any search would nullify my journalist cover story.

★

'Mr Faris asks that you get down in your seat and let me put this jacket over you.'

The young guy sat next to me in the rear of the SUV must have seen the scowl on my face, but he had his orders. We already had darkened privacy glass in the rear and this clown wanted me to hide under a jacket.

'Why? What's happening?'

All I needed. A drama on my last night in Baghdad during a magical mystery tour. Not that I'd seen anything to cause alarm.

'Mr Faris says the area we are going to, Al-Adhamiya, is a very strong anti-American neighbourhood and they must not know you are there.'

Just fucking great. What about the people inside the meeting? I certainly didn't have control of the situation and things could start going wrong pretty fast. If it was such a big deal, then why the hell was the meeting being held there?

My concern rose that it might be fine getting in, but, after I'd been presented like a debutante at a summer ball to the waiting audience, how long would it take for some undesirables to crash the gig and upset my evening. Assuming that didn't happen, leaving and getting out of there might prove trickier than the move in.

'We need to keep this meeting short, mate. Very short.'

'Mr Faris agrees that the meeting should not be a long one.'

The kid must be telepathic because Faris, sat in the front passenger seat, hadn't said a word. That meant they must have already discussed this point, and he knew we were headed into a potentially dangerous situation. He was a Sunni who served under Saddam. If he was concerned about it then I had every right to be.

Ten minutes later, with me huddled under a dark jacket on the back seat keeping low, Faris murmured to the driver and I felt the vehicle turn left, bump down an incline, and stop.

The doors opened. 'We're here.'

Thanks, kid.

We'd driven into a small integral garage underneath a house. It was dark outside, but the lights on the two gateposts up at street level provided enough illumination to make out a doorway in the gloom and reach it without tripping over anything. There was no space to turn around, which meant reversing out when we came to leave. What was it with everyone in this country? Why did no-one ever think to reverse in and be ready to exit in a better tactical position? I took some deep breaths to calm my frustration as I shook my head and muttered under my breath about 'fucking idiots'.

Once allowed inside the house by a big, sullen guard with a holstered handgun, we entered a large room full of Faris lookalikes sitting round a huge conference table at one end. At the other end, the identity of the resident Mr Big was clear: behind a huge desk sat a large, clean-shaven man in his late forties/early fifties with an intelligent face who emitted a naturally powerful aura solely by his presence, a perception undoubtedly helped by the dominant size and position of both him and his desk. He spoke with an off-putting deep growl and I had to concentrate to understand his English.

'Welcome, Mr John. Faris tells me we have little time. You'll forgive me if we begin immediately.' And so began the interrogation.

When I say interrogation, I don't mean in a torture sense. Instead, Mr Big, aka Abu Saif, had his minions rapid-fire questions in my direction for the next twenty-five minutes about me, my business, what I was doing in Baghdad, and what I hoped to achieve in Iraq.

It's lucky I had experience blagging business meetings as an investigator because this was brutal. Abu Saif eyed me intently throughout, interjecting with an occasional question directly to me, and comments in Arabic to the minions.

'You must excuse me, I have visitors.'

The hairs on the back of my neck stood up as Abu Saif left the room. A young, fit-looking guy with a holstered Glock-type handgun had darted in to give him the message announcing the apparently unexpected guests. After which, Abu Saif had immediately risen from his sumptuous leather chair and strode out of the room with a curt nod in my direction after he spoke.

The lack of a handshake concerned me, but then maybe he would be back in a couple of minutes. Faris looked directly at me with a slight frown. A short while later he wrapped things up with the interrogation tag-team as they finished their copious note-taking.

'Mr Faris says we need to go.' No shit, Sherlock. The kid was only doing his job, but his 'Simon says' way of talking was beginning to get on my nerves.

'Tell him we need to be very careful leaving here.' Faris seemed to be on top of things, but I wanted to make doubly sure we were all on the same page.

There was no sign of Abu Saif as we exited through the same basement door out to the SUV. I had mixed feelings about the three rugged-looking men armed with AK-47s stood inside the gate. They were taking no notice of me and I wanted to get out of there ASAP in case that changed to unfriendly interest. I didn't know whether they belonged to Abu Saif or his visitors, but they held themselves and their weapons like they knew what they were doing. If things went noisy as we left, I hoped they'd be on our side.

I held my hand up as the kid turned to me with his eyes sweeping down to the jacket laid on the seat beside me.

'Yeah, I'll deal with it.' I grabbed my baseball cap out of the daysack and pulled my own jacket collar up high. No way I was leaving this place curled up on the back seat like a cat under their jacket.

'Mr Faris…'

'I don't give a fuck.'

The sound of the slide racking on my Makarov prompted a comedy look of shock on the kid's face. Cultural sensitivity was all very well, but this wasn't the time for pussyfooting about.

The kid was speechless, which suited me fine.

Faris turned from the front seat with a concerned look on his face and made downward motions with his hands. 'It's okay, it's okay.'

The expression on his face said it might not be okay.

'Let's not hang about when we get outside, yes? Go, go, go, yes?' This wasn't the time to be all 'Driving Miss Daisy.'

The armed guards opened the gates and stepped out onto the road in front of the house as we inched backwards until we pulled level with the pillars. The engine revved and we reversed into a left turn with screeching tyres before shooting forward down the road.

People stood clumped together on the street and outside most houses as I searched for signs of weapons and threats. Christ, it seemed like every other person had an AK-47. Ten rounds in a handgun felt like very small beer.

We swerved left past a shouting figure stepping out from a house gate fifty metres or so down from Abu Saif's pad. More yells sounded behind us, but no gunfire, no pursuit, no drama. I blew out a breath as we turned onto a main road until I looked behind and saw a dark Mercedes come flying round the same corner we'd recently emerged from.

'Behind, behind.' I chopped a hand towards the following vehicle.

'No, no, no. With us.'

We'd arrived alone, but it appeared Abu Saif had supplied an escort for our journey home. Faris nodded as his eyes searched out mine, checking I understood.

'Okay, good,' I offered.

If they were an escort, then great. Mind you, I didn't know who was in the vehicle or whether their intentions were in fact friendly. I guessed we'd find out soon enough.

Faris certainly appeared to have relaxed now we'd cleared Abu Saif's neighbourhood and he spoke to the driver without any urgency in his voice. It was probably a home from home for him, or perhaps he even lived there. Maybe if knowledge leaked out of the presence of an infidel, it could have a seriously adverse effect on him. Selfish I know, but I hoped so. If it was in his interests to keep me out of harm's way, then that suited me just fine.

The driver manoeuvred through the evening traffic at speed and the Mercedes soon dropped out of sight. It had indeed only been an escort out of the neighbourhood by the looks of it.

When we arrived outside the pedestrian gate entrance to the hotel, I realised Faris didn't know I'd be leaving in the morning. I cleared the Makarov and made it safe as we pulled up, prompting another wide-eyed look from the kid. As I handed it to Faris, I let him know my plans.

'Bukra?' he asked in Arabic. Then switched back to English. 'Tomorrow, Mr John? You should have told me. We have so much to do and I haven't made any arrangements to escort you to Amman.'

CHAPTER 12

It had been a tough call. Either head back with Thamer and take my chances with the unsupported, low-profile approach, or rely on Faris, a new and unproven contact. I'd made the decision during the last get-together with General Imad.

First, the General surprised me when he didn't express a ringing endorsement of the blossoming relationship with Faris. It sounded like they didn't know each other as well as I'd initially assumed.

'Be careful with Faris. Him and his type may have links with some very unpleasant people. Unfortunately, this is the future of Iraq unless the Americans act quickly.'

'Thanks, General. Are you saying you don't trust Faris?'

The General snorted. 'Of course I don't trust him. He was state security and now he mixes in circles where money is everything. Some of these people would sell their mothers for dollars.'

Okay, so they definitely weren't as close as I'd thought. Faris had been a useful person to meet, but it was a reminder I needed to be very careful where things went next.

Secondly, with his son Ahmed now coming along, the General reassuringly informed me, 'We have friends along the way, so you will have a safe journey.'

Walid confirmed what Ahmed had said about the General having lots of friends in the military and amongst the tribal leaders in the western Anbar Province, so I made sure Imad's number was stored in my UK phone, the local Nokia, and the sat phone. For good measure

I'd also given his and Walid's numbers to my ex-bootneck mate, Jim, in case I disappeared off the grid.

As I checked out of the Palestine Hotel, I felt surprisingly wistful to be leaving. The last ten days had been like beaming into a completely different, exciting, dangerous universe. There were no guarantees I would ever return.

Optimistically, I'd tucked myself and my gear into a sheltered doorway thirty metres from the pedestrian gate. The hotel staff appeared genuinely sorry to see me leaving and one of the doormen had insisted on wheeling my bag to the gate for me. It can't have been because I was a big tipper; I'd been relieved to have enough money left to cover the outstanding hotel balance. But I had chatted to the staff whenever I bumped into them and engaged in several friendly discussions about Premier League football results and the Champions League progress of Chelsea and Arsenal.

The arrogant attitudes from some of the press corps and executives strutting around the place made me wonder how many guests treated them with decency and respect. Almost every time I passed the reception desk, I heard someone registering a complaint about water, power, the standards of cleaning, lack of Internet, poor food, broken air conditioning, or just venting about Baghdad. It's not a job I would have fancied.

My Nokia rang and Ahmed announced their imminent arrival at the gate. I grabbed my gear and yomped off in that direction.

One of the armed guards was still complaining to Thamer and telling him to move, even while I threw my larger bag into the boot and assumed a position on the back seat with my daysack. Perhaps he needed to attend the next customer service course.

We left Baghdad only fifteen minutes later than scheduled and were soon cruising past Abu Ghraib on the western outskirts and hitting the open road. I vetoed a stop at the local version of motorway services near Falluja. I'd read the book and got the T-shirt for Iraqi service stations and didn't intend to chance my arm in this area again.

Ahmed in the car with his excellent English gave me far more control over the journey. And with General Imad's assurances the journey would pass without incident, I hoped an unseen, wider presence offered protection along the way.

★

The American Humvees were travelling at speed on the opposite side of the carriageway back towards Ramadi. We weren't hanging around either. The speedo regularly nudged 130km/h as Thamer's freshly-serviced taxi zipped through the scorched desert air. The road ahead of us was empty as a second packet of Humvees came into view, charging down the other side of the road.

Without warning, a huge explosion of dust about 400 metres ahead of us obscured our view of the lead Humvee. The deafening road noise in the old car helped to muffle the sound to that of a distant peal of thunder.

'IED.' I knew what had happened immediately.

Surprisingly, the Humvee fired out of the dark dust cloud followed by the second and third vehicles. The bomb must have exploded too early and missed its targets.

I'd reached for my camera to get the shot I imagined would adorn the front page of *Time* magazine. That would give my journalist credentials and my bank balance a serious boost. Unfortunately, it was only a low-spec digital camera, so by the time it responded to my frantic clicking of the button, we'd slid to a halt 100 metres or so from the seat of the explosion still in front of us, and the Americans were long gone. Instead of a glorious photo of Humvees emerging through the dust of an IED explosion on the western highway, I got a puff of dust and an empty road. Bollocks.

It was a reminder we weren't out of the woods yet. I interrupted the excited chatter in the car.

'Excuse me, guys. Can we get moving?'

Instead of setting off again, both Ahmed and Thamer opened their doors and began to get out of the car.

'We're stopping for a break as we're at the side of the road already,' said Ahmed.

'Oh no we're fucking not. Listen mate, if that bomb was operated by radio control, mobile phone, or command wire, then someone is probably sat out there watching us right now. Someone, I might add, who's just let off a big fucking bomb trying to kill Americans and might just fancy taking out an English dude as a consolation for screwing up. So, before they start shooting or, even worse, the Americans turn up and start vittling up the only vehicle sat near the site of an attack, let's Foxtrot Oscar the hell out of here, okay. NOW.'

Ahmed cast fearful glances into the desert as he scrambled back into the car and called Thamer, raising his voice after the driver replied with a whingeing tone recognisable in any language. He must have made his point because Thamer suddenly darted back into the driver's seat and wheelspun us back onto the road and away.

'I'm sorry. I didn't even think of those things. Have you seen them?' Ahmed's eyes were out on stalks peering into the passing desert. Probably a mirror image of mine, which had been sweeping across every sandy hillock, depression, bush, and tumbleweed in the vicinity since I put the camera down.

'No mate, but it's better to be safe than sorry. Let's get well away from this area and then you can stop for a toilet break.'

As we accelerated away from the scene of the explosion, Ahmed asked, 'What is "vittling"? I haven't heard this word before.' He smiled. 'But I understand "Foxtrot Oscar".'

'Vittling? That means shooting. Effective shooting. You might not find it in the dictionary though.'

'You mean the Americans would shoot at us?'

'Maybe. We were the only people in the vicinity. With the VBIED threat – you know, car bombs – our friendly GI Joe might not fancy bimbling up for a chat to check if we're a bunch of rabid jihadis determined to fast-track our way to heaven or not.'

'Bimbling?'

I laughed. 'It means having a leisurely stroll over to us. Walking slowly, taking your time, not a care in the world. Thumb up bum. At this rate I'll have you talking like a bootneck by the time we reach Amman.'

After briefly pulling over half an hour up the road, the only other stop before reaching the border was the world's fastest pit-stop for fuel. Thamer moaned about my refusal to let him get anything hot to eat. Apparently, the snacks I'd brought along just didn't cut the mustard. Tough. I'd taken enough chances over the last ten days and was in full risk mitigation mode for this final leg of the journey.

Weariness rolled over me as the Iraqi Turaibil border post came into view in the distance. Desperately trying not to switch off for the final few minutes, I forced myself to keep scanning for potential threats amongst the intermittent traffic and out into the passing desert scrubland.

As we pulled into the border post, I felt shattered and hoped the exit visas would be processed as fast as those on entry. That hope proved wildly optimistic. Even at this time of the afternoon, vehicles crowded both the Iraqi and Jordanian sides. It didn't take much of a queue to overwhelm the officials on either side and it wasn't a surprise the Jordanian border guards took far more interest in those entering their country than those leaving. I resigned myself to the wait.

★

Ahmed insisted I was dropped off first. It sounded like he'd be going on to meet with a former student friend, probably a girl judging by his excitement. He'd been a real asset for me on the drive across from Baghdad and we parted with a warm handshake.

I couldn't know it then, but we were never to meet again. Later that summer he was kidnapped and tortured in Baghdad, although fortunately rescued by a police raid, along with several other shackled and blindfolded hostages held in a disused factory.

Hamad and his family treated me like an old friend and I relished the chance to relax properly for the first time since passing through less than two weeks ago. Mariam cooked a delicious meal which I savoured before excusing myself and going to bed early. I slept right through until my alarm had to wake me the following morning.

As the Royal Jordanian flight went wheels up after take-off, I finally turned my attention to life back in the UK. Our financial situation was poor, but I had a real sense of optimism Iraq could provide the money that would lift us out of the day-to-day struggles and change our lives infinitely for the better. 'Fortune favours the brave' as they say; well I should be due some good fortune if I kept this up.

Back home was like coming down to earth with a bump. From the fear and excitement of Baghdad, Epsom could only ever appear boring and mundane. It often did when a big project ended or I returned home from a tour, only this time it felt acute.

Great to see Claire and the girls and get out in the spring fresh air with Taz, but over in Iraq I'd been a player in a much bigger game. Here I was scratching around to find the money to back up my ambitions while trying to fit in some paying work before I went back.

Despite the risks, there was never any real doubt I would go back. The siren call of adventure was drawing me inextricably to Baghdad. Now I'd started down this road, I remained determined to see where it would lead, hoping desperately that success would be quick to arrive. But first, I had to find some money.

CHAPTER 13

EPSOM – LATE MARCH 2004

The collar nipped at my neck as I tried to adjust it. I wasn't used to wearing a shirt and tie, but for the visit to the bank I'd suited up and even reacquainted myself with tying a half-Windsor knot instead of using one of my clip-on security ties. Next time I bought any shirts I needed to remember to go up a collar size.

The grey-haired bank manager, with his sensible shoes and a cheaper-looking suit than mine, flicked through my updated business plan, studied the bullish financial forecasts, and listened with apparent interest as I described my recent visit to Baghdad and exaggerated the value of work here in the UK. His attitude throughout had been more open and positive than I'd expected.

It was my first port of call for finance although I wasn't optimistic a bank manager in leafy Surrey would be itching to fund my ambitious international expansion plans. Friends I spoke to made it clear they believed I was wasting my time, so I'd also enquired about getting a secured loan on our house. The computer at our building society said no, but some other mortgage providers claimed people like us – with less than stellar credit scores – could get a deal with them, with the accompanying higher interest rates. Funny how the more money troubles you had, the more you had to pay compared to those in a better position.

The bank manager returned to the room and sat down with a friendly smile as I finally gave in and undid the top button of my shirt.

'So, Mr Pierce, just to recap. This loan will be used to set up an operation in Baghdad, but you do understand it is a loan to your British limited company and the liability falls squarely with that company here in the UK?'

'Yes of course. Most of the money will be used for office rental, equipment and supplies, and a cash float for expenses. My partners in Baghdad will also be putting in money and paying their own costs separately. But I understand the liability for this loan would be with my company here alone.'

'Fine. It sounds like a very interesting project. Based on your business plan and financial projections, and a review of your account standing, your application has passed the credit checks and I'm happy to endorse the loan. I wish you all the best with your new venture in Iraq.'

I punched the air as I left the bank, even whilst kicking myself for not asking for more, like a one-man band of competing emotions. Getting the bank to say yes to a £15,000 business loan had been a lot easier than expected. Finance sorted, my thoughts turned to Baghdad.

★

Sat in the Churchill Hotel again three days later, the future seemed full of promise as Mohammed and I discussed plans for both of us to travel together to Baghdad at the end of the month.

'I have the money for my flight ticket to Amman,' said Mohammed. 'Should I give it to you, so you can book both tickets together, or buy my own ticket?'

'If you give it to me, I can book the tickets as soon as we agree which day we're going.'

'I'm ready to go, so what do you think?'

I'd been invited to a rare get-together with some other ex-bootnecks the following weekend and it would be a shame to miss it. 'Let's fly next Monday, 29th March. That gives Thamer seven days' notice from today for the Amman to Baghdad drive on the 30th. I know he needs to get to Amman, but that should be enough time, yes?'

'Let me call him now and find out.' Mohammed pulled out his phone and scrolled through the contacts.

Five minutes later and we were all agreed for the following week, subject to my booking the seats with Royal Jordanian or British Airways to Amman. With next Tuesday pencilled in for another desert odyssey to Baghdad, memories of my last trip flashed up and triggered a gentle fluttering of nerves. At least Mohammed would be with me this time and he didn't seem fazed by the upcoming journey.

'Walid shouldn't have introduced you to this man, Faris. You can't trust state security people.' Mohammed had slipped back into the disapproving stance he'd adopted since first discovering the involvement with Faris on my return from Baghdad.

'It wasn't Walid's fault. I asked him to introduce me to people, and it was actually General Imad who suggested meeting with Faris. And Faris isn't so bad. He seems to know a lot of people involved in business over there. This Abu Saif guy I met could be a useful contact.'

'I don't know them, and you should be more careful who you meet with,' replied Mohammed. 'Be careful with that old rogue Imad as well. He's related to Walid's wife, but he doesn't really know what's going on outside of the Baghdad Hunting Club.'

Suffice to say Mohammed wasn't enamoured with the involvement of Faris and didn't appear too fond of General Imad. These were issues to keep an eye on and try to smooth out once we were back in town. He refused to share offices with Faris, which was fair enough as I wasn't convinced about that myself. Mohammed had raised some money to put in alongside mine and said he'd find us good places to view at decent prices after registering his criticism at the rental quotes I'd received.

The UK company was mine alone, so I agreed we should set up a company in Baghdad with Mohammed as the director and shareholder. A key consideration was preventing any hostile interest that could arise if my name appeared on the records in Baghdad. It would also be easier administratively and sharing the profits from our Iraq venture would be straightforward with a written agreement between my UK company and the new firm in Baghdad. The deal wouldn't include my unrelated investigation and surveillance business. My other work wasn't paying big bucks, but it was all I had to try to cover the mortgage, bills, credit cards, and loans.

It was disconcerting to hear a Swedish guy I'd met at the Palestine had been killed at long range by a gunman while in traffic on a busy Baghdad road. This reflected the reports of a deteriorating security situation. My hair was fairer than usual because of the recent Middle Eastern sunshine. Even though my trip had started in February, the midday temperatures had been over eighty degrees. If insurgent gunmen were targeting Western-looking individuals in Baghdad, then pitching up with a blond beach boy look wouldn't be ideal. I considered dyeing my hair darker and Claire volunteered to do the honours, but I imagined I'd end up looking like an oddball with mismatching hair and eyebrows, so decided against it.

★

On the Saturday afternoon, two days before the flight to Amman, I met up with a few ex-bootnecks congregated in London for a celebration. I didn't know the guy it was all for, but one of my old oppos, Steve 'Jacko' Jackson, persuaded me to get on a train and head up to join them at the Victory Services Club in Seymour Street, off Edgware Road. There were some familiar faces stood round the bar, and it was great to have a few beers with friends I hadn't seen for a long time.

Jacko and I had different views on the 1-1 draw between Chelsea and Arsenal in the Champions League quarter-final first leg earlier that week, and especially on the likely outcome of the second leg at Highbury – me being Chelsea and him a Gooner. A lot of bootnecks considered football players all overpaid fairies, and we were interrupted with derogatory comments from our big rugby-loving mate, Mark 'Chewy' Barker.

'Stop talking about shitball you pair of wankers,' chipped in Chewy as he walked past on the way back from the heads. We threw a couple of insults his way about his huge rugby-ball-shaped 'heed', which were met with a raised finger over his shoulder back at us.

'Come on then, get the wets in. You must be loaded earning all that dosh in Iraq.' Jacko wiggled his empty pint glass under my nose.

'Some chance of that, mate. I'm spending money like water over there.'

'Eh, gen? How come? I thought it was all a thousand dollars a day swanning round with your Oakleys on, looking ally, bronzing up on your time off.'

'Not for this call sign, mate. I'm going for it, shit or bust. Setting up on my own to make my fortune. By next year I'll either be driving an Aston Martin or dossing under Waterloo Bridge.'

'Fuck. I didn't know that. I'll throw you a few coins when I see you under the bridge.'

'Cheers Royal, you throbber. That's if I even make it back. The taxi rides between Amman and Baghdad last time were... entertaining. Not really looking forward to it all again next week. Baghdad had its moments an' all.'

'So, what sort of security do you have? You're tooled up, yeah?'

'Hang on mate.' The barmaid had reappeared and I caught her eye. 'Excuse me love, two beers please.'

Chewy appeared at my elbow. 'Two beers my arse. What he means, darling, is twelve pints and twelve shots.' He smirked while he selected the poison of choice from the top shelf.

'No need to thank me. I've sorted it for you.'

'Have you mistaken me for someone else you prick? Does it look like I'm the duty baron?'

Chewy blew me a kiss. 'You look essence, mate. And I know you're coining it in over in Iraq you tight-fisted twat.'

'I don't fucking think so, mate. I'm riding round in taxis between Amman and Baghdad with no weapon, no security, no nothing. Relying on my gleaming personality and ninja skills to stay out of the shit.'

'Well you're fucked then, mate. What size boots are you? Tell your missus I'll be round to sort through your kit when you get caught and fucked. Pretty boy like you, they'll be queueing up to give you the good news from behind. Make sure you ask for a reach-around to get the full benefit. Although you'll probably enjoy it anyway you tart.'

As the pints and shots began to arrive on the bar, our conversation was interrupted by an influx of piss-taking, laughing idiots I called friends – old and new – grabbing drinks and downing them ridiculously fast to the disapproving look of both the barmaid and the manager helping her serve the order. Luckily for us the bar was otherwise empty. The Victory Services Club isn't a drinking den, and we'd soon need to move on to somewhere our increasingly boisterous behaviour would be less out of place.

After paying for a round that would have stress-tested the central bank of a developing country, I turned back to Jacko and caught the tail end of him telling the others I had been roaming Iraq unarmed in a taxi. There was a brief silence before one of the lads, Simmo, piped up, 'You fucking knobber,' and everyone dissolved into laughter, including me.

When Jacko found out I was returning to Iraq in two days, he got straight on the phone to another ex-bootneck mate of his, Dan, the security team leader for a US TV news crew. Despite being half-cut, I recognised the offer to join their convoy leaving Amman the following Tuesday was a godsend. Through the alcoholic haze I gave no thought to the practicalities of Thamer's ageing taxi tagged on the end.

With security for my trip unexpectedly beefed up, I settled in for another beer or two, my intention to get back home early to spend the evening with Claire temporarily forgotten in the laughter and banter. Much later than planned, I finally extricated myself from the group, bid my goodbyes, and headed home – to plenty of catcalls, orders to 'grow a pair', and claims my balls were firmly in Claire's handbag. Although I'd left Central London by nine, I didn't make it home until 10.30pm. Claire had given up on me and was almost asleep.

I tried to sound upbeat. 'Sorry I'm a bit late. Come on, we've still got time to watch a video or something.'

'It's gone ten-thirty and you're half-pissed. I should have known you wouldn't come back early. I'm tired and I just want to go to sleep.'

Claire turned her back on me as I tried to find a witty response that would make everything better. 'I suppose a blow job is out of the question then?'

It wasn't top draw, but it sounded like a snigger came from under the covers. My silver tongue had worked its magic. I stripped off, jumped into bed, and applied some tender loving touches with my ice-cold hands.

'You bastard. And don't even think about it.'

A less than encouraging response, but within ten minutes I was being ordered to grab a shower and clean my teeth. On my return we were soon trading comedy stage whispers to stay quiet as we made the best of what was left of Saturday night.

Claire was still upset we hadn't spent the evening together and I couldn't blame her. She understood I didn't see my old friends very often, but the following night would have a blanket of apprehension about it as I finished my travel preparations. We'd been through enough separations over the years to know Sunday would be a write-off. I suspected I'd given away too much information about a couple of the riskier moments from my previous trip to Baghdad. That and the debate about dyeing my hair to avoid increased threats, and she had every right to worry whether I was doing the right thing by returning.

CHAPTER 14

AMMAN – END OF MARCH 2004

'What the hell is in those?' The bags had appeared out of nowhere. They certainly hadn't been with us on our journey out from Heathrow.

Mohammed was struggling to lift them into the boot of Thamer's taxi as he answered, 'They're the chandeliers for our family house.' As though it was the most normal thing in the world.

'What? Did you say chandeliers?' About to set off in the morning darkness for the Jordan-Iraq border and here we were loading chandeliers into the boot.

'Yes. I brought them here for safekeeping before the war. They're really valuable.'

I stopped myself from saying anything further as he closed the boot with our luggage and the new cargo wedged together inside.

I'd tried to call Jacko's mate Dan to tell him we wouldn't be able to make it to the RV and to wish him good luck for his trip. Although it would have been great to have the added protection of armoured SUVs and an armed security team nearby, Thamer's taxi would never be able to keep up with Dan's group of vehicles. We'd either slow them down and piss everyone off, or more likely I'd be quickly told I was a knobber and 'see you in Baghdad'.

My judgement was to prove uncannily accurate as a rear tyre blew a mile inside the Iraq border. Curled up on the back seat trying to get some sleep while Mohammed jabbered away to Thamer up front, the loud bang from the tyre had sounded like a gunshot. So much for trying to relax at the start of another lengthy journey along the dangerous road to Baghdad.

'It was a retread? For crying out loud.' I was making a conscious effort to reduce my swearing, with mixed results. 'Thank fuck we weren't travelling with Dan's group. Please tell me we have a decent spare.'

A check if any other vehicles were emerging from the border crossing revealed only the natural stillness of the desert morning. The sun hadn't yet eliminated the last traces of the cold night air, causing me to shiver as I inspected the other tyres with trepidation, while Thamer and Mohammed cursed their way through the enforced wheel change.

I felt slightly less vulnerable with Mohammed alongside me this time, not that he and his chandeliers would be much help if we got into trouble further up the road. At least control of the journey should be easier, the same as when Ahmed had accompanied me back to Jordan some three weeks before. There'd be no outings to dangerous towns along the way or doing a tour of the mean streets of Baghdad to meet the wife and kids.

We'd made the border thirty minutes later than planned, so Dan's armoured convoy should already be ahead on the same road. Although we would rapidly fall ever further behind, the 'friendly forces' in front allowed me to hope any dubious activity might have been identified and cleared before we came through. Of course, the further we dropped behind, the less we might benefit from this perceived advance clearance.

Once back on the road, I smiled to myself when we motored past the Rutba turn-off this time. Replacing the shredded tyre had cost us about twenty minutes but, more than time, I was concerned about the poor state of the other tyres. Hopefully we'd just been unlucky with the one that blew.

After making good progress through the barren reaches of the western desert, I watched with dismay as Thamer slowed down to pull into the same Ramadi services we'd visited last time.

'Don't worry, just don't say anything. If anyone asks, I'll tell them you're my cousin from Mosul… who's mute.'

It wouldn't be the last time Mohammed suggested this cunning plan to outfox any nosey locals, and fortunately we never had to use it to see if it worked. Anyone who noticed the obvious Westerner alongside him kept it to themselves.

Not long after our stop we began to encounter more and more American military vehicles and personnel on the road. Before reaching Falluja, the highway ahead was barred by a roadblock.

'What's happening here?' Mohammed called out to the nearest American soldier, whose sunglasses reflected the knot of traffic in the bright sunshine. If Mohammed expected the sergeant to engage him in friendly conversation because he had a British passport and there was a blue-eyed, fair-haired expat in the car, he was to be sorely disappointed.

'That way.' The American made chopping motions with his hand down towards a track running to the left at a ninety-degree angle to the main road.

'But we're going to Baghdad.'

'I TOLD YOU. THAT WAY.' More chopping motions as Mohammed settled back into his seat with a pout.

Whatever had caused the road closure, we couldn't see any evidence of it. My concern was the slowness and density of traffic as we bumped our way along the dirt track to God knows where. It wasn't yet a name on everyone's lips, but Falluja wasn't a place you wanted to be hanging around.

Mohammed and Thamer engaged in shouted Arabic conversations with drivers slowly making their way past in the opposite direction, in an effort to find out what was going on. I pulled my baseball cap down lower and tried to shrink out of sight in the back.

'Another mile and we join the old highway,' Mohammed finally ventured.

'What's that road like?'

'It's fine. The same as the other one, only older' – and throwing a thumb in the direction of a lorry behind us – 'That truck driver said the Americans had a big fight in the town earlier and to be careful around here.'

Once we reached the old highway we started moving faster again, but I was grateful once we'd finally crossed back onto the new road after another torturous spell on a dirt track. The military presence had only been concentrated near Falluja and we closed on Baghdad without any further hold-ups. I braced myself for the Baghdad traffic jams. At least I'd forcefully established we wouldn't make any unplanned house calls on the way to the Palestine.

CHAPTER 15

BAGHDAD

The Baghdad approach roads and suburbs weren't as congested as on my first trip from Amman although we'd come via a different route. I suspected our diversion to Thamer's house last time caused more issues than he'd bargained for.

We arrived at the Palestine Hotel to find that the pedestrian entrance had been moved and combined with the vehicle gate on the smaller road running next to the river. A positive change that ought to reduce the threat in the immediate vicinity.

The hotel was busier than when I'd checked out earlier in the month. As we entered, Mohammed told me Walid had needed to plead with the general manager to get me a room because the hotel was fully booked. When they realised who he was talking about, they'd released one of the reserve rooms held back for special guests. As I reached the reception desk, the manager smiled and held out his hands.

'Mr John, it's so good to have you back at the hotel. I'm sorry about the problem with your reservation. We are fully booked this week. Don't worry, I have arranged a good room for you. You are a very welcome guest.'

It would be great to report this room as the epitome of decadent luxury hidden away from the 'ordinary' guests, but it wasn't. The amenities and layout were similar, and it had to be directly below my previous room judging by the identical 'CNN reporting from Baghdad' view. The only discernible advantage I could make out compared to last time: one less flight of stairs to climb.

The following morning, Mohammed and I headed into the city to meet with the family lawyer, Yasin. It took us to another little oasis of calm in the centre of Baghdad where we sat in a pleasant garden under the shade of a big golfing umbrella, drinking juice and chai. Yasin wasn't exactly Perry Mason, but he seemed like a decent enough guy and Mohammed had known him since growing up and trusted him. His advanced years meant he might not be as dynamic and on-the-ball as we might need though. Company incorporation was fine, but he admitted corporate law wasn't his field. I made a mental note we needed to find an international lawyer operating out here. Of course, we'd need to have a contract in hand before we could commit to the sky-high fees that would entail, so all in good time.

That night in the hotel bar, I watched with grim fascination as the news being broadcast from a balcony upstairs detailed how a four-man Blackwater security team had been captured, killed, and strung up in Falluja in front of a jubilant crowd. We'd only travelled through Falluja the previous day. Another of my nine lives could probably be crossed off. There's only so much time you can keep riding your luck before it all goes south.

The American media portrayed the indignation felt by the nation that the Blackwater team, deployed in support of reconstruction efforts, had been mutilated before cheering mobs of locals. This would mark an immediate sea change in the atmosphere in Iraq; as though a valve had been opened and the mindset of insurgency had flowed out and covered the land. There had been plenty of attacks in the year since 'Mission Accomplished' but this changed everything.

There was a sombre mood at the hotel when Mohammed and I left the next morning to walk down to the bazaars near Al-Rashid Street where his cousin had a shop. With the television screens full of the corpses of the Blackwater team hanging from a bridge over the Euphrates, walking through downtown Baghdad was about last on my list of preferred options. If I'd known it would be two miles yomping down the main drag, I would have flat out refused to set off. I didn't have a weapon and the uneasy conversations around the early morning breakfast tables had prickled with tension. But Mohammed suggested we could drop into one or two shops on the way to buy a jacket and local-style shoes, which would help me to blend in, from a distance at least. He still believed we'd get away with the 'cousin from Mosul' bullshit, but the clothes were a good idea, I had to give him that.

The shopkeepers in the stores we visited were friendly and polite. It always helps when you're buying rather than simply browsing, but they did appear genuinely pleased to be serving a British businessman. They'd be waiting a long time if they thought I represented the vanguard for an influx of Western shoppers. Despite the heat, I donned my new black 'leather' jacket and changed out of my trail shoes into a pair of black slip-ons. Topped off with a black Nike baseball cap popular amongst the locals, I reckoned the figure in the mirror could pass muster at a distance without everyone standing, pointing, and screaming like the final scene from *Invasion of the Body Snatchers*.

★

Compared to the emptyish pavements on the main roads, the bazaar was teeming with people. The jostling crowds made me wary and I tried not to catch anyone's eye as I alternated lowering my gaze with surreptitious scans of the surrounding faces. Dropping your head provides better peripheral vision, so my posture had a dual purpose apart from simply avoiding recognition. Mohammed knew I wanted to grab a few souvenirs, and he soon led me into an open-fronted shop filled with the kind of tat on my shopping list.

On holiday in Tunisia years ago, Claire, Natalie, and I had enjoyed the bartering process with various stallholders and shop owners, which began in Monty Python fashion with mock outrage at our low opening bids. This experience in Baghdad started in similar style and for the next half an hour I almost forgot where we were as the jolly owner served me chai during a negotiation with the pace of the Korean War peace talks. He acted as though having an Englishman drop into the shop was the most normal thing in the world. We finally agreed on an insignificant amount of Iraqi dinars for an Aladdin-style lamp and a small brass teapot with matching tiny cups. I'd only had my eye on the lamp, but he smiled triumphantly when he talked me into the tea set as well.

As we left the shop, a pack of shopkeepers surrounded us. Bony fingers grasped at me and pointed towards nearby stores.

'Mister, mister. Here, here.'

'Carpets. Persian carpets at cheap.'

'This way, mister. My shop is just here.'

Anglo-Iraqi commercial relations may have taken a hit as I ripped my arms away from the sea of hands. 'Fuck off. Get your hands off me.'

We pushed through them and moved deeper into the bazaar towards our destination: an electrical store owned by Mohammed's cousin. Much as I'd enjoyed the bartering, I was conscious we'd stayed far too long at the souvenir store and allowed plenty of time for any adversaries to mobilise. The mob of shopkeepers demonstrated word had leaked about a foreigner in the area. I hadn't seen any other Western faces since we'd left the hotel two hours earlier.

The cousin's eyes almost popped out of his head when he spotted me trailing Mohammed into his shop. He clearly didn't know we were coming, and he most definitely wasn't happy his cousin had brought a Westerner along. Angry Arabic flowed between them as I checked outside through the window. Unsurprisingly, the pistol in the hand of the large guy striding purposefully towards the shop caught my attention.

'Mohammed. We might have a problem.'

A problem I would not be well placed to deal with. We hadn't met with Faris yet, so I didn't have a weapon apart from the KA-BAR knife in my jacket pocket.

As I retreated into the interior of the shop, Mohammed and his cousin moved the other way towards the front door. I was motioned to a narrow door behind the counter by one of the staff. Before making a decision I turned back to assess the situation. The large guy holding the pistol marched straight past the front of the shop just as Mohammed and his cousin reached the entrance. He led a small posse of other dubious-looking men with more handguns visible. These guys might have been the local neighbourhood watch out on patrol, but there was a lot of shouting going on out there.

'Go out the back,' Mohammed yelled, as the posse turned back towards the shop. Someone must have alerted them to where I'd gone.

I didn't need telling twice and followed the counter clerk through the small stockroom to a side door as the shouting intensified from the front of the shop. Breaking glass, the clatter of falling boxes, and the sounds of a violent altercation indicated we now had a very real problem. I didn't know what was on the other side of the door, but I knew what was on this side and it wasn't looking too healthy to stay here. With the KA-BAR in my hand, blade running up the inside of my forearm, I motioned for the clerk to open it.

'Yella,' I said quietly. *Come on.*

As I bolted out of the door, I was immediately faced by a shemagh-wearing man, about my height, with a gun in his hand. I had no idea if he was part of the posse trying to break through Mohammed and his cousin to get to me and I wasn't going to stop and ask. His eyes widened as he must have caught a glimpse of the knife in my hand flashing towards his face, but it wasn't the knife I was leading with, it was my elbow. With the momentum of my charge through the door it connected with his face with a satisfying crack and he immediately began falling to my left as I tore on, heading in the opposite direction to the shopfront. I didn't have a clue where I was going, but I was going to get there fast.

Time to go Anglo-Saxon with the locals.

'GET OUT THE FUCKING WAY.'

I smashed into men and women alike, bouncing them out of my way as they strolled through the local market for their morning shopping.

'I SAID GET OUT THE FUCKING WAY.'

It was working. I scythed through the crowds leaving carnage in my wake by the sounds of it. A growing hubbub followed as I desperately searched for signs of a main road.

Jinking left and right to try and shake off any pursuers, the narrow walkways of the bazaar changed into wider, emptier back streets. I risked a glance over my shoulder. The expected assailants on my heels were nowhere to be seen.

Finally, I charged back out onto Al-Rashid Street with its recognisable columns lining the road and turned immediately left and then right onto the main road in the direction of the Palestine about two miles away. I still didn't know if anyone was chasing me, but I was determined to outrun them if they were, even in my new slip-ons rather than the trail shoes crammed inside my rucksack. The gridlocked traffic meant I didn't dare try to grab a taxi, much as I wanted to get off the street; an expat sprinting down the main drag in Baghdad was guaranteed to attract attention. The last thing I needed was to run into the uncertainty of local police or security forces although an American patrol would have been a welcome sight.

A few hundred metres later the traffic was running more freely on my left, so I darted out, forcing an empty taxi to brake sharply.

I yanked open the passenger door and jumped into the seat. 'Palestine Hotel. Yella, yella.'

The taxi driver made like a statue as though stunned. His quiet morning had just taken an unexpected turn.

'Fucking move.'

His widening eyes dropped to the KA-BAR in my hand and followed the blood smeared along my forearm. That did the trick and we spurted forward to a chorus of car horns and howls of complaint.

In calm, perfect English he asked, 'Are you in trouble?'

For a city with relatively few English speakers, I was making a habit of bumping into the cream of the crop.

'Yes mate, whatever you do, don't stop.'

I strained to look behind using the mirrors and through the rear window despite the constrictions of the daysack on my back. No sign of pursuit. Provided the traffic kept moving, we'd arrive at the Palestine shortly and I'd be sprinting in through the gate. The driver took the right turn towards the river road leading to the new entrance. In my haste I'd have probably forgotten the pedestrian entrance had changed, so a good job I'd jumped in the cab and not found myself screaming in frustration by arriving at a bank of concrete and razor wire marking the old entrance.

As we pulled to a halt, I threw a twenty-dollar bill back at the driver and yelled 'Shukran' behind me. The guards at the entrance hardly stirred as I ran into the safety of the Palestine Hotel complex. I slowed down but didn't stop running until I'd turned the corner and moved out of view from the entrance.

A check of my right forearm revealed I'd nicked myself just below the elbow with the KA-BAR, so at least some of the blood on my arm was mine. Unsure whether I might have seriously hurt one or quite possibly a lot more people during my mad dash for safety, I changed direction and headed for the emptiest part of the gardens rather than the throng of people in hotel reception. I found an empty table shielded from the rest of the hotel to patch myself up. I cleaned away the blood with water and applied a plaster from my daysack as I tried to get my breathing under control. The sweat poured off me in rivers.

I rang Mohammed. 'Are you okay, mate?' He'd answered the phone on the first ring which should mean he was all right.

'Yes, everything is fine. Those criminal bastards.' Mohammed was his normal cheery self. 'Where are you?'

'Back at the Palestine. Is everyone okay there?'

'The police are here, although nothing will happen. There was one man very hurt, but he's gone. I have a cut and my cousin will probably never speak to me again. Apart from that everything is fine. But why did you hit the women?'

I was momentarily stuck for words. 'It was an accident. Some people were in my way.' What could I say? Not my greatest moment.

I'd got away with it that day, but it was a stark reminder the security threat in Baghdad needed to be taken seriously. As the coming days would show, Baghdad was changing for the worse. Much worse.

CHAPTER 16

At my insistence, we met with Faris later that day. It was clear from the outset him and Mohammed were never going to be the closest of friends, but after the morning's events I wanted to give him the opportunity to offer me a pistol again.

I wasn't disappointed and this time I had an upgrade to a compact Glock 19 with a spare magazine of fifteen rounds. That gave me thirty rounds in total with a reliable weapon. The chance to test fire it would have been ideal, but I was happy enough. Faris had even supplied a decent holster. The Glock doesn't have a safety catch; instead it is equipped with three separate safety features which mean it won't fire unless you mean it to, provided you handle it correctly. Compared to the Makarov, for instance, there's no possibility of it going off accidentally when dropped.

Unlike when on patrol with the military or out on a security task, I usually carried any weapons loaded but not made ready, known as condition amber. That meant the immediate action if I encountered a serious security threat would be to cock the weapon. The Israelis tend to practise this technique, but I had American friends who would vehemently disagree with not being ready to fire at all times. The practicalities of sometimes needing to give my weapon up when meeting important people or entering places with a firearm ban meant I thought it appropriate. Believe me, if the situation escalated then I'd be made ready at condition red in a heartbeat. I might not be Billy the Kid, but I could draw and cock the weapon pretty fast, even with one hand using the heel of my shoe if required. The chances of a threat emerging that required the extra split second this would cost me was small, but I recognised it was possible. It was a trade-off, like so many other things.

Mohammed and Faris locked horns almost immediately. The Arabic between them didn't sound at all friendly, so I interrupted.

'Hang on a minute. What are you saying?' I asked Mohammed.

He finished his sentence and dropped the finger he'd been wagging at Faris. 'I told him we didn't need him. I have places to visit and will find a good office myself.'

Faris spoke up. 'Mr John, I don't understand the problem. When you were here before, we took you and showed you some good places. Were you not happy with them?'

Before Mohammed could start up again, I spoke quickly. 'Yes of course, and thank you for all your help. This is just a misunderstanding. Because Mohammed wasn't with me last time, we need to discuss and agree the best way to do things this time.' My eyes locked onto Mohammed's. 'We may need to alter things slightly, but the objectives are still the same. We all want the same thing here: to get the business up and running so we can work together and make good money.'

Mohammed's face read as though he didn't want the same thing if Faris stayed involved.

'That's right, Mohammed, yes?'

Whatever inner battle raged behind his eyes, the reasonable side won this time. 'Yes, you're right. But we don't need any help to find and set up the office.'

I'd take that. 'Right. So Faris, you don't need to worry about the office side of things any more, so instead can you focus on the business side? Opportunities we can follow immediately and in the short to medium term.'

At the conclusion of the meeting Faris was pissed off, but thankfully not so much to make him take back the Glock. He'd clearly realised that Mohammed's influence meant a different and looser relationship between us compared to the one he'd anticipated.

In some ways it was easier the two men didn't like each other. Any thoughts Faris might have had to relieve me of my money should be snuffed out. And Mohammed had declared he wanted nothing to do with Faris's contacts, which left me free to explore those opportunities without him charging in and upsetting people like Abu Saif.

The change in atmosphere in Baghdad in those early April days was palpable. Restaurants suddenly became scared to have Western diners unless they could be hidden away in private. Stories of grenade attacks at eateries in the city and a multitude of direct warnings had seen to that. Even the exuberant Mr Saleh had lost his appetite for meeting with me again and instead made plans to take his family to Jordan until the outlook improved. That spelled the end for the drinks factory project, although the way things had changed I'd probably be lynched if I showed my face there again now.

Reports of Westerners being kidnapped soon filtered in and Faris warned me to be careful. 'I am worried if you are going out without our protection. Something might happen to you. Baghdad is very dangerous for foreigners, especially British and Americans.'

He might only care because he thought I could help make him money, but he still cared. How touching.

'Yes, I know. I'm keeping on top of the news reports. We're being careful when we go out, but thanks for your concern. Any time you have any specific information, then let me know so we can alter our movements if we need to.'

Faris spoke without any emotion. 'The danger is everywhere now. I advise you not to go out with your other friends. We too are having to take many precautions. Abu Saif wants to meet with you again, but now it is too dangerous to take you to Al-Adhamiyah. Perhaps we will meet in Mansour, near to the Green Zone.'

'Does Abu Saif have some new business to discuss?'

'Yes, plenty of business. As soon as he heard you had returned to Baghdad, he told me he wants to meet with you. He is very busy, but you will meet soon.'

'Okay. Well tell him I'm looking forward to meeting him again and let me know when he's available.'

'But when you meet it must just be you. Not the others.'

'Don't worry. Mohammed isn't interested in meeting him. He's concentrating on getting the local company and offices up and running.'

★

While Faris sought to arrange a suitable time and venue for the meeting with Abu Saif, Mohammed and I went about the business of setting up the new company and finding an office.

We visited a new business centre in Palestine Street on the eastern side of Baghdad, conveniently located near Walid's home where Mohammed stayed. However, it was also near to the Shi'a district of Sadr City, which was featuring heavily in the news after the Shi'a Mahdi Army had ambushed US military patrols and seized police stations. It was to mark the start of an uprising that would see heavy combat in the area for the next four years. As we looked round the new building, I doubted I'd be seeing it very often if we took an office there. I was right. Although we operated from the building when it opened, I never visited again.

★

The Palestine Hotel planned a grand opening party of its refurbished rooftop bar to coincide with the first anniversary of the end of the 2003 war. In the days leading up to the party, leaflets appeared warning all the workers at the hotel to leave because the insurgents were going to blow it up. The attack never materialised, but the threats prompted the cancellation of the event and the opening.

Although several other Western contractors and journalists had recently been kidnapped, on 9th April the American media focused on the disappearance of US national Nicholas Berg. This particularly resonated with me because Berg appeared to be doing the same thing as me: trying to win contracts using trusted Iraqi contacts. The feeling of a spiral into deadly insurgency and war grew ever stronger as news of the US Marines assault on Falluja filled the airwaves. However, it was the news Sunni insurgents had seized a stretch of the main highway between Baghdad and Falluja that guaranteed there was no way I'd be taking a taxi to the Jordanian border when it came time to leave for home. Baghdad felt cut off from the outside world.

While the local news was depressing, I've always been able to compartmentalise. Chelsea were playing Arsenal in the Champions League quarter-final second leg which I was determined to watch. The bar staff had confirmed the match would be shown live in the bar and I was the only guest down there when the game kicked off. With so much going on all over the country the news teams were working flat out. Little chance any of them could watch the game, even if they were interested. When they realised I was an ardent Chelsea fan, the hotel staff all cheered the Blues on with me. For ninety minutes I forgot all about the spiral into despair outside in the city and the potential effect it could have on my business plans. Instead I spent a memorable evening celebrating Chelsea beating Arsenal to qualify for the semi-finals.

★

Returning to the hotel one afternoon via a long walk from the closest drop-off point, Mohammed and Walid stopped at a street vendor on a corner a hundred metres from the hotel entrance gate. I wasn't hungry after the lunchtime chicken, rice, and beans in the small, friendly restaurant we'd finally located. The two brothers were ready for a top-up though and bought a drink and a hot snack each from the old guy's wheeled stall.

It was a hot day and I wanted to get back to the unsatisfying shower in my room before checking online if Royal Jordanian had any plans to add to the once-daily flights between Amman and Baghdad. One-way cost upwards of $750 if you could get a ticket. Not something I'd budgeted for, so I needed to be very careful with my cash situation. I hadn't enquired about availability for the rest of the month yet, but the throng we'd passed in the morning outside the small RJ office in the Palestine Hotel complex didn't fill me with optimism.

I tucked myself into the corner and observed west along the river road we'd traversed and then checked the narrow road leading north to the main road between Firdos Square and Liberation Square. Although I was scanning for threats, I hadn't really expected to see some cheeky git with a scarf over his lower face raise an AK-47 in our direction from fifty metres away.

'Take cover.'

I drew the Glock and cocked it in one movement as I dropped into a crouched position by the concrete barrier behind the street seller's kiosk. Mohammed and Walid stood rooted to the spot, each holding a cone of fava beans and regarding me with a confused look.

The outbreak of automatic fire soon had them rushing to join me in cover though. The closest rounds snapped past and zinged off the road and barriers. Both now prone in the dirty street, Mohammed had somehow managed to keep most of his beans intact while Walid's decorated the road surface.

I peeked round the barrier to see the gunman already running off. With only a handgun and no weapons permit, this wasn't the time to be trying to make a citizen's arrest, so I watched as he rounded the corner and disappeared.

The three of us just looked at each other. The street vendor hadn't even budged from behind his cart. Had it even really happened?

'It's time I was heading back to the UK.'

There was no disagreement; the situation was getting out of control. The French had told all their citizens to leave the country, various NGOs were pulling out, attacks were multiplying rapidly, and American casualties were escalating fast.

★

The following morning, I was in my room when a loud explosion rang out close to the hotel, accompanied by the sound of breaking glass and multiple car alarms. I dived into the bathroom, out the way of potential flying glass in case of further explosions, and listened for sounds of any follow-up attack. With the chaos being reported in Baghdad and Falluja heralding a huge upswing in the insurgency from two different forces (Sunni insurgents and Shi'a militia), there was always the possibility of a large-scale attack against a heavily defended target like the Palestine. With the US tanks and troops stationed at the hotel it was unlikely to be successful, but it would be a PR coup for the insurgents whatever the outcome.

After a few minutes, nothing further had happened and my friends upstairs at CNN provided an update via the television. They were showing live shots from their balcony and describing the incident as a rocket attack. I looked outside my window and back to the TV. Near identical views.

Less than forty minutes later, Mohammed arrived at the hotel and spoke excitedly about the attack. 'I heard the explosion while I was at the checkpoint. The American soldiers thought there might be an attack coming and started shouting at everyone to get back. Was it a car bomb or a rocket?'

'The news channels say it was a rocket. I didn't see it land, but it's caused damage at the Sheraton.'

'Ah, a rocket. Usually they hit the Green Zone. Maybe more rockets will come.'

It's a natural reaction to get caught up in the excitement when an incident like that occurs, although I wasn't quite as enamoured with the idea of rockets starting to get hurled in the direction of my hotel. As per usual, the rocket had hit the Sheraton rather than the Palestine and I hoped a couple of guys I knew over there were okay. Media reports indicated minor damage and no casualties, so hopefully we'd all got away with one today.

CHAPTER 17

Faris had a different assistant with him as we drove through Baghdad to the meeting with Abu Saif. I didn't know what happened to the kid but compared to his characterless replacement he'd been a veritable feast of entertainment.

The car was silent as we passed Saddam's giant unfinished mosque, before leaving the traffic and turning into the quieter streets of an upmarket residential neighbourhood in the Mansour district.

As the armed security guards closed the villa gates behind us, I noted there was plenty of room for the driver to turn the vehicle and face forward on exit for a change – a good start. We were in Baghdad's 'Red Zone' but I knew this area to be one of the most secure outside the Green Zone. There were a handful of embassies nearby, more than one security company headquartered down the road, and the Iraqi National Intelligence Service operated from the China House complex at the southern end of the neighbourhood, near Beirut Street.

As I entered the room, Abu Saif stood to greet me with his trademark low growl.

'Mr Pierce. It's very good to see you in Baghdad again. I must apologise for the way our last meeting ended. I had very important and unexpected guests who I had to deal with. I hope you can understand.'

'Not a problem at all. I'm sure we'll be able to cover a lot more ground today than would have been possible last month.'

The big man held my gaze and a humourless smile crossed his face. 'Yes, today we have plenty of time. And there will be no interruptions.'

This time it was a far more personal affair, with only three minions in attendance matched by me, Faris, and his new assistant. We had an escort car with us, but Faris's men had parked on the quiet road outside the gate when we had driven in. There was little small talk as we got straight down to business.

Abu Saif dominated the room again, both physically and with his self-assured manner. His large frame and gravelly voice gave him a touch of the Bond villain. He was refreshingly direct and came across as intelligent and shrewd.

He spoke about long-established Iraqi construction and oil services companies working with him, suggesting they would be ideal partners for international corporations seeking to win contracts in the country. We agreed a mixture of foreign expertise and local capability was going to be key to winning the cream of the business opportunities.

The discussion moved on to overseas companies with whom he already had relationships, including companies in UAE, Saudi Arabia, and Lebanon. I got the impression he considered a working relationship with me might provide him and his Iraqi contacts with an important touch of international credibility with potential Western suppliers and partners.

He hardly knew me, but I suspected Faris had been reporting back to him. With the security situation deteriorating rapidly, I sensed an opportunity to remain involved with reconstruction efforts, even if I might need to limit my exposure in Iraq in the future.

Specific topics included prospects for the oil sector, healthcare, and cement factories. None of these were areas in which I had any deep knowledge. However, the sourcing and procurement of international expertise, equipment, and supplies, including pharmaceuticals for hospitals, had my mind working overtime as Abu Saif outlined where he thought the best opportunities lay. The financial sector was another significant area he sounded well placed to move into, with mention of both a Jordanian bank and an insurance group.

As we paused for a substantial lunch that covered most of the large conference table, I looked out at the tidy garden area and a young lad cleaning surface debris out of the swimming pool. It looked clean enough and big enough for a decent swim. By comparison, the pool at the Palestine Hotel was a dusty, empty reminder of better times. The tops of the surrounding high stone walls glinted in the sun with shards of glass to deter intruders. My wandering thoughts returned to the table as Abu Saif switched from an Arabic conversation back to English.

'I've talked about all these areas of business I'm engaged with. The companies, the partners, how we can provide the logistic support here in Iraq. But can you help me to access the American money? The international funding? What can you do for me?'

Up to that point he'd done most of the talking, which had been both unexpected and welcome. I'd picked at a couple of the dishes and already filled myself up, so the chance to speak for a while instead of eating came at the right moment.

'I can give you that link to the Coalition and to the West generally. To the outside. Right now, businesses and people only see the news of the bombs and the violence. A lot of companies are interested in getting involved in the reconstruction, but they don't know how. And even if they could manage to win a contract with, say, the US military, most would have no idea how to go about implementing it on the ground. That's where we can come in. Not only can we try to win projects for ourselves, but we can work with others who have won contracts and help them. For a share of course.'

As Abu Saif mulled that over, I continued.

'Which brings me on to something else. I'm not interested in making judgements or trying to imply anything improper, but it would be good to understand where you can operate.'

He frowned at the question.

'I mean, I understand you have powerful business interests and from Faris, you, the meeting in Adhamiya and now here in Mansour, I assume it's the Sunni areas where you will be strongest.'

He held up his hand and started to protest. 'That's not...'

I spoke over his objection and he let me continue. Doubtful that happened often.

'Sorry, I don't mean that to be taken anything other than literally. What I'm trying to say is Sunni Islamist groups appear to be at the forefront of this growing insurgency. Can we... erm... can you use your influence to provide protection for our projects? As I said, I don't mean to imply any link to the... insurgents, but it would be prudent to explore any contacts who could reduce the threat against our interests.'

The rest of the room had fallen silent and a scan round the faces at the table indicated I wasn't explaining myself very well. Faris stared at me with confusion in his eyes.

'That might not have come out the way I wanted, but I believe it is better to be direct and make sure we all understand the situation and the potential strengths or weaknesses we might have together. If you have lines of communication that would allow us to operate in areas where others might face... difficulties, then it's something we can focus on. Obviously in a discreet way.'

While the others maintained looks that made me wonder if I'd spoken way out of line, Abu Saif began to nod. And smile. This time the smile even reached his eyes.

'You're right,' he said. 'Iraq is becoming a dangerous place and religious and tribal alliances are more important than ever. The American military are making huge mistakes if they think they can occupy the country without bloodshed and plunder its resources. The simple answer to your question is I know how to operate here. I can protect my business interests. But no-one can protect everyone, everywhere. I mean that as a friendly warning to you. Be very careful with these other Iraqi friends or partners of yours from Britain. I cannot protect you while you are with them and I advise that you only work with Faris in Baghdad.'

His last comment annoyed me, so I snapped back, 'It's important I have people around me I trust, the same as it is for you. Mohammed and Walid are my friends. They won't get involved in our business together. They don't want to get involved.' My voice softened. 'But I appreciate your warning and I understand how the situation has changed here over the recent days.'

The conversation petered out into an uneasy silence round the table. I reached for a bottle of water and gulped down the remaining half. My appetite hadn't returned but I needed to focus my attention on something. I reached over and spooned more rice and chicken onto my plate.

It was Abu Saif who spoke again to break the silence. 'The key quality I need with a business partner is trust. We've spoken about plenty of different business sectors and opportunities, but the question I ask myself is: can I trust you?'

I took it as a rhetorical question until he asked again.

'So, Mr Pierce, *can* I trust you?'

I glanced down at the business card he'd given me at the start of our meeting to check his surname. 'Yes, Mr al-Tikriti, you can trust me. If we agree a course of action, I will complete it to the best of my ability. And, just as importantly, I'll tell you if there's a problem, or it can't be done, or we need to change our approach. So yes, you can trust me. Honesty and loyalty are two areas I believe are vitally important in business... and in life.'

Okay, so my nose could have started growing as I said that last bit, but with my blagging background I didn't mean the honesty part in a literal sense, more in the 'honour amongst thieves' way.

After our exchange, we took chai outside in the sun at a small table by the pool. The setting cried out for a couple of cold beers and some bikini-clad eye candy, although I settled for the improving atmosphere and warmer conversation with Abu Saif about family and children. There was no further mention of business. I assumed he'd made his mind up one way or the other about working with me.

Half an hour later we parted in a relaxed and friendly manner. It wasn't clear if we would work together, but I hoped so. This was a man who could make things happen round here. As we left the villa in the late afternoon sun to join our escort vehicle for the ride back to the Palestine Hotel, Abu Saif and the others also prepared to leave. Interesting.

'Faris, is this Abu Saif's villa?'

Instead of answering the question, he replied, 'Why do you ask?'

'I just wondered. Seems like a nice place, with the pool and everything.'

Faris turned back to face the front without adding anything. Probably meant he didn't know either.

★

The TV news broadcasts were filled with daily attacks, kidnappings, hostage releases, and murders. Some who got lucky and some who didn't. And that was just the international community. For the locals, similar kidnappings and murders were occurring on an industrial scale.

The morning after my meeting with Abu Saif, I sat with Mohammed and Walid having a coffee in the Palestine Hotel gardens. We hadn't been out together since our close shave with the gunman outside the entrance two days beforehand, and Abu Saif's friendly warning also deterred the idea of anything but essential travel outside.

'They kidnapped our neighbour's son from school yesterday,' said Mohammed gloomily. 'They want $10,000 in forty-eight hours or they'll kill him. The message was left on the doorstep where his daughter was playing. Our friend is terrified they will take his other children as well, but what can he do? It's getting so bad that people are too scared to let their children go to school any more or even to the local shops. The Americans have destroyed Iraq.'

'I'm sorry to hear that, mate. If it's that bad at a local level, what do you reckon it means for us? What do you think we should do?'

'I don't know any more,' answered Mohammed. He sounded more downbeat than I'd ever heard him.

'We need to be very careful,' said Walid. 'There are rumours they are watching all the hotels and getting ready to take more foreigners. People are leaving our neighbourhood; Sunnis and Shi'a. Warnings are being left on front doors and, as Mohammed said, some of our neighbours have had family kidnapped by criminals.'

Fuck it. This was getting out of control.

'I think it's time for me to fly back to the UK before our luck runs out. If they're watching the hotels, and after the threats here and our fun and games a couple of days ago I'm sure they are, then the longer I stay the more danger I put us all in. And if they find out you're working with me, then...' The rest didn't need saying.

Walid lived in a mixed Sunni-Shi'a neighbourhood and he was clearly anxious about the safety of his family, even without the added risk the wrong people discovered he was working with a Westerner. My woeful cash position and the rumoured scarcity of thousand dollar tickets for the once daily flight to freedom were running up big red flags. I needed to get my arse on a plane out of there ASAP.

'Get yourselves away, guys,' I said to the two brothers. 'I'll finish this and go straight round to the RJ office and see what's what.' I knocked back the rest of my coffee and stood up. Neither Mohammed nor Walid were arguing.

★

The Royal Jordanian office was mobbed with a multinational mix of frantic souls in amongst the fray. Finally managing to force my way through to the ticket desk, the weary ticket agent informed me the next availability for Amman was in two days at $1,000 for the last seat, or $800 for the flight in three days' time. I didn't have enough cash for the first one, but I could run to eight hundred. With my back being accosted by the mutating scrum like I was having a Thai massage, I counted out the eight $100 bills, which left me a fifty and a wedge of dinars. The money counter rejected one of the notes with a beep.

He handed it back to me. 'No good.'

'Wait a sec.' I didn't have another hundred in US currency, but I didn't want to lose this seat. 'Dinars?'

'No, dollars.'

As he handed the other $700 back, I sensed my fellow desperados saw an opportunity to take my place like sharks moving in for a kill.

I swore under my breath as a guy in Arab dress pushed in front of me while I juggled the cash back into my wallet. Mohammed and Walid were back in the hotel garden and might have enough US dollars on them. Shit. I really didn't want to give up my place after taking so long to battle my way to the desk. Freedom felt tantalisingly close, but at the same time frustratingly out of reach.

I stayed put and sharpened my elbows as I pulled out and sought to flatten my eight Benjamins. I reordered them and pushed past the guy in front as he turned to leave with an infuriated look on his face. Either he wasn't happy with the price being quoted or it was because my elbow had accidentally caught him under the ribs. More importantly, he hadn't bought a ticket, so, although there was another clerk serving at the table, I hoped my precious seat out of here was still available.

'There you go.' I handed over the same eight $100 bills.

If there's such a thing as ESP then I was using it, willing this to go my way with everything I had. The room was heaving with body odour and desperation, some of it mine, as I watched him knock my bills together and feed them into the machine. This time the money counter was silent, and I had a shit-eating grin like I'd just scored a winning goal at Wembley. I was down to the last of my cash and it would be touch and go whether I could cover my final hotel bill, but I was going home.

★

Mohammed gave me the extra 150,000 Iraqi dinars needed to cover the outstanding hotel charges when I checked out three days later. The hotel manager shook my hand before I left and said, 'Good luck, Mr John.' But without his usual smile.

From the look on his face, he must have guessed we were heading for the airport and would have to transit 'Route Irish', as the US military called the airport road, which was fast gaining the reputation of being the most dangerous section of highway in the world.

Mohammed would escort me to the airport in a local taxi without Walid. There was no need for all three of us to run the gauntlet. And if Walid drove his car then he might get pegged by surveillance at the airport entrance as being involved with infidels. Instead, Walid and I had said our goodbyes the previous afternoon in the tranquillity of the hotel gardens. A tinge of sadness and finality was unavoidable given the recent events and the growing siege mentality of the expats in Baghdad. It was difficult to see me returning any time soon unless things unexpectedly improved, although he said he hoped to visit the UK again soon.

'Keep your head down. Stay careful and be lucky. I'll see you when you come to London.'

Walid smiled as he repeated my message a couple of times like a mantra. 'Stay careful and be lucky. Stay careful and be lucky.' Before adding, 'I can be careful, but the rest... Inshallah.'

CHAPTER 18

I'd never been to Baghdad International Airport (BIAP) before, so this was my first time on the airport road. The section known as Route Irish was a twelve kilometres long artery linking the Green Zone at the eastern, city end, with the airport itself at the western end. For traffic joining the road from the south rather than emerging out of the Green Zone, there were three major junctions with bridges crossing the carriageway and ramps leading on and off.

Set back from the highway were densely packed Sunni districts of the city, able to spit out and swallow heavily armed assailants at will. As the primary route between the city and airport, and the only route for civilian traffic, it was an insurgent's dream scenario.

Mohammed had chosen our transport wisely. Inside it was decorated with furs and jingly mementos hung from every available vantage point. Verses of the Koran indicated Allah's guidance and protection for travellers. I was happy for all the help we could get. But it was the meaty sound of the engine and the lack of the usual red-and-white Baghdad taxi colour scheme that had me nodding my head in appreciation.

'No, no, no. Here, you sit in the front,' said Mohammed, indicating the front passenger seat after I'd grabbed the rear door handle.

'No mate. I'm going to stay hidden in the back. Keep myself as invisible as possible so we don't attract any unwelcome attention.

'Of course, but what about if we run into Americans? Maybe with you in the front it will help.'

'To be honest, I don't think they'll notice in this car. Anyone seeing us will expect it to be full of locals. If we hit a local checkpoint, I'll slouch down quietly in the back with my cap pulled down. If we run into Americans, I can speak to them.'

Mohammed had a dubious expression as he considered what I'd said. I couldn't blame him for being nervous about running into trouble. After all, this was also his first time along the airport road since the war. 'Okay,' he said at last. 'Inshallah we will have no problems.'

'Inshallah,' I agreed.

We bypassed the Green Zone to the south side, getting stuck in heavy traffic at the Jadriya Bridge taking us out of the central district of Karada. Then across the Tigris River and towards the junction where we turned right to join Route Irish from the south. There was a tranquil normality as we sped down the airport road. If it hadn't been for the charred skeletons of a destroyed convoy and occasional shells of other burnt-out cars, it could have been any other highway in the country. Like many dangerous places, it all looks calm and normal until the shit hits the fan.

'Tell the driver, if we see any Americans then stay well back. At least a hundred metres. Don't try to overtake them.'

'He knows,' said Mohammed.

'I'm sure he does mate but tell him anyway. Tell him I'm saying he has to stay back, or I'll be fucking angry.'

The driver's head twitched as I swore, so I followed up by catching his eye in the mirror and said, 'You see Americans you stay back, right?'

He glanced at both of us and shrugged his shoulders, which Mohammed answered in Arabic. I recognised the word 'Amrikiyyan', meaning Americans. I hoped my belligerence had helped get the message across.

Numerous Iraqis had been killed trying to overtake military convoys and private security teams displaying 'Keep Back 100 Metres' signs in Arabic and English. This was one road where you couldn't blame the security forces for being extremely wary of the suicide vehicle-borne IED (SVBIED) threat, even if the trigger-happy nature of some reports led me to regard them as potentially dangerous as the bad guys. For some reason, the locals just didn't comprehend the seriousness of the threat and many innocent men, women, and children lost their lives due to a cultural misunderstanding of the new rules of the road.

As the airport loomed in front of us, I spotted an American military call sign ahead. We were doing 140 km/h, so I yelled over the road noise to Mohammed that we needed to slow down and follow the Americans into the airport cautiously. By the time the driver braked, there were flashes up ahead as the Americans came under fire from the right-hand side. A boom as an RPG landed close to one of the vehicles and it wobbled left.

We screeched to a halt along with two SUVs in front of us. The road bent round to the left in a sweeping U-turn to join the opposite carriageway and head back towards the city. We were hidden by a small grassy mound as the crack and rattle of small arms and automatic fire continued out of sight to our front.

I was relieved to see an expat security commander jump out of the front SUV, although he didn't look anywhere near as happy to see our jingly taxi joined on the end of his team. A look of surprise crossed his face as I emerged from the rear door and called over. Turned out he was the British team leader of a security team escorting US journalists to the same flight as me. It dawned on me that failure to make the flight would be a disaster as I doubted the RJ refund policy would be much help to get my money back, let alone the issue of when the next seats might be available.

We were in cover from the firefight which appeared to be dying down as quickly as it had erupted. However, sitting here could make us vulnerable to the American soldiers if they unexpectedly came across us when clearing the area.

I removed my baseball cap to reveal my fair hair and took off my jacket to expose my white forearms below the rolled-up shirt sleeves. The first time I'd ever been disappointed to note how brown they were from my 'pusser's tan'.

'I'm going to let them know we're here.'

'Are you sure that's a good idea?' The team leader had a point, but I was picturing US soldiers sweeping through the area and catching sight of our local vehicle positioned in cover not long after an attack had hit them. Any decision to shoot first and ask questions later would put a dent in my travel plans.

'There's no way I'm missing this flight.'

I had my hands up as I rounded the hillock. There was at least one American casualty on the floor being treated about seventy metres to my front. As I moved forward gingerly, none of the Americans appeared to have seen me. That could be bad, so I shouted out to make sure they were aware of me.

'BRITISH.' And again. 'BRITISH. Three vehicles.' I waved three fingers of my raised left hand back in the direction of the hillock.

That did it. Before I'd finished shouting, weapons were taking a bead on me and a cluster of American voices were screaming at me to halt.

'British. Three Vehicles,' I repeated, but the Americans were screaming at me to 'GO BACK, GO BACK.' They'd just been attacked and at least one of their mates was wounded, so I didn't blame them for not wanting to stop and chat about it.

I about-turned with my hands even higher in the air and started to head back the twenty metres or so to the vehicles. Up ahead I could see a jam of other traffic stopped a hundred metres up the road, aware of the scene ahead of them and conscious of the threat.

Once back in cover I let my hands drop to my sides as I updated the security team leader. 'They know we're here, but we're not going to get past them for a while.'

'Fuck,' was his simple reply. My thoughts exactly.

If we thought we were staying put until the road was clear again, we were badly mistaken. Within a couple of minutes, a Humvee tore around the corner and we were told in no uncertain terms to: 'Get down the fucking road back to the Green Zone.'

All my money was gone, and the flight was due to leave in three hours. My shoulders sagged as the American sergeant shouted at us to get a move on while they set up a cordon and began directing traffic to take the sweeping U-turn back towards the city.

'Is there anywhere we can stop and wait without having to go back to the city?' I asked, more in hope than expectation.

I didn't relish the idea of bouncing up and down Route Irish all day, but I had no idea if any of these neighbourhoods were quiet residential areas or seething with insurgent menace. The problem now was all Westerners seemed like walking dollar signs to anyone with a gun who wanted to make money by selling you to the highest bidder. You might end up in the hands of the insurgents, but it would probably be local low lifes who first took you. It was clear we couldn't go to the north side: that was the direction the attack on the Americans had emerged from.

Mohammed conferred with the taxi driver in Arabic and we took an immediate right turn off the highway.

'The driver knows somewhere. A restaurant not far away.'

I wasn't hungry, but if there was a friendly location where we could wait for half an hour without having to drive all the way back down Route Irish into the centre of the city, then it got my vote.

★

'I'm sorry. He won't let us in.' Mohammed had been sure he'd be able to persuade the restaurant owner to find us a discreet table, but he was having none of it. His eyes blinked ten to the dozen as he stared at me like I carried the plague.

The driver and I walked the ten metres back to the parked taxi by the kerb while Mohammed waited for the takeaway food he'd ordered, making no attempt to hide his anger at the refusal to allow us inside.

As I dropped onto the back seat, vowing not to touch any of the food in case it was tainted, a car turned into the road a few metres away and I caught the gaze of the driver. Loud music was blaring out from the open windows as he braked and slowly drove past. I could see three other young men crammed into the car, with the nearest passenger also giving me the once-over. At distance I might be okay in my local clobber, but up this close they would make out my European features and hair colour. Being the mute cousin from Mosul wasn't going to cut it here.

'We need to get moving.' But I was wasting my time with the driver. He didn't speak a word of English.

'MOHAMMED, come on, we need to get moving.'

He waved his hand dismissively as a waiter handed him a bag. Through the back window I saw the car of young Fonzies had pulled up less than a hundred metres down the road.

'COME ON.'

'All right, all right.' As he started back towards the car, Mohammed had a half-smile on his face as dismissive as his earlier wave.

By now the suspicious car had completed a three-point turn and then begun to accelerate as it approached again. Although initially appearing oblivious to the situation, Mohammed broke into a slow jog. He'd spotted the problem.

'Let's go. Tell him to go. GO.'

Mohammed barked an order as the carload of young men pulled up beside us. Our driver must have seen the same as me and stamped on the gas as a passenger began to emerge with the familiar black accessory of a handgun.

We barrelled round the corner into the main road and careered into the traffic to the blare of car horns from braking drivers. Our adversaries turned into the road to follow us but made little effort at any serious pursuit. A few turns later we were anonymous again amongst the lunchtime flow.

It had only been twenty minutes or so since we'd been ordered to leave the incident scene outside the airport, but already I wanted to try again. I was conscious of the clock ticking towards the departure time and didn't have a clue how long the check-in and security process would take even if I did manage to reach the terminal before the flight had left.

After a brief conversation with the driver, Mohammed advised me we needed to rejoin the highway at the same junction close to the Jadriya Bridge from earlier. I didn't relish the thought of cruising down almost the entirety of Route Irish again, but at least it would mean nearly an hour might have passed before we reached the site of the earlier attack on the Americans. With any luck it would now be clear, and I might still make the flight after all.

We passed the same skeletal remains of shattered vehicles as we sped back towards the airport with grim determination. I think the driver had a 'fuck this' moment and tried to call time on things. Mohammed pulled out a wad of dinars and used his powers of persuasion to keep us on track. He didn't tell me what was said, but I could tell this was more than the driver had bargained for and he wasn't at all happy about it.

There was barely any sign an incident had occurred as we passed the site of the earlier attack and closed on the airport entrance. To my consternation and the taxi driver's obvious satisfaction, I had to disembark at a large chaotic parking area to cram myself and my luggage into a crowded bus to get to the terminal building.

At the bus door I shook hands with Mohammed.

'Be careful on the way back, mate.' I looked up at the faces in the bus windows peering back at me. 'You could have been pinged dropping me off, so get away now and I'll see you soon in London.'

I tried to make contingency plans in case I missed the flight or it got cancelled, but Mohammed was confident it would leave as scheduled and I'd be on it. We agreed to meet again as soon as he arrived back in London. He planned to drive with Thamer when the roads heading west opened again. However, in the end he followed me to Amman on an RJ flight a few weeks later.

I felt vulnerable as I bouldered my way onto the bus not more than 400 metres from where the Americans had come under attack. There were no other white faces looking up from the packed seats. Not a surprise because other expats would be driven all the way to the terminal in their armoured escort vehicles. Yet another reminder I was firmly at the low budget and higher risk end of things.

★

As we corkscrewed up and away from Baghdad and settled into the flight to Amman, there was a collective sigh of relief from me and my fellow passengers. Everyone had endured Route Irish, security queues that seemed out of all proportion with the number of passengers actually flying, and an extra security check of all hold baggage on the hot tarmac next to the plane.

I'd already decided to treat myself to a decent hotel in Amman where my credit cards would give me access to funds again. In the end I might as well have stayed at the airport hotel because after one beer I fell into a deep sleep and hardly stirred until the morning, apart from taking a second shower and ordering burger and chips from room service.

★

Claire was happy I was home. Despite my tiredness from the journey, we hopped into bed the moment we thought the kids were asleep. After renewing our acquaintance with a quick bout of 'hello again' satisfying sex, we laid together and caught up properly for the first time. She didn't watch the news much, but you'd have to be living on a desert island not to know Baghdad was going to hell in a hand basket.

'Is it really bad over there?' she asked. 'My mum was really worried the other morning after seeing some news reports and I'm sure your mum feels the same. They've both been round and phoned so much I started getting worried. Worried something might have happened I didn't know about.'

I gave a measured answer. 'It's not good. Things happened soon after I got there to stir the situation up. I don't think I'll be going back again for a while.'

Claire kissed me and smiled. 'I'm pleased you're not going back.'

I returned her kiss. 'I didn't say I wasn't going back, just probably not for a while.'

Her face fell, but quickly brightened again. 'Well it means we have time to plan for Natalie's sixteenth birthday party next month. You'll definitely be here then?'

'Yeah, I should be. Depends on work, but I'm pretty sure I'll be here.'

Claire kissed me again, draped her arm across my chest, and pressed herself into me. The last traces of tension from my trip melted away.

★

The escape from Baghdad had dominated my recent focus, but out running with Taz over Epsom Downs on my first morning home I began to appreciate my predicament in Iraq. After so much time, effort, and money to establish a foothold in Baghdad, was it time to take a step back and reconsider whether to continue? The country was descending into a hell and I couldn't foresee returning anytime soon. Mohammed remained over there, but was it going to turn into a pit that swallowed money until I had nothing left, or was there still a chance I could make a healthy return on my investment?

Then there was my family. While away I thought about them, just not with the immediacy I felt when at home. It might not make sense, but usually it was only at home that the risks seemed so apparent and foolhardy. When I was in Baghdad, I felt I had a semblance of control most of the time, even when things weren't going to plan, or at least the ability to influence events around me. Watching the reports of the carnage being wrought across Iraq from afar like everyone else, it looked like heading back into that maelstrom was almost guaranteed to be a one-way trip.

As far as my daughters were concerned, like most teenage girls Natalie had plenty of problems of her own to occupy her as she approached her sixteenth birthday. If she was aware her old man was taking reckless chances with his safety in Iraq, she didn't show it. And with her total innocence, little Becky made me smile nearly every time I looked at her and I couldn't help but feel enormous guilt for the risks I had been taking.

★

The two periods I'd spent in Iraq had caused me to miss some interesting sounding projects I'd had to pass on to other investigators. And with all the money I'd spent in Iraq for no return, I needed to start bringing in alternative revenue fast. It was still several months before the annual arrival of Middle Eastern sheikhs would herald 24/7 work and the accompanying boost to cash flow for me and many others on the London 'circuit'. A promising answerphone message raised my hopes.

'John, it's Roy. I've got an urgent job in London so call me if you're home. It starts next week and hopefully should run for a few weeks. Speak soon, bye.'

Normally Roy's business partner, Dave, contacted me, so this was a little unusual. Dave was a former para and Met Police detective whose son was an old oppo of mine from the Corps. He called on me regularly when he had close protection or investigation work available, and I hoped Roy's message meant more of the same.

CHAPTER 19

LONDON – SUMMER 2004

'I've got a good mind to get out and give this guy a round of applause. What a legend,' I murmured to my partner in crime, Jez.

It wouldn't have been practical to jump out of the surveillance van and compromise ourselves, but this average-looking old man had livened up our afternoon no end.

He had his hands in his pockets and a spring in his step – not a mean feat considering he must have been about eighty. Apart from Jez and me, the only other people who knew what he'd been doing for the last couple of hours here in Chelsea were the two Asian hookers he'd treated with champagne and a back catalogue of cracking dits.

There was no way we'd have picked him out as the potential client on his way to the flat, but I made sure to be in position to ID our mystery Romeo when he left. I'd been given a running commentary all afternoon from Jez in the rear of the van as he listened to the guy sharing a drink, enjoying a bath, and raising plenty of laughs with Mai Ling and Alicia.

Calling up the 'Creme de la Femme' office after he'd gone past, it turned out we now had two hours clear until the next appointment at the other flat near Paddington Station.

'McDonalds here we come,' I told the voice on the other end we'd christened 'Moneypenny'. She said her real name was Sindy, but we reckoned she only used it for work, like the escorts.

'Stay ready in case we get a new booking,' warned Sindy. She sounded gorgeous although my attempts to get an invite to the next works party and see for myself weren't getting anywhere.

'We'd eat you alive,' she'd teased.

'Sounds like a great way to go. Put us down for four tickets,' I said hopefully. Unfortunately, all that ever came back over the phone was a giggle rather than an invitation. Oh well, you can't blame guys for trying. I don't think Claire would have seen the funny side though.

The protective surveillance job had been running for over two weeks and I worked all day every day. Two listening devices had been installed in each of a pair of flats in Paddington and Chelsea which housed girls from the escort agency as they worked their magic on the variously horny, sad, lonely, and/or pathetic men who came to see them. A spate of attacks had resulted in Dave and Roy's company being hired to protect the girls. It wasn't a complicated security plan although it was a little unclear in the important places.

'So, if you hear an attack taking place then you're to get in there ASAP and deal with the attacker,' Roy had explained during the initial briefing for the job. 'Don't worry about the police, I'll deal with them if it comes to it. Just make sure you call me straight away if something kicks off.'

Roy was former Met Police Flying Squad and still had strong contacts on the force. Over the years, I'd had my fair share of jobs that threw up obvious warning flags and without doubt this fell into that category.

'But surely we're going to be bang to rights if we've kicked seven bells of shit out of this prick, even if he has attacked one of the girls?' Jez had a good point, and I was keen to hear Roy's answer as well.

'Listen guys, when you get this scumbag, just make sure you don't leave him in the flat. You get me? If he's not in the flat, then there shouldn't be anything to tie him to the agency or us.'

'Apart from the witnesses who see two men dragging a guy out the front door and dumping him on the street,' I threw in.

Roy turned and glared at me. 'I told you, if it comes to it then I'll deal with the Met. Oh, and whatever you do, don't kill anyone. Do something stupid like that and no-one can help you.'

Not exactly a rousing pep talk, but it did signal the start of some well-paid work bombing up and down between the two flats, parking within range of the bugs planted in the hallways and outside the bedrooms, and listening intently for the sounds of a struggle, attack, or anything else untoward.

For some reason no-one else wanted to drive the van, so I took that on for the duration of the job whilst three other guys, Jez, Billy, and Smudge, rotated the listening role in the back of the van to fit in with their other work. It suited me because it meant I took the van home at night rather than having to catch a late-night train and then another early the next morning to get back up into town.

The news coming from Baghdad worsened by the day: the latest showed kidnapped American businessman Nicholas Berg being decapitated by a knife in a video released by al-Qaeda in Iraq, reportedly killed by their Jordanian leader Abu Musab al-Zarqawi. With depressing reports from Mohammed about the deteriorating situation and no sign of progress with any of the business opportunities, a long-running gig in London was very helpful financially.

I'd told Claire it was a surveillance job; no need to get into the details with her. The bugs weren't located in the bedrooms anyway, so the listener in the back wasn't getting his kicks from the sounds of rampant sex all day long. From what my partners in the van reported, they were more likely to be heading home about ready to slit their wrists after listening to a procession of losers pouring out all their troubles to a basque and stocking-clad escort girl, before seeing if spilling their beans helped take the edge off their problems.

Several days later I heard something in the back hitting the floor or sides and the van swayed as Jez must have stood up.

'Jesus, mate. This guy Clive isn't our man. Sounds like his missus wears the trousers in their house. Apparently she "doesn't understand me" and their sex life is non-existent. I'm not surprised you idiot. You're paying £200 an hour for a blonde goddess and you're sitting there boring her to death. I don't understand you either. Nice work if you can get it, I suppose.'

I'd seen the pictures on the website of this statuesque Russian girl and tried to imagine the scene. 'Yeah, I bet she's not bothered. Better to get paid for listening to some loser than have to shag him for an hour. By the way mate, careful about walking round in the back. The van starts to rock and that could get noticed. The local neighbourhood watch might think we're a mobile gigolo service.'

'If I wasn't hidden in this sweat box, pissing into a bottle, then I'd be beating them off with a shitty stick.' Then Jez swore quietly about the headphone cables getting snarled up.

'That's what you get for throwing the kit about.'

I opened the door to the cab and stepped out to stretch my legs in the fresh air. That caused Jez to start chuntering about who had to do all the work on this job.

'Keep it down, mate,' I said back into the van, which only prompted more but quieter grumbling.

For me, it was a case of parking up and acting like a fibre optic cable engineer as per the magnetic sign displayed on the side of the van. Drinking tea, listening to the radio, and reading a newspaper seemed to fit the bill perfectly.

Less than a month later and the job ended. We never did intercept any attackers or get an invite to any staff parties, but it generated some much-needed income before the Qataris came back into town. Unfortunately, they had plans to spend most of their summer holiday in Paris, so the security job with them only lasted a couple of weeks instead of the more usual six or more. I still enjoyed playing football with the two elder sons and had introduced them to the time-sapping delights of Championship Manager on the laptop, but soon I faced another empty work diary and needed to make a decision about the future of the operation in Baghdad.

During this time, Natalie chose to hold her sixteenth birthday party at her boyfriend's house, which meant I had little involvement in the planning and organisation. The lad and his parents seemed a decent bunch and we mixed easily without becoming real friends. Claire became more involved as the day drew closer, but the momentous occasion for our eldest daughter seemed to pass us by in a flurry of GCSE exams and growing up. The party was a good night though, and Natalie appeared to be relaxed and happy which was the most important thing. And on the plus side, chipping in to share the costs meant it hadn't proved as expensive as feared.

★

My main business marketing efforts focused on the Internet. I'd knocked up the company website myself using online guides. It wasn't great although many of the images were photographs I'd taken in Iraq and I thought they evoked an air of authenticity. Using a small budget on Google AdWords and the Yahoo pay-per-click service, I received regular requests to quote for work, some of which turned into paying jobs.

Not enough though, so I went back to the bank for more funds to give me time to get better established. They agreed an increase in the loan and a £10,000 overdraft facility, but only if I guaranteed both personally. I didn't even need to think about it and signed on the dotted line. With the additional money I expanded my marketing budget and rented a small serviced office not far from where we lived. Far better than working from the dining-room table and it meant being closer to a train station that could whisk me into Central London in thirty minutes if required.

What I really needed now was a big meaty project, either out in Iraq or closer to home.

In the early nineties, when I'd left the Corps for three years before rejoining, I'd posted an advert in the back of *Combat & Survival* magazine that read: *Former Royal Marine seeks interesting work UK or abroad* with my home telephone number underneath (well before the days of mobile phones). It led to several interesting experiences, including an appearance as a prosecution witness in a conspiracy to commit murder trial and adventures in the former republic of Yugoslavia.

By 2004 the Internet was changing a lot of things, but there were still people out there who needed the same kind of irregular jobs doing. The trick was to try and avoid the time-wasters and instead concentrate your efforts on projects with real earning potential. At the end of the summer I was approached via my website contact form with an invitation to discuss an ambitious project called Football to the Summit.

Sport had captured the national mood that summer and mine with it. England had reached the quarter-final of Euro 2004 before losing on penalties to Portugal. Although the country wallowed in the disappointment, it soon perked up with the rest of the home nations during the Athens Olympics a month later as Britain achieved its best medal haul in the modern era. What better time to get involved in an international sporting project?

Football to the Summit was the brainchild of a smart-suited, young British-Indian businessman with a passion for the sport. He intended to dribble a football hundreds of miles through India in thirty-two stages, accompanied during each stage by local kids representing one of the thirty-two teams qualified for the 2006 World Cup. Training sessions and small matches would be scheduled throughout, with one of the goals being the introduction of football to the youth of cricket-loving India. The final stages would see us move into Nepal before playing a game at Everest Base Camp, which would be the highest altitude match ever staged. An unlikely but ambitious goal was for the match ball used in the Everest game to be used to kick off the opening match in the 2006 World Cup.

As I sat through the presentation in London by the three men running the project, I understood immediately it could be the making of me and my company – provided it had the funds to go ahead. They asked me to submit a proposal for a comprehensive security support package, so the costings could be included in the financial projections. There was mention of FIFA approval and discussions with various high-profile brand names but, when push came to shove, the funding to date all appeared to have come from the founders. I'm a big football fan and love the occasion of the World Cup, so it was a given I'd prepare an extensive and comprehensive proposal for this project in any event. However, these guys did seem to have the contacts who could make this thing fly.

Over the next couple of weeks, I coordinated with Jim to add a communications package to my security plan. It was his area of expertise and he wrote a slick document which dovetailed with my main proposal. The total figure for the security side totalled over £2 million plus costs. It was difficult not to get excited as the plans came to life in my research, concept of operations, and risk assessments, but it wouldn't generate any revenue unless and until the funding was in place. Therefore, I needed to avoid being sidetracked too much and instead keep focused on developing new business.

★

The investigation and due diligence work often included interesting cases, usually with overseas elements to a greater or lesser extent. This reflected my website, which made no mention of standard UK private investigator fare such as process serving or tracing debtors. It meant the jobs coming through the door paid well; there simply weren't enough of them. My target was the corporate market where I could provide the same level of service as the big companies, but at less than half the price. Unfortunately, many law firms preferred the accountability of the larger companies. Outside of that, they only engaged trusted individuals with whom they had a long-standing relationship.

I considered pretty much anything which came my way. It led to investigations in France, Italy, Germany, Eastern Europe, and the US. While I achieved great results in complex cases, the costs of employing surveillance teams, overseas agents, and technical experts always reduced the net profit to disappointingly low numbers come the end of each month. I needed to increase the margins and increase the volume, but it was a very competitive market.

★

Mohammed had returned to Baghdad to run the office and try to generate some revenue; until our last phone call earlier that week had been interrupted by the sound of automatic gunfire.

'Where are you?'

'I'm downstairs by the reception. There's fighting outside in the street. Things are getting even worse.' He sounded dejected.

'Keep your head down and get home to the family as soon as you can, mate. There's no point risking your life.'

When he called me again later that night from Walid's house round the corner from the office, we agreed not to renew the six-month office lease when it expired the following month. Gunfights taking place outside the entrance to the business centre were the final straw. Mohammed would move all the furniture and computers into storage at his brother's place and come back to the UK. Our efforts to establish a trusted business beacon in Baghdad had failed.

The only potential bright spot for Iraq was an ongoing discussion with a German company about the feasibility of exporting HMS 1 & 2 scrap metal through the ports in Basra in the Shi'a south under British control. The south had its own problems but compared to Baghdad it sounded like a haven of peace and solitude. Mohammed said he knew people down there, so we agreed to meet up on his return to discuss the support options in the south. Maybe there was still a chance to salvage something out of the Iraq adventure after all.

★

The previous year, my full-time consultancy work for Pete had been short-lived once he'd quickly realised winning the big corporate jobs would be more difficult than anticipated. Even so, we'd been friends for over twelve years and I continued calling into his office in SW London at least once a week.

If I thought I met some interesting characters and got involved in weird and wonderful schemes, it was nothing compared to Pete and his small team. I'd first worked with him in the early nineties while on my sabbatical from the Corps. It had been a similar story back then with debt collecting, car repossessions, process serving, and investigations. Always on the edge of acceptable, but Pete got results.

Although I no longer worked with Pete on a retainer, I did join up with him and the team for specific corporate jobs as and when they came up. My once or twice weekly visits gave us a chance to compare notes about enquiries we'd received. Sometimes I used the expertise of him and his team to subcontract on my cases, but usually it was Pete bringing me in on one of his corporate jobs.

Pete seemed to be involved in various wild and complicated projects with high net worth clients in the UK and abroad. The last time I'd visited his office he had complained bitterly about having a cheque seized from him by customs at Gatwick during a random search.

'They searched all my bags, found the cheque, and started asking me questions about where it came from. I mean, what right have they got? Next thing I'm pulled into an interview room and they're telling me I should have declared it and they need to make some enquiries. Before you know it, they've snatched it away and given me a receipt. Strewth, what sort of country is this? Seventy-five thousand bloody euros for Christ's sake.'

Not a lot you can say to that. Apparently, the cheque originated from some Spanish casino owner. He'd mentioned an important client down in Spain, but I didn't know enough to understand how all of this fitted together. I hadn't even been aware customs could seize a cheque in that manner, not that travelling with large quantities of cash and cheques was a problem likely to affect me anytime soon. Still, visits to see Pete always made for an interesting break from my quiet little office in Ewell.

It was a sunny day as I parked up round the back of the supermarket, grabbed a microwave Rustlers cheeseburger on my way through the shop, nipped over the road through the traffic, and entered the code on the external office door. After climbing the stairs, I was about to get an offer I most definitely should have refused.

CHAPTER 20

SOUTH WEST LONDON – OCTOBER 2004

'The problem is, John, no-one's got any balls any more.'

The next time I hear that, I'm going to steer well clear of whatever they have to say next.

Pete was railing against the lack of take-up for his generous offer to get involved in a small 'sleight of hand' operation to protect his main client. He went on to outline what he described as a simple task, undoubtedly intending to lure me into accepting a role in his scheme. He was flat out of luck. To me it appeared clear it was more a case of no-one wanting to risk getting involved in a plan with 'potential fuck-up' written all over it.

We were having a coffee in his office near the River Thames in South West London. Lately, Pete had spun tales of an investigation involving VAT carousel activity, stolen oil shipments off the coast of Nigeria, and meetings with British intelligence. The British intelligence part supposedly included being led on a curious circuit of London, which ended in a meeting at the *Cutty Sark*. His main client was somehow adversely affected by all these shenanigans, although I didn't pay close attention to the details.

A few weeks earlier, he'd taken me to meet a new contact at the Special Forces Club in London; an interesting experience even if the club rule of wearing a jacket and tie had me sweltering as we sat having drinks at a table in the bar during the still heat of a summer afternoon.

Pete's contact, George, was an old and bold member of the club who seemed to know everyone there. I suspected this new relationship was at the root of Pete's claimed dealings with elements of the British intelligence agencies, who were also entitled to join the SF Club. Added to his Spanish casino client causing him no end of problems, it all sounded complicated and messy. Good job I wasn't involved.

The latest development was a plan to distance Pete's client from two businessmen implicated in the VAT carousel investigation, with whom the client had other, legitimate business dealings. Pete's attempts to rally a team together for the plan had failed, apart from two dubious-sounding characters from the local pub. He was openly frustrated by my refusal to join in.

'Sorry mate, I'm busy all next week due to this scrap metal thing. Probably be in Germany.'

Unlikely, but I didn't want to leave any scope for arm-twisting. The plan was being put into action the following week, so the limit of my involvement would be listening to a recap after the event next time I visited the office. He gave up talking about it and turned to one of his guys who used the name 'John' in the office. An unfortunate coincidence that meant I was frequently still referred to as 'Jack' from my time working with them.

Shortly afterwards, Pete made a phone call to a lawyer while masquerading as a customs officer, which set in train a fuck-up that tangled me firmly in its web.

★

LONDON – THE FOLLOWING WEEK

The train passed through Wimbledon on time on its way to London Waterloo as my eyes dropped back to the page of a new book I'd started reading. My efforts to avoid getting caught up in Pete's plans to help his client had failed, although my role was a minor bit part. That morning he'd called with a final plea for my assistance.

'I can't do it, mate. I've got a meeting this afternoon at four at the Churchill Hotel with my Iraqi guy.'

That should have been the end of it, but Pete was nothing if not resourceful, and had called back to inform me enthusiastically he'd been able to switch the location of the 'op' to the Churchill Hotel at the same time I'd be there. Therefore, I needed to meet with him and the team for a quick briefing in Berkeley Square at three o'clock, and there was free curry and beers for all the team afterwards. It was only some counter-surveillance. What harm could it do?

The part about my meeting with Mohammed was true. The German company interested in exporting the scrap from Basra were keen. I didn't know anyone in Basra, so I needed to pick Mohammed's brains and find out if any of his southern contacts might be able to assist. Baghdad continued to spiral into a dark place as sectarian killing dominated the news. It didn't look as though we'd be setting up shop there again anytime soon.

The next day I'd also arranged to meet for a coffee with an old army officer friend of mine. Ian was in the UK on leave from Iraq and had called me earlier in the week to catch up. Even if I might not make it to Basra myself, I knew Ian was deployed in southern Iraq. He just might have information useful to the German firm.

I reached Green Park Tube station early, made my way to the Costa Coffee near the south side of Berkeley Square, and dropped into a comfortable chair to read more of my book. I'm a fast reader and busted through a couple more chapters before checking my watch. Almost ten to three. I finished my coffee and wedged the book inside my leather folder alongside a few notes about Iraq.

As I walked into Berkeley Square, I immediately spotted Pete and a group of guys wearing suits right in the centre by a wooden bench. I changed direction to head their way instead of into the Regus office block on the right-hand side where we were due to meet. What the hell were they all doing out in the middle of the square? I could see Scotty, another ex-bootneck who sometimes worked for Pete, over by the road at the edge of the square. He was also walking back towards Pete and the group.

'Hey, Jack. I didn't know he'd got you involved in this shite.'

I only knew Scotty through Pete rather than from service in the Corps and he was used to calling me Jack from the previous year. He knew it wasn't my real name, but I've been called a lot worse.

'Not really, mate. I've got a meeting at the Churchill, which it sounds like you lot are all going to crash. What's going on here?'

'I tell you, there's something not quite right. I've told Pete I spotted a guy talking into a Coke can earlier and I'm sure I just spotted another one. I reckon there's eyes on. And I cannae understand why they're having a dry run through in the middle of the park?'

So, Scotty was in a counter-surveillance role and had been totally ignored when he spotted something suspicious. It didn't surprise me, but I was relieved. This nonsense clearly needed to be knocked on the head and I headed over to Pete to tell him this should all be stood down. Pete turned from chatting to two guys I hadn't met before while his Asian client sat serenely on the wooden seat.

'Scotty tells me he thinks he's spotted dickers. I assume that's not a complete surprise or why have you got him here? You're knocking it on the head, yeah?'

Pete was having none of it. 'No mate. He's just seen a couple of winos talking to themselves and got all excited. We're just about done here. Meet...'

Pete introduced me to a barman and a bookmaker who both worked near to his home. Later I couldn't remember their names, so I referred to them as the Barman and the Bookie. The Barman was a big fella and the Bookie shorter and slimmer. Both looked nervous.

'So... what are these guys here for?' I didn't know the plan, but there were six of us involved who would be enjoying the curry and beers later.

'They'll be the customs guys who make the approach and serve the papers.'

He'd wanted seasoned blaggers involved in this charade, but with everyone else turning him down, he had to make do with the two local lads from back home. Pete pulled out a form, some sort of seizure notice, and explained how the 'customs officers' would approach the client during the meeting with his allegedly dodgy acquaintances at the Churchill Hotel.

The seizure notice was a prop intended to spook them into distancing themselves from his client because they would believe he was under suspicion and investigation from Customs and Excise. Even if that failed, Pete's client would excuse himself from whatever scheme they were proposing due to the heat he was supposedly feeling from the authorities.

It all sounded overcooked to me. Quite a grand plan to basically tell a pair of chancers to get lost. My part involved being inside the hotel in the tabled area to the left of reception on the ground floor, acting in a mixed surveillance/protection role as close to the client meeting as possible. I'd forced Pete's hand because I insisted on being sat inside for my scheduled meeting about Iraq, but he managed to shoehorn me into his plan anyway. Whether I'd be able to position myself anywhere near his client's meeting was a different matter. Provided the meeting occurred in the public areas I should be able to keep eyes on, if nothing else.

If it all went to ratshit, I would need to intervene if things got nasty. Pete thought this might occur in the aftermath once the Barman and the Bookie had played their part and left. He and Scotty would be outside ready to join me if I needed them. Not the best-laid plan, but how much could go wrong in the lobby bar of a five-star London hotel?

'What are you doing this out here for?' I asked, with a sharp look left and right. Berkeley Square occupied an open piece of land in the heart of London, surrounded by buildings, overlooked by a thousand windows, and filled with people all day long. Pete was an experienced guy and it made little sense.

Pete brushed the question off. 'It's only a quick dry run-through for the guys. Nothing that would mean anything to anyone else. It's a nice day for this time of year and it's good to get some fresh air. Come on, let's get a coffee in the office before we set off.'

He collected his seated client before leading the way into the Regus Business Centre.

I knew the hotel better than anyone else in the room, so I drew the layout on a whiteboard up in the client's office to show the two alternative doors to the street other than the main hotel entrance. Scotty could cover the main door and the northern side door from his position parked up on Portman Square, while Pete would cover the main entrance and the southern door from the other side of the square from his van.

If the client went to leave with his two business associates, then we needed a clear distress signal agreed so I didn't kick off when they might in fact have kissed and made up. We agreed the client would drop his pen if he required intervention and go down on one knee as he bent to pick it up. In case I missed seeing the pen being dropped, a stumble and dropping to one knee would be good enough on its own. A move to quickly help him would appear natural to any onlookers and get me in the mix. From there I'd need to improvise.

To avoid arousing suspicion with the use of radios, communication would be via mobile phones. I thought there might be other entrances and exits for the staff, so if they all took off somewhere other than the three public entrances I needed to be on my toes and calling for back-up.

My meeting with Mohammed was arranged for four o'clock. Scotty drove me round to Portman Square and parked up, with the others due to follow on about thirty minutes later. They were waiting for a final confirmation that the targets were en route to the hotel. Not that it would have bothered me in the slightest if they'd cancelled. Scotty found a parking spot which gave him a decent view of the two doors he needed to cover. We had a quick chat about the best curry house to visit that night before I made my way into the main hotel entrance a few minutes early.

After stopping to say hello to a doorman I recognised from a job during the summer, I entered the hotel and turned left, scouring the tables for sight of Mohammed. He hadn't arrived yet, so I grabbed a table at the far end with a good view of anyone passing the reception desk from either the main or the northern side entrance, and anyone entering the hotel from the nearer southern entrance. I ordered an orange juice and settled in to see how late Mohammed arrived and what kind of drama Pete's crew would serve up.

★

By 4.30pm we had agreed the decision to give up the lease of the office in Baghdad was warranted. Even Mohammed was loath to travel back to the city and he was clearly worried about Walid living in a mixed Sunni-Shi'a neighbourhood.

'There's no reconstruction happening now. Everything has stopped. Everyone is scared. The criminals are running all over the city as they like, and the Americans don't seem to care. I can't see how we can keep the business going.'

He was right. Baghdad still seemed to be a total bust, so all the more reason to follow up with Basra. If these Germans got an operation going, then we could forget about Baghdad for the time being and concentrate down there.

'What about Basra then? Did you speak to the people in the south?' I asked.

We were engrossed in our Basra discussion when I noticed Pete's client walking towards us from the direction of the reception desk. He turned immediately right as he reached the corner a few metres from our table and greeted two Asian men sat at a table positioned fifteen feet away on its own across the passageway.

Anyone walking in between our two tables would turn left to find a short passage leading to toilets on the right, a bar on the left, and the southern side door to the street a few metres ahead. I was ideally placed to keep eyes on the meeting, but too far away to hear anything they were saying unless they started raising their voices.

I hadn't told Mohammed anything about my secondary role at the hotel. If it came to it, he might prove useful; after all he was a broad guy with a fiery temper. But if I'd let him in on the plan, he'd probably have shone out like a beacon and compromised everything.

As for Basra, although he had some distant family connections involved in import/export down there, I was disappointed when he told me he doubted he could arrange reliable support in the south. He did, however, offer to join me if I intended to travel there, just as I spotted the Barman and the Bookie approaching from the main entrance.

The two of them performed better than I'd expected. They looked every inch like officialdom as they strode purposefully through the hotel lobby and stopped at the table where the meeting was taking place. They spoke with Pete's client as the other two men sat back and watched on. The client made an open gesture with his hands. I assumed to indicate they could talk to him there rather than going somewhere quieter.

I couldn't hear the conversation, but it gave all the appearance of a plausible scenario, at a stretch. After a couple of minutes, the Barman pulled some papers out of an envelope carried in by the Bookie, pointed out parts in apparent explanation, and handed them over. The two 'customs officers' then turned and left. They walked past the reception desk and out through the main entrance.

Back at the table the three men engaged in a quiet conversation; no sign of anything out of the ordinary. I excused myself from the table, walked down the passageway past the gents' toilet doorway, and made a quick phone call to Pete to report everything appeared to have gone okay and there was no drama inside.

'Okay mate, tha…' The phone signal dropped out and cut us off.

CHAPTER 21

As I put the phone back in my pocket, three people began marching our way from near the reception desk. Two tall, lean guys in dark suits, one in his forties and one at least a decade younger, and a slender woman in her late twenties/early thirties, wearing a smart skirt suit and with her brown hair tied in a ponytail. The trailing man and woman stopped at the table with the client meeting, and the leading man's eyes flicked across the nearby tables and on to Mohammed, before he focused on me. Hardly breaking step, he veered towards where I stood, still trying to reconnect the call with Pete.

'Can I ask what you're doing in the hotel today, sir?'

Although his two colleagues had stopped to engage our target meeting, an indication something was afoot, my first thought was that hotel security might be looking to move Mohammed from the table. The waitress had taken our cups and glasses, so he was sitting there alone without any food or drink in front of him while the place filled up with the paying early evening crowd.

'Sure. I'm here meeting with my colleague to discuss our business in Iraq,' I said, indicating Mohammed sat at the table ten feet away.

As hotel security, this guy was probably ex-job (police) or military so I expanded on the Iraq angle. 'We've had to close our office in Baghdad and we're reviewing the options for Basra. Things are really fucked up over there. Why, what's the problem?'

He studied me closely, then looked at Mohammed who rose out of his seat.

'What's wrong, John?' he asked.

I looked at Mohammed as he spoke and then back to the suited guy who appeared to be wrestling with a decision.

'It's nothing to concern you. Sorry to have bothered you,' he said grudgingly, before moving to join his nearby colleagues. He leaned in to speak to Pete's client who rose out of his seat. The two men then walked towards the main entrance.

'What was that about?' asked Mohammed.

Two more guys came in through the front entrance and spoke with the suit who'd just questioned us.

'I don't know, mate. But something's obviously going on.'

I tried to call Pete and then Scotty from my unregistered 'pay as you go' mobile but both calls went to answerphone. From the looks of it, Pete might have been working with the authorities on a genuine operation. Maybe one linked to his VAT carousel investigation. That might explain the earlier dry run-through in Berkeley Square, intended perhaps to indicate to a watching team who was involved from his side; a watching team Scotty might have detected. However, the alternative red warning flag was the cheque Pete had told me about. The one he said customs recently confiscated when he flew into Gatwick Airport. There were no guarantees here that he was on the same side as the authorities.

I forced myself to remain outwardly calm as I went back over the events of the afternoon in my mind. I couldn't believe customs would have sanctioned a Mickey Mouse op with an actual barman and bookie – civilians. So, either they were genuine customs officers, which was unlikely, or Pete had really been messing with the big boys and it had turned into a clusterfuck. I knew where my money lay.

Neither Pete nor Scotty were picking up calls. I considered my options. If this was the mess I suspected in the pit of my stomach, then I really didn't want to get snared in it any more than I was already. To get up and leave now might appear suspicious, so, fighting every instinct to get the hell out of there ASAP, I ordered another orange juice for me and coffee for Mohammed.

When the drinks arrived, I asked Mohammed if he could get me a pen from the reception desk while I made a phone call. I did have a pen in my pocket, but I needed an excuse to send Mohammed to find out what was going on. I also had pens in my folder, which I realised wasn't with me. Bollocks. I must have left it in Scotty's car or back at the client's office. Oh well, there wasn't anything important inside. I'd pick it up later.

'Ask Jerry what's going on, mate. He'll know.'

Jerry was one of the senior doormen who I'd seen on my way in. We both knew him to say hello to, from working with the Qataris that summer and in previous years.

'Okay. I need to get something from the shop anyway.' Mohammed set off towards the reception desk. Through the doors behind the reception desk was a passageway leading out to the northern side door. There were slightly posher toilets on that passageway, a small function room, a stairwell, and a general shop.

Five minutes later and Mohammed reappeared, stopped to try and talk to the suited guy who'd questioned me, and returned to our table after being waved away. He sat down with a satisfied glint in his eye. I still hadn't got hold of Pete or Scotty and had now turned that phone off as a precaution. I had my contract phone with me, but it was registered in my name; calling from that one might be a bad idea. As unobtrusively as possible I switched it off under the table. My other unregistered pay as you go phone would be useful. Shame I'd left it in the forgotten folder in Scotty's car.

'When I spoke to Jerry, he told me there's been a raid and a couple of guys have been arrested by customs and police. I could see some men with baseball caps; I think they might have been armed police. Two guys were on the floor in handcuffs. They lifted them up and then put them in the back of a Range Rover.'

Shit. That didn't bode well. I glanced at the customs/police officers chatting amicably with the client's two Asian business associates across from our table. It didn't strike me they were being treated as the bad guys here. The younger man and woman were still with them and they had now been rejoined by my suited inquisitor. As soon as they all got up and left towards the main entrance, I moved to the edge of my seat.

'Right mate, we need to get going.'

And before Mohammed could say anything I added, 'Let's go this way.'

I took off down the passageway towards the nearest side entrance past the bar. On reaching the pavement, I turned right heading towards the busy Edgware Road. Mohammed struggled to catch up.

'What's the rush?' he panted as we crossed the road.

'I've remembered something I need to get done.' Better he didn't know the real story.

As soon as we reached Edgware Road, I gave Mohammed a quick handshake and said I'd call him, before turning left and heading down towards Marble Arch at speed. The pavements were busy with early evening crowds and I wanted to get lost amongst them and as far away from the Churchill as possible.

I dodged the traffic as I crossed straight over Edgware Road. On reflection, this was a good time to be paranoid. Scotty had detected possible surveillance during the peculiar dry run-through of Pete's operation in the middle of a public London square. Now arrests had occurred; an indication Scotty had not been mistaken.

It was safe to assume at least two if not all the other guys involved that afternoon were in some sort of custody; whether friendly or hostile remained to be seen. If I also assumed the area around the hotel was under observation during the raid, the watchers might well have acquired me as a target and perhaps followed me when I left. Time to throw in some amateur counter-surveillance. I didn't care about detection, this was all about avoidance.

I cut left down towards Hyde Park and considered whether to head for a bus or tube at Marble Arch. Marble Arch underground walkway has multiple entrances/exits to all the surrounding streets and looks like the kind of setting George Smiley would use to shake off a KGB tail. As the closest underground station to the Churchill Hotel, it would be the obvious place for me to go, so bollocks to that. I headed into Hyde Park. If it came to it, I'd literally run for it across the park. If anyone was following and managed to catch me, then it would be a fair cop.

I knew the various routes in the big Central London park very well from many hours of training in the mornings before work over previous summers. If I broke into a run it would look suspicious, but I maintained a fair old walking pace. I passed the bandstand and moved into cover, taking a few seconds to observe the people in my wake. No obvious customs or police officers struggling to keep up. Everything appeared normal.

Three-quarters of a mile from Marble Arch was Hyde Park Corner, another London Tube station with multiple entrances and exits, but I wanted to avoid obvious transport hubs. I dropped out of the park onto Knightsbridge and kept heading south, skirting Belgrave Square Garden and onto Belgrave Place to keep parallel with the main road, Grosvenor Place, which ran along the side of Buckingham Palace Gardens towards Victoria Station two-thirds of a mile away. Victoria had trains that ran to Epsom, but it would be another obvious location where surveillance or arrest teams might try to pick me up.

I kept on moving towards Victoria as I weighed up my options. It wasn't worth the risk. I circled to the south of the station, then swung left past the Passport Office and a large Argos shop onto Vauxhall Bridge Road. A number 36 Routemaster bus came into view heading south towards the bridge and stopped on the other side of the road. I darted across and jumped on the open rear platform just as it scooted off. A ticket inspector shook his head in disapproval as I flashed my One Day Travel Card.

A couple of minutes later I jumped off the bus at the end of Vauxhall Bridge with the modern MI6 headquarters looming on my left. I dashed up and over the footbridge before picking my way through the complaining traffic to Vauxhall station where I could catch an Epsom bound train coming from Waterloo Station.

I took the stairs two at a time up to Platform 8 and squeezed through the closing doors of a train about to depart. All Epsom departures left from this platform, although the driver announced this train was headed elsewhere. Not a problem. It stopped at Wimbledon, which connected to Epsom.

After changing at Wimbledon for the right train I let myself relax a little. It was irrational to think I would be under close surveillance, but better safe than sorry. Rather than stay on the train all the way to Epsom, I jumped off at Ewell West and walked the mile or so towards home. The other commuters going the same way might have included watchers. If they were still with me I wouldn't shake them off now.

The nerves began to build again as I got closer to home. If they knew my identity, then all the dicking about I'd been doing since the incident at the Churchill would have been a waste of time. In that case, they might be parked up outside the house, or worse still sat in the living room with Claire and the girls waiting for my return. I needed to assess the situation at the house.

I passed the small row of shops on the main road and prepared to turn right into a side road with a pub a hundred metres down on the left. Directly opposite the pub was the entrance to the small close where we lived in our three-bedroom semi-detached house. The pub itself was a quiet locals' place and plenty of cars usually sat parked outside. Once I turned the corner, I might come into view of hostiles who would have eyes on the front of our house, if they were there.

I stayed in the shadows close to the fence after making the turn. An access road thirty metres away on the right ran behind the row of shops and the bottom of the gardens for one side of the close, including our house.

With my jacket pulled up around my face and my baseball cap fished out of my pocket and onto my head, I walked naturally towards the access road turn. After making the turn into the narrow, potholed road, I ran over to the trees marking the start of our back fence about forty metres further along. I slipped into the trees, clambered over the fence as quietly as possible, and dropped down into the soft earth behind our garden shed.

There was no-one in the conservatory and the curtains were closed in the living room, although light leaked out through the gaps. I stayed still and listened for a minute, straining for the sounds of anything out of the ordinary. Music drifted from the pub and a woman laughed loudly nearby, but I caught no discernible fleet of running engines, squawk of radio transmissions, or grumble of waiting officers. I took out my two remaining phones, checked they were both switched off, and slid them under the far corner of the shed. Best to take every precaution until the situation was clear.

I slowly made my way up the garden towards the rear of the house, taking care so as not to alert Taz to start barking at a potential intruder. I trod carefully through some toys scattered on the patio, moved up against the living-room window, and peered through a chink in the curtains. Claire sat on the sofa watching the television with the dog lying on the floor in front of her. That made it highly unlikely any strangers were in the house. Good. Although I made a mental note of the hound's failure to detect my approach.

I knocked softly on the patio doors. Taz immediately sprang up and barked as she ran to get her head through the curtains. She hadn't barked until reaching a year old, and the first time had been at a doorbell ringing on the TV. We didn't even have a doorbell in our married quarters, so it must have been some deep-rooted dog instinct. Well she had her voice now and barked even though it was me standing in front of her. I quickly removed my baseball cap and pulled my jacket collar down, but it didn't stop her growling through the glass. Claire pulled open the curtains and the light spilled over me. She unlocked and slid the patio door open.

'What are you doing?' With a look that said she knew she wasn't going to like the answer. She probably suspected some sort of drunken antics even though it was still before 9.00pm. She'd known it might be a late one after a free curry and beers.

'Just being careful. Has anyone called round?'

'No. Anyone? Like who?'

'Like the police or other authorities.' It sounded quite reasonable to me.

'No. What the hell have you done?'

'I haven't done anything. I'm just being careful. Something happened up in London with Pete and I'm sort of caught up in it' – and before Claire could say anything else – 'I need to grab a few files and my laptop. If anyone rings or calls at the door, then you haven't seen me.'

With the dog trailing behind me, I kept the light off as I moved into our dining room at the front of the house. After grabbing the files containing current work in progress, some company documents, and my laptop, I took everything and a black plastic bin-liner out into the garden. Once I'd recovered the phones and notebook from under the shed, I wrapped the lot in the black bag and buried it in a shallow hole in the left-hand flower bed. I tried to camouflage any sign of my excavation as well as I could in the dark and returned to the house where Claire was eager to begin an interrogation.

'Are you drunk? Have you been fighting?' Based on past misdemeanours these weren't unreasonable questions.

'No sweetheart, it's a job that seems to have gone wrong.' Quickly adding, 'Not my job. One of Pete's.'

'If the police are involved, then shouldn't you go to them?'

I didn't want to even try and explain the background. It was confusing enough to me.

'I don't really know who's involved. I'm going to sleep on it tonight and see if I can get hold of Pete tomorrow to find out what's going on. Once I know, then I can work out what to do about it.'

Claire had a general idea of what I did for a living, although I never went into the details. For anything work-related, she usually trusted my judgement. She clearly wasn't happy about tonight, but then neither was I.

CHAPTER 22

I spent a fitful night half awake, imagining a van screeching to a halt outside followed by a thunderous knock at the door and shouts to 'open up'. I got up early and nipped out in the cold morning darkness to retrieve my buried hoard. After a quick breakfast, I showered, dressed, and headed out the front door to the dog's obvious disgust that we weren't going for a run. As I parked up in the empty car park behind the business centre, I wondered if I'd be receiving any visitors to my office today.

I still hadn't contacted Pete by the time I left the office for the station and a train to Waterloo to meet with Ian to discuss Basra over coffee. As I travelled up to London and walked the same streets that had felt so sinister the night before, I was struck by the normality of the day and everyone, including me, going about their business as usual. Fear that the previous day's events might negatively affect my business gnawed away inside, but for the time being I needed to get on with things.

Ian was already sitting at an outside table when I arrived at the cafe near Carnaby Street. We'd known each other since before he went to Sandhurst for army officer training, originally meeting when he joined a close protection job I was running in London because the boss knew his dad from old army days. We'd worked on a few jobs together after that first one and always got on well. He'd rung when he got home on R&R to catch up and I'd started pumping him for information about the ports of Umm Qasr, Khor Az Zubayr, and Abu Flous because of

162

the German client interested in the scrap. Ian said it would be much easier to explain face-to-face, so here we were.

'Hi Ian, long time no see,' I said as I dropped into the seat opposite.

'Hello John. You've survived Baghdad without any bits missing then. Last time we spoke it sounded pretty hairy over there. What do you want to drink?'

'I'll have a coffee, mate. Much as I'd love a beer, I could do with the caffeine hit after the last twenty-four hours. As for Baghdad, yeah, I got out by the skin of my teeth last time. It's horrendous up there now. Trust me to start investing time, money, and effort just as the whole place goes to ratshit. So how are things in the south? As I mentioned on the phone, I've got a client interested in export from Basra, so it would be great to pick your brains about the situation down there.'

'Export? They'll be lucky. What on earth are they thinking of exporting?'

'Scrap metal. The law has changed to allow it to be exported and they want to get in early. God only knows if the depleted uranium the Americans used will make half of it contaminated and worthless, but for now I need to look at the logistics. See if it can work.'

That piqued Ian's interest and by the sounds of it he was the ideal guy to be speaking with about the southern Iraqi ports. As a junior officer he was out on the ground with his men rather than back at HQ, so he possessed the kind of information I needed to help assess the logistics required for the export of scrap metal.

Although he was able to reel off plenty of information about the three ports and the local operating environment, he didn't know anything about the political or regulatory side of import and export. He offered to ask some questions on his return and then made an intriguing suggestion.

'Why don't you mosey on over and let me give you the grand tour. Then you can check it out for yourself.'

Ian was satisfied he had built up trusted relationships with various locals during his tour who could help support a business operation in the south. He reckoned it should be safer and easier than the experiences I'd described in Baghdad.

A fleeting image of flying into Kuwait and driving to Basra was bludgeoned out the way by a jolt of financial reality. 'Unfortunately, I don't have the money for a fact-finding trip right now. But I'll ask the Germans if they'll agree to fund it. If they say yes, then I'll be straight in touch.'

'You need to be quick,' said Ian. 'Our tour is finished in another month, so it's now or never.'

We agreed a simple message protocol I should use in the unlikely event I convinced the Germans to fund the trip. Provided I could give him seventy-two hours' notice, Ian said he should be able to arrange to pick me up on the Kuwaiti side of the Safwan border post. All I needed to communicate was a 'yes I'm coming' and a date/time when I'd be at the shops opposite the border, preferably midday or early afternoon.

As I returned towards Ewell on the train, I worked on a draft email to the Germans asking to fund a recce. It wasn't easy ignoring the chaos of the previous day's events at the Churchill, but the more I thought about it, the more I considered it would be worth trying to somehow make the Basra trip happen.

By the time I arrived back at the office in mid-afternoon, I still hadn't heard from Pete. Not that I'd tried to call him again yet. Our conversation needed privacy, which wasn't available on the train.

With a fresh coffee to hand I tried again. This time Pete picked up. 'Pete, it's me.'

'G'day mate. You coming over to the office?' He sounded tired.

'Can we meet somewhere else? How about the cafe in an hour?'

'Fine, mate. See you there.'

As an Aussie, Pete was a huge cricket fan and helped with coaching at his nearby cricket club. There was a cafe close to the cricket ground where we'd often met in the past.

★

I'm sure there was plenty he left out, but Pete gave me the gist of what had happened. Apparently, the blag phone call he'd made posing as a customs officer the previous week prompted the lawyer he'd rung to contact Customs and Excise to complain. That in turn resulted in customs tracing the suspicious call back to Pete. From there the whole thing escalated as they suspected they had stumbled on an organised crime ring. A suspicion no doubt enhanced on realising they'd recently seized a valuable cheque from him as he re-entered the country.

Although it would be inadmissible evidence, Pete suspected customs had been intercepting his phone calls and probably his emails. From early the previous morning, he, Scotty, and the others had been under surveillance by customs, who thought they were going to intercept a major criminal undertaking. While I was inside the Churchill with Mohammed wondering what had happened, customs were arresting everyone outside. The Bookie and the Barman must have been the pair Mohammed had seen on the ground outside the main entrance. Pete was detained sat in the van and Scotty in his car. When I'd seen the client being led out of the hotel, he was being taken to a waiting vehicle and off for questioning.

We now knew Scotty had detected surveillance in Berkeley Square because Pete was shown photos of my arrival and asked questions about my identity. Pete had told them it was a casual contact of his, Jack, who occasionally worked security at the Churchill Hotel and had provided some background information about the layout. Of everyone involved, including Scotty, Pete was the only one who knew my real full name, so I might be in the clear. However, he said the senior customs investigator was convinced the mysterious Jack was in the hotel working with the team and desperately wanted to identify him – me. I tried to imagine his face when he must have recognised me from the surveillance photos as the guy he'd questioned at the hotel immediately following the arrests.

That wasn't all. Simultaneous to the arrests in London, Pete's office had been raided by customs officers and his wife answered the door at his home to gun-toting police demanding to know the location of the safe containing the 'drugs and guns'. In the office, 'John' had professed to know nothing, and Sam had pretended to be the cleaner. She'd always joked she had a duster and cleaning gear for just such an eventuality and she'd given it her best shot when it happened for real.

'How the hell am I supposed to run my business now?' Pete was incensed they'd seized all the computers, files, photocopier, and even the laminator.

He and the others spent most of the night at customs headquarters before being charged at a nearby police station. The wealthy client had an expensive lawyer on speed dial and I think he'd organised appropriate legal aid lawyers for the others, including Pete.

Pete didn't seem overly concerned about the whole thing though, apart from the equipment seized from his office and the furious reaction of his wife when he finally got home that morning.

'Customs arrest and charge everyone. They make the decision themselves whether to prosecute or not, unlike the police who have to take it to the CPS *(Crown Prosecution Service)* and persuade them to prosecute. These guys are more powerful than the police. It means they can keep everyone on the hook and only drop off the bit-part players just before going to trial. It sucks but don't worry mate, there's no way this is going to trial.'

When Pete told me he and the others had to surrender their passports at the bail hearing that morning, I started getting worried. I needed my passport or my business would be seriously screwed up. Pete said it could take months before the whole thing blew over and that wouldn't work for me.

Before we parted, he gave me a business card for the legal aid lawyer he'd used – reckoned he was a switched-on bloke.

'If they catch up with you, then you could do a lot worse than speak to Denis.'

★

The following day, I sat in my office finishing off a report based on an excellent piece of detective work by my French agents for a case in Monaco when the phone rang.

'Mr Pierce, my name is Tim Dryden. I'm a customs officer and I believe we met yesterday afternoon at the Churchill Hotel. I need to speak to you urgently and I want you to come to Custom House in Lower Thames Street, London at the earliest opportunity.'

Fuck.

'Okay. Well I'm quite busy this week, but how about…'

'Mr Pierce, you need to come to Custom House at ten am tomorrow morning or a warrant will be issued for your arrest.' Blunt and to the point.

Denis the lawyer's business card was on my desk. 'I assume I should have some kind of legal representation?'

'That's your choice. Ten o'clock tomorrow.' And he hung up.

CHAPTER 23

CENTRAL LONDON – OCTOBER 2004

I suggested meeting up with Denis somewhere else first before going to Custom House on the north bank of the Thames in East London, but he said it wasn't necessary. 'Don't worry, we'll have plenty of time.'

Fair enough. He already understood the outline of the case from representing Pete, and he knew how this worked much better than I did.

We met at 9.55am outside the entrance to the Customs and Excise headquarters building and made our way in. We were met by an officer who escorted us upstairs in the lift.

Denis agreed to the opportunity for a private discussion in a small interview room, listened to my outline of the events, and then suggested we prepare a written statement. The investigating officers would then question me about the statement and anything else they wanted to raise before deciding whether I should be charged or not.

It took over two hours to prepare the statement, which presented a reasonable reflection of what happened. I hadn't thrown anyone under the bus, but made it clear I believed it had been an extravagant plan, and one in which I had minimal participation. I hadn't mentioned any of Pete's dealings with the intelligence services or his VAT carousel investigation, mainly because I didn't understand how they fitted in and to introduce them without any evidence could have made me sound like a fruitcake.

In the late afternoon, the two interviewing customs officers left us to consider my fate. It had been a long afternoon answering questions, although mostly straightforward. During the interview I discovered they'd established my likely identity and contact details from a business card in the folder I'd left in Scotty's car. Forgetting the folder in the car had been unlike me and now I was reaping the consequences.

Towards the end, the proceedings took a more adversarial turn as they questioned my use of unregistered mobile phones; why I hadn't volunteered to talk with the officers at the scene; the supposed curry and beers in lieu of payment; and their doubts as to my claimed role in the proceedings. The bottom line: they thought I was lying through my teeth.

'So, you claim you were going to put yourself at risk to protect a man you didn't know from others you believed were hardened criminals, and all for a curry and a couple of beers? Do you really expect us to believe that?' This from the fatter customs guy, who was really starting to get on my nerves.

'Yes, that was the plan. Not great, but as I've told you I was primarily there for a meeting about my business in Iraq. It wasn't my plan, it was just a favour.'

'The problem I have with that, Mr Pierce, is why would you agree to it?'

'Because I'm an ex-bootneck and that's who we are. A mate asked me for a favour, and I said I'd do it. Maybe you customs people are a different breed, but it's just who I am.' I spat that out with more venom than intended. It had been a long day and this guy was pissing me off.

By the look on his face the feeling was mutual. He looked at his colleague and they left the room. I asked Denis what he thought would happen next. He was non-committal. Surely when they reviewed everything, they'd just let me go. I hadn't done anything.

'Mr Pierce, you will be charged with…'

'You're fucking joking?' I didn't even listen to the three conspiracy charges as he read them out. It was all bullshit anyway.

Resigned to my fate, I joked with Denis at the desk in nearby Shoreditch police station about who would play us in the movie about this whole bizarre mess. Customs couldn't charge me, that had to be done by the police, so I was there to be fingerprinted, DNA swabbed, and charged before being released into the early evening. My next engagement was a bail hearing at the magistrates' court, for which I was ordered to bring my passport.

'I need to keep my passport, Denis,' I told him as we went our separate ways until the following morning. There was a doubtful look on his face.

★

The bail hearing at the magistrates' court turned into a full-on battle as Denis tried to convince the magistrate I needed my passport to continue operating my business. The female lawyer for the Crown was having none of it, but in the end the magistrate decided the bail conditions were to report to my local police station every Saturday morning at ten o'clock, unless I was out of the country.

It felt like a victory after the sense of bitter frustration and injustice from being charged the previous day. Denis told me bail hearings were normally very straightforward affairs and it had been the feistiest one he'd ever experienced.

The next step would be a pre-trial hearing at the Crown Court, unless customs elected to drop the charges beforehand. Denis couldn't tell me how long all this would take but he reminded me to inform the police if I did travel abroad. And that was it.

CHAPTER 24

EPSOM – LATE OCTOBER 2004

I'd submitted the report and invoice for the Monaco job; a job well done with a sizeable invoice total, although yet another disappointing profit margin. My personal overdraft was almost exhausted and the outstanding balances on my credit card statements read like telephone numbers. My director's account for the business still had some leeway, but unless I generated more revenue soon, everything would grind to a halt. I tried to ignore the Customs and Excise situation. Pete was adamant that elements within the Security Service would see to it that the case was quashed, so I focused on that outcome.

'There's no way this is going to trial, mate. Too many people knew what was going on. There's a lot more to it than those muppets at customs know.'

'And there's a lot more to it than this muppet knows as well, mate. Because I know fuck all. What's this got to do with the Security Service?'

'Don't worry. I told you, I was a source for them, for MI5. Giving them information about those idiots and the VAT carousel, the oil theft in Nigeria, all of it.'

There was either a lot more to this than I knew about or a lot less. 'So why have customs arrested us all and had us charged then? It doesn't make sense unless they know absolutely nothing about your secret squirrel stuff. I tell you mate, no one's going to come out fighting for us if this was just some complicated blag done off your own bat.'

'No John, you're wrong,' Pete said, but I could see I'd struck a nerve.

Fuck. It seemed more and more likely this was all caused by a madcap scheme and the authorities had the wrong end of the stick. Customs probably assumed they'd caught serious players with their pants down. Little did they realise it was only us bunch of clowns putting on a Billy Smart's performance to top the lot.

★

As I checked the spam folder of my Hushmail account, I noted an encrypted email from Faris. I'd set him up with a free account requiring access every three weeks to avoid being disabled. A surprise he'd managed to keep it going. He'd only sent me a handful of emails and none since shortly after I'd returned from Baghdad at the end of April five months earlier. Maybe he used it for other stuff. Not that I should be affected; other than our meagre correspondence, it wasn't linked to me in any way.

Hushmail uses PGP encryption to send secure emails between users. It also functions as regular email if the other party doesn't have a reciprocal PGP secured account. Faris had sent me an encrypted email which decrypted automatically on my computer. In theory the contents couldn't be intercepted and read by anyone else, government or otherwise. I had my doubts. We had nothing to hide but it was good professional practice to keep communications confidential.

Mr Jon,

Please refer to me if you can travel to Dubai next week to meet with partners of Mr Al-Tikriti. The discussions will focus on a new project in Iraq and should only take 1 day.

I will wait your reply and ready to send 2.000 Dollars by Hawallah to you in London for your flight and expense.

Please reply soon to confirm.

Faris

Abu Saif had mentioned companies in the United Arab Emirates at our meeting in Baghdad. With them offering to pay a generous sum towards my flight and expenses it was a no-brainer. Time to start looking at cheap flight and hotel options in Dubai.

Hawallah was the unofficial money transfer system used widely in the Arab world for centuries. In recent decades it had remained relevant due to the lack of widespread international banking facilities. With Iraq in turmoil and very much a cash economy, it was how money flowed in and out. Just like Western Union, Faris would hand over a wad of cash in Baghdad and the reciprocal contact in London would pay out when I produced ID and gave the correct code word. The system is hated by Western law enforcement and intelligence agencies because it makes the flow of money untraceable and can be used for money laundering. For me, it was an ideal way to get immediate cash to fund a return ticket to Dubai.

*

The desk sergeant at Epsom police station had a sceptical look on his face when I started wittering on about my travel to Dubai. I said I ought to be able to report for bail the following Saturday, but I was informing them of my travel 'just in case'. Even if he suspected he was wasting his time with a local lunatic, he agreed to make a note of it.

I headed off to Edgware Road in London to collect the money sent by Faris. Edgware Road was a focal point for Middle Eastern expats far from home, with its coffee shops, shisha pipes, Arab and Kurdish-owned restaurants, and currency shops. The latest email from Faris had directed me to collect the cash from a dry cleaners rather than a currency shop. Real money laundering in action.

*

The suspicious vibes from the shop staff soon dissolved.

'Mr John, please wait one minute.'

I'd only mentioned my name and Faris in Baghdad, but it had done the trick.

'Two thousand dollars is one thousand and ninety pounds.' He counted it out against the backdrop of suits, dresses, and other dry cleaning. 'Here you go.'

All done on trust with nothing to sign.

After taking the money, I hurried out and headed for the Tube station. The way things were going it would be just my luck for the Security Service to have this place under surveillance and for me to be accosted with some other ridiculous charges. I gave a half-hearted stab at anti-surveillance drills at Marble Arch and again at Hyde Park Corner, but nothing that would have caught out anyone determined and professional.

The return flight only cost £360. Even adding on two nights at a hotel left 500 quid in my back pocket. And there was the potential this new business opportunity could lead to more money. After the difficulties of the last few days it felt good to focus on something positive.

CHAPTER 25

DUBAI – END OF OCTOBER 2004

As I checked into the hotel in Dubai, I felt a renewed sense of purpose. And I wasn't slumming it. There had been a great deal on two nights at the InterContinental. My hotel arrangements reflected on me and the business, so the InterContinental was a good choice in the sense it wasn't opulent luxury, but it wasn't a fleapit either. A car would pick me up at 10.00am the following morning after my late arrival. I grabbed a shower, checked my emails, and then drifted off to sleep in the comfortable bed.

I was picked up on time the following morning by a smartly-suited young executive and accompanying driver. After a short journey we glided to a halt outside an impressive glass office building. The inside proved even more luxurious than the outside had suggested. A good job I'd brought one of my better suits, which had survived the flight without needing much of a touch-up from the iron that morning.

'Mr Pierce, welcome to Al-Nura Engineering. My name is Essam, I'm the general manager. And you've already met my assistant Ibrahim.' He indicated the young executive who had picked me up and then reached into a suit pocket. 'My card. Please take a seat. Chai? Coffee? Water?'

Essam must have been mid-thirties, slim, clean-shaven with short, dark hair, and came across as a smooth operator. His business card had a plush feel without being over the top. *American Psycho* Patrick Bateman would have approved.

'Coffee would be great, thank you.'

As Ibrahim left to arrange the drinks, I took in the breathtaking view from the top floor of the building. The blue waters of the Persian Gulf shimmered in the distance, disrupted only by the new Palm Jumeirah islands development which jutted out five kilometres from the shoreline.

Essam appeared next to me by the floor to ceiling window. 'The view is incredible, don't you agree?'

'It's fantastic. I see the Palm is taking shape. That's an amazing project.'

Out of the corner of my eye Essam nodded. 'We have been involved in the project. Maybe if there is enough time I can show you the Palm? A tour tomorrow morning perhaps?'

'Unfortunately, I fly back to the UK in the morning. Next time for sure though.'

Essam smiled. 'We'll see. Maybe your plans will change. Let's get down to business. I know you British like to get the small talk out of the way.'

I turned and laughed. 'You know the British well then?'

'I studied in London. It has stood me in great stead.'

Now it was my turn to nod. 'Well your English is very good. Better than mine in fact.'

As we both laughed, a young woman entered through the door carrying our drinks and two bottles of water. She breezed across the room and deposited the tray on the table. In an assertive voice she said, 'I don't know why you trusted Ibrahim to make coffee. I had to take over, so he didn't end up poisoning your guest.'

She looked at me with an impish smile, her eyes a striking light green and decorated in a way I'd call smoking hot: alluring colours and flourishes à la Arabian Nights. A colourful headscarf adorned her dark hair at a jaunty angle, covering little and giving the impression of a fashion accessory rather than anything religious.

'Hi, I'm Amira,' she said, holding out her hand.

Any physical contact with Arab women can be a minefield, especially if they're young and pretty, so I hesitated before reaching out and briefly shaking hands.

'Amira, this is Mr Pierce from London. He's come to discuss a new project in Iraq,' said Essam.

'John. Nice to meet you,' I added.

'Nice to meet you too, John,' she said, still smiling at me before turning to Essam with a frown. 'A new project. I don't think I'm aware of it.'

'It's early days,' said Essam. 'Mr Pierce may be able to help us with some of the groundwork. I'll speak to you about it later.'

Essam said the last sentence with a hint of annoyance and ushered her out with an exchange in Arabic before striding over to the table and grabbing one of the drinks. From the sound of it, Amira wasn't too happy about being kept out of the loop. Join the club – I didn't know anything either yet.

Essam tried to brush the encounter off. 'Women! And Amira, she's a talented engineer and the owner's niece.'

He didn't add any more in explanation. Instead, he moved behind the large desk, sat down, and sipped at his tea as Ibrahim slunk in with a sheepish look on his face after his fail with my coffee. The room was quiet as we all sipped our drinks until Essam put his cup down. 'That's better. Now let's get down to business.'

For the next hour and a half, we engaged in easy discussions about Iraq, Al-Nura, and my business set-up in Baghdad. These guys were Westernised and smooth. With my due diligence head on, I didn't see much evidence of engineering activity taking place, although the engineers may have been on a different floor or based at a completely different location. When I asked Essam about them, he said it wouldn't be possible to visit the engineering section today. It didn't necessarily mean anything, but I liked to 'kick the tyres' when I visited a new company. See everything that was going on and get a feel for the real business and not just what some flashy website or brochure claimed. I didn't push the issue but made a mental note all the same.

During a tour of the conference room and management offices, we did pass an open office door with a handful of young staff beavering away at computer workstations, including Amira perched behind a desk, concentrating on the screen in front of her. Photographs of power plants and petrochemical storage tanks adorned the walls of the offices and conference rooms, indicating the focus of the company's activities. That chimed with our earlier discussions although a glossy brochure hinted at a wider range of activities.

After lunch at a nearby restaurant, we returned to the offices and the talk turned to specifics in Iraq. With the country's only ports located in the south, that area was very much of interest to Al-Nura. Not wanting to appear lacking, I regurgitated some details Ian had provided the week before. Essam was keen to know if I had the capability to support business activity moving through the ports and I mentioned a possible visit to the area in the near future.

'That's very interesting,' said Essam, 'because I would like you to travel to Basra for Al-Nura and compile an assessment of the security and logistic infrastructure and the extent of any issues we might face. We need more information before we can make an imminent decision about shipping valuable equipment and machinery to Iraq.'

I started calculating a quote in my head.

'We'll pay five thousand dollars for your time and one thousand for expenses,' he added.

That would do nicely, but I made out it needed consideration first.

Essam continued. 'We need a detailed report of the situation at the various ports, the options for secure storage, and an assessment of customs clearance times for inbound goods. Preferably with recommendations how to reduce this to a minimum, if you understand my meaning?'

'I understand yes. Who we need to know and how much they charge for the fast-track service.'

'Exactly. You know how things work in this part of the world, especially over there right now. We also need to understand the security risks. Many companies here are passing up opportunities in Iraq because of the risks, but no-one I speak with has a clear understanding of what is happening in Basra. There are reports that Iran is sponsoring local militias to attack the British.'

'I can certainly look into all those aspects and produce a comprehensive report. If you can provide me with a detailed list of what you want, then I should be able to gather the information and send you a written report within two weeks of arriving in-country.'

I tried not to let my excitement for the job show, but in my head I was already spending the money. Firstly, it was vital cash in the lead-up to Christmas, and secondly it would allow me to check the exact same issues for the Germans investigating the scrap opportunities in the region.

Essam began getting ahead of things with an assumption I would jump straight on a plane and get on with it.

'So, you could fly in the next twenty-four hours and report back to us within two weeks,' he said.

'Err, no. That won't work. I need to return to the UK first. My flight is already booked for tomorrow morning, and I won't change it.'

'But Mr Pierce, we really want this report as soon as possible. Why do you need to return to the UK? Surely it will be quicker and easier to travel from here.'

'Because I don't have any kit and equipment with me. I just need a couple of days to plan and prepare before travelling.' I also needed to give Ian at least seventy-two hours' notice.

Essam made no attempt to hide his annoyance with my timeline, but I'd travelled light with only minimal hand luggage for the trip to Dubai. There was no way I was rocking up to Basra wearing my best suit and without my essentials.

His obvious annoyance with the delay showed a different side to his character and it jarred with me. I was about as 'seat of the pants' as anyone, but to expect a deployment to Iraq at zero notice was unreasonable. We clashed as he tried to pressurise me to change my mind.

'But I still don't understand why you can't buy what you need here and travel sooner. The owners will not be happy with the delay.'

'Listen, I'm not flying directly from here. These things need to be planned properly or they go fucking wrong.' Oops. The bad language had been unintentional. 'Sorry, I didn't mean to swear.'

Essam waved away my apology and backed down now I'd made it clear I wouldn't be changing my mind. It was a reminder I didn't know these people. I moved the discussion to payment terms.

'I'm happy with the five thousand dollars, but it will be easier for me to book the flights from London myself. If we make the expenses two thousand dollars, then it'll cover the flights as well as hotels, drivers, subsistence, and incidentals.'

'That is reasonable, but we do need the visit to take place as soon as possible. How soon can you travel from the UK?' he asked.

'If you pay me straight away, then I should be ready to fly out in… four days' time. I'll need to stay overnight in Kuwait. I could be crossing the border in five days. I have arrangements in place I can activate.'

Essam and Ibrahim left the room for five minutes and returned with an envelope containing the seven grand. It was all smiles again when Essam handed it to me.

'Mr Pierce, I have another engagement I must attend, so if you'll excuse me, I need to leave you in the capable hands of Ibrahim. He will give you a briefing document detailing our requirements for your assessment.'

'Of course. Thank you for your time today. I hope this is the start of a long-term business relationship.'

What had really caught my attention was the fact that they already had the briefing document ready. Maybe someone in the office had put it together over lunch, but I had my doubts. More likely our meeting had been arranged to confirm my suitability for a prepared task. Whatever the process, they'd made the right decision because it was right up my street. I wouldn't forget to thank Faris and Abu Saif for setting this up for me.

'I hope so too. One final thing, we have some important contacts in Basra, and we ask that you convey a personal message from our CEO to one of our most important friends, Sheikh Mustafa.'

I picked up my pen and notebook from the table. 'Okay, let me make a note…'

'Ibrahim will provide you with some details to help you contact Sheikh Mustafa, who is a very influential business figure in that region and will be of great assistance to us there. The message itself is contained in this sealed envelope. I must stress to you that safe delivery of this letter is of critical importance to our business in Iraq. Please ensure that you personally hand-deliver it to the Sheikh at the earliest opportunity once you arrive in Basra.'

The letter was sealed to prevent tampering and inscribed with handwritten Arabic on the front. They clearly didn't trust email or phones for this message, which resonated with me. I half expected him to ask me to sign a register, similar to checking out a classified document in the military.

'I'll make sure to get all the details from Ibrahim, so I can arrange to meet with this sheikh. I assume he'll know I'm coming? And there are no security implications I should be aware of?' Ian out in Basra might have heard of this guy if he was a player, but it didn't hurt to get a heads up while I was here.

'Unfortunately, we are having trouble reaching the Sheikh, but he is a wealthy businessman and I am sure you will be able to find him quickly and relay the message for us. He is also a powerful man and there is no doubt your safety will be his highest priority while you are his guest.'

Once Essam had left, I sat down with his sidekick Ibrahim and read through the briefing notes. There was a list of specific questions they wanted answering, which would help in the structuring of both my assessment and written report. Happy with the task, I looked at the envelope containing the message for the Sheikh.

'What does the writing say?' If I was going to be waving this around, then I ought to know what was written on it.

'It is marked confidential and private, and addressed personally for the Sheikh's eyes only. As Mr Essam said, this message is very important, and you should expect to receive a reply to convey back to us. On your return you will receive a further thousand dollars plus your flight expenses.'

Great. Now they were turning me into the Postman Pat of the Middle East. I only hoped it would be as straightforward to find this guy and deliver the letter as they expected.

CHAPTER 26

LONDON

By the time I'd flown back into London late the following day, I only had two days to make the preparations for Basra before flying out to Kuwait. Claire's voice contained a hint of regret even as she congratulated me for winning new work.

'I'm pleased, really, but be careful. I know you've been paid and you're meeting with Ian but, if anything, I'm more worried for some reason than when you went to Baghdad. How safe is it there?'

I tried to reassure her. 'It's because the news from Iraq is relentless and always terrible. Don't worry, this time I'll be embedded with Ian and the Brit Mil guys and Basra is a lot safer than Baghdad.'

She didn't look convinced, but I was buzzing after getting this unexpected and paid opportunity to head into the south. With any luck, I'd be able to help both Al-Nura and the Germans to establish business operations and make some decent money. Even if Baghdad was presently a lost cause due to the nightmare security situation, perhaps the time and effort there earlier in the year had been worthwhile after all; the connections I'd established leading me to the British-administered south. And that might prove to be an easier place to work for a British businessman anyway.

When I looked at the map, the very short distance between the Kuwait border and Basra looked a piece of cake compared to my epic journeys across the deserts of western Iraq to and from Baghdad.

Ian was great when I reached him by phone the following morning. I kept it short and cryptic as agreed during our coffee in London. A quick hello and then a date and time: three days later at midday. He acknowledged with the correct 'green light' phrase and cut the call. No pleasantries or small talk. I'd given him the requested seventy-two hours' notice, if only just. There wasn't enough time for me to get an Iraqi visa in London, which had been introduced since my previous visits, but it shouldn't be an issue. Ian had assured me when we met that passports didn't get checked in the military lane.

Once I'd booked a British Airways flight to Kuwait and a hotel for the night of my arrival, I turned my attention to background research. With the money already in my hands, I didn't need to worry about being paid. However, time spent planning is seldom wasted. I searched the Internet about Al-Nura Engineering, Sheikh Mustafa, the ports in the Basra area, and the current situation in the south.

Al-Nura's generic website didn't really say a lot. A bit like mine I suppose. There wasn't much information about them on the Internet either, but then Middle Eastern companies were often tricky with regard to due diligence. I'd used the Middle East as a business cover several times in the past for just this reason. They were difficult to check out unless you put considerable time and resources into it, neither of which I had in abundance.

Sheikh Mustafa had some hits, but only mentions in passing and nothing of any use to me. I'd have to rely on making enquiries on the ground using the details Ibrahim had provided.

The ports and the security situation were areas I'd already been researching. Even so, I checked the latest updates and had a closer look at relevant maps and topography. I printed off the best two maps at different scales before remembering to head over to Epsom police station to update them on my movements for the bail conditions.

I hadn't been away for a bail reporting day whilst in Dubai, but I needed to leave for the airport early the following Saturday and would miss at least a couple of bail attendances. The same desk sergeant made a point of repeating everything as I explained my trip to Kuwait would last at least a week, maybe a fortnight.

'Very good, sir. I'll make sure those who need to know are aware of your travel plans to... Kuwait.'

I was worried my bail conditions might suddenly be changed and my passport snatched away, although he gave no indication that was on the cards. I'd reported my return from Dubai as soon as I'd got back, which hopefully demonstrated I wasn't a flight risk. After the focus on Iraq of the previous few days, the visit to the police station was a stark reminder of the crappy situation Pete's scheme had landed me in.

I dropped in to see him the day before flying out to Kuwait and he remained positive all the charges would be dropped, and he'd be getting compensation for the seizure of his computers and business equipment. I didn't stay long. Unlikely, but he might still be targeted by surveillance. I had enough on my plate organising the trip to Basra without worrying about being tangled up in more nonsense which didn't concern me.

★

POOLE, UK

My former colleague Jim had been a military communications expert. He'd furnished me with a satellite phone and BGAN when I first travelled to Iraq at the start of the year. I hadn't been able to cover all the bills yet, and I needed to call him and warn him there might be some more imminent usage. This time I'd only packed the sat phone and not the data hungry BGAN. It meant there shouldn't be any shocking bills arriving on the doormat.

As we spoke on the phone about my forthcoming trip, he asked if I could trial a new tracking unit for him while I was there. But given his workload and my imminent departure, I'd need to drive to Poole on the Dorset coast to pick it up. Two hours' drive each way would eat into the limited time I had left before flying out, so I convinced him to agree to meet me at the services on the M27 north of Southampton.

It would only save me forty-five minutes to an hour each way, but I didn't have much time to play with and every little extra helped.

Jim showed me the tracking unit in its waterproof case. 'It's a prototype, but fully functional. It's going to be really useful to deploy it in a hostile environment and use that tracking data in future presentations.'

I was grateful for his help again and Jim was also throwing in £450 for my trouble, despite my intimations that I'd trial it for nothing. The panic alarm feature was a bonus, although he did warn me that pressing it wouldn't bring the 7th Cavalry charging over the hill to my rescue. He'd monitor things when he could, but generally that would be in the mornings and evenings, three hours behind Iraq time.

'I'll be running the tracking software on my laptop both at home and in the office, and keep meetings and travel to a minimum while you're out there, especially in the mornings. If you stick to moving in daylight hours, you should be firm somewhere by early to mid-afternoon my time.'

'Thanks mate. I'm grateful for whatever monitoring you can do. Resistance to interrogation isn't my bag, and I'll run out of scintillating conversation to hold them off with pretty fast.'

This much was true. Start pouring water over a towel wrapped round my face and it wouldn't be long before I'd be spilling whatever beans someone wanted to know. I'd been through some of the training and knew that was a fact. Everyone breaks in the end and I was unlikely to have any reason to hold out on any persuasive new acquaintances whose paths I might cross.

Jim's voice took on a more serious tone. 'Yeah, sure mate, I understand. I'll do what I can, but I can't guarantee being able to keep on top of it while I'm at work.'

'Mate, let's face it, if I'm in a situation out there where I need to press that button, then I'm fucked. In fact, I'm proper fucked.'

CHAPTER 27

KUWAIT – EARLY NOVEMBER 2004

It was my first visit to Kuwait, which is very modern and Westernised, although completely dry. Not that I'd wanted a beer, but it was the first time I'd been in a country where you couldn't get one legally even if you wanted to. I'd mentioned it to my driver Khalid as we headed the 100 kilometres or so towards the border with Iraq.

'Does that mean no-one here drinks at all?' I asked.

'Oh no, people drink alcohol, but they are very careful about it,' answered Khalid. 'Small gatherings at home, or I hear the embassies have proper parties. For normal people, well, a lot of my friends regularly drive through Saudi Arabia to Bahrain if they want to party. There's a place that knows how to have a good time.'

It sounded like a lot of hassle just to get a drink, but I made a note to check out the nightlife in Bahrain one day.

He hadn't shown any surprise when I told him my destination, which made me feel slightly better about the wisdom of the plan. The road was empty as we drove north, save for the occasional truck heading up or down. After less than ninety minutes, he pulled over by a group of shops and pointed out the Safwan border post further up the road.

Once Khalid had dropped me off, I checked my watch and examined the surroundings. A couple of the shops were open, including the one I stood outside. There were few other signs of life apart from a convoy of trucks heading towards the border. It was 11.30am, thirty minutes early for the RV, so I bought some water and chocolate to snack on while I waited in the shade. Just after 12.15pm, two British Army Land Rovers came through the border and headed in my direction. They pulled up near the shop and Ian climbed out of the lead vehicle.

'Mr Pierce? We are your escort today. Are you ready?'

'Yes Lieutenant, thank you.' I supposed his men would simply assume the mission was a scheduled escort task, so I played along.

We whizzed through the military lane without pausing. Ian was right: the lack of a visa hadn't been an issue. I'd been concerned about getting refused entry at the border and had been frugal with the cash from Al-Nura in case everything fell over at the outset. Failure to even make it into Iraq would have looked very amateurish to my paymasters. At least now I could forget that scenario and focus on the job at hand.

Traffic was light even though it was Sunday, which is the first day of the working week in Iraq – like a Monday in the UK. The vehicles we passed were either commercial trucks or old and weary-looking cars. With the ubiquitous sunny blue skies and desert sand as far as the eye could see, it looked the same as most other desert roads in this part of the world. The only difference between the Iraqi side and the Kuwaiti side of the border was the far superior quality of the road in Kuwait.

After the vast distances I'd had to travel on my trips to Baghdad, the appearance of a British military base close to the border came as a surprise, even though I should have expected it from studying the maps. It provided a feeling of Coalition presence and protection I hadn't felt at all when crossing the western desert. Of course, travelling with a British Army patrol probably had a fair bit to do with that as well, but the proximity of potential support was warming me up to the idea of operating here.

Within half an hour we entered the huge Shaibah Logistics Base where the men had been promised a chance to do some shopping at the large NAAFI and grab some fast food. They'd therefore seen the Sunday morning task to pick me up from the border as a positive rather than a pain in the arse and it sounded as though there had been some competition for the seats in the vehicles. Ian and I tucked into a Cheese Feast from Pizza Hut and quietly caught up as the others enjoyed the facilities. He asked if I'd made arrangements to stay anywhere, which caught me a little off guard.

'When we spoke in London, you said you'd be able to arrange that.'

I had no idea of the options here, only that a British journalist had recently checked into a hotel and been kidnapped almost immediately. We hadn't had a chance to discuss anything in detail until now, but it ruled out the hotels as far as I was concerned.

Ian shrugged. 'We'll get back to the base and chat with Hassan about some options. There is a secure place he's mentioned.'

A couple of hours later we set off for the British base at Basra Airport ten miles to the north, which Ian and his men called home. The corporal sat next to me in the back of the Land Rover explained why we needed to avoid Basra city.

'Things are tricky in the city. Apart from routes to Basra Palace, any military units going in have to be coordinated with the locals. Casualties are starting to rise and it's getting worse. I'm glad we're leaving. Right time I think.'

Not what I wanted to hear. I'd read reports alluding to increasing levels of violence, but this made me wonder if much of the news from Basra was being heavily polished with positive spin rather than reflecting the real situation.

As we entered via the ECP leading to the main base and the airport, I was conscious I didn't have either a visa for Iraq or any permission to enter the British base. However, Ian seemed to take it all in his stride. He acted as though it was the most natural thing in the world for me to be with them. On reaching the single-storey containerised accommodation, Ian called his translator, Hassan, to the team office. It didn't take long for me to veto the suggestion by Hassan to stay at a guarded farmhouse owned by one of his relatives.

Ian didn't have an alternative to hand. 'It's difficult, John. Now we're getting so close to handing over to our relief unit, we're having to give up accommodation left, right, and centre to their advance party. Most of the guys have just been moved into group transit accommodation. I just don't know if I have anywhere for you.'

'Well mate, I'm not staying in a farmhouse and I'm not checking into any of the hotels. You know what happened to that journalist. There must be somewhere I can stay close by your lines.' After a pause I added, 'What about your cabin?'

If that thought had already occurred to Ian, he disguised it well.

'Well, I do have a bunk bed to myself and as the platoon boss that shouldn't change.'

I didn't know if he was offering, but I wasn't going to wait for a written invitation.

'Great, that works for me. I'll throw my stuff in your place.'

It might not have been quite what Ian had been planning, but he nodded and smiled. 'Okay, I'll show you to my humble abode.'

The arrangement suited me perfectly and I doubted we'd identify a better solution. As the platoon commander, Ian should keep hold of his room right up until they were due to leave for the UK a couple of weeks later. It provided enough time for me to get the job done and get dropped back over the border, although we'd need to be ready to adjust quickly if Ian's situation changed.

Outside his cabin, Ian stopped and indicated down the row of accommodation to the right. 'The CO lives about fifty metres away, up there and around the corner to the left. Let's keep clear of that area and be careful not to arouse suspicion.'

He pointed to a cabin opposite, 'It helps that a BBC crew is staying just there.'

Good. Plenty of new faces to blend in with. In the cookhouse (or galley for us bootnecks) I made sure to sit near the BBC team because they were the only others in civilian clothes for every meal. It was a good job I hadn't used my press credentials and journalistic cover with Ian and his guys; the BBC team would probably have smelled something was off if we started talking shop and comparing notes.

Ian provided a discouraging security summary. My suspicions about the inaccuracy of the reporting from Basra were right on the money. The situation was deteriorating, even as the British high command were still crowing about British success in the south compared to the American failure to retain control in the rest of the country. Violence in Basra was steadily rising, with the Shi'a Islamist parties vying for control of the city. Targeted assassinations, kidnapping, sectarian violence, gun battles, and widespread criminality were common.

'We're containing the problems for now, but we're undermanned and the tempo of attacks is rising. Without flooding the place with overwhelming force to impose security by sheer weight of numbers, this is going to turn into a real mess. In my opinion that is. The generals at the top seem to think differently, but everyone who comes here can see the writing on the wall.'

An influx of additional troops simply wasn't going to happen. The British were pursuing an alternative strategy of trying to work with the various local religious and political factions, but it was a mess of competing groups. They all blamed the British for the problems in the region while being the root cause themselves. The soft-touch approach made the British appear weak, and the troops were growing increasingly frustrated with a strategy they didn't believe was working.

Minimising the military presence in Basra city was an example: it allowed armed groups a free run to pursue their criminal intent. The strategy was meant to dictate that the police and other local security forces maintained control. An optimistic concept, given that Ian reckoned many of them were part of the criminal networks.

More worrying for Ian and other British troops was the emergence of Iranian technology in the hands of anti-British Shi'a militant groups, the strongest of which was controlled by Muqtada al-Sadr. Advanced IED attacks were now targeting British patrols, involving activation by new methods such as mobile phones, radio control, and Passive Infra-Red (PIR) sensors.

Iranian forces were suspected of training the militants in the region or across the nearby Iran-Iraq border. If the IEDs weren't a big enough headache for the lightly armoured British patrols, there was an even more lethal form of IED able to defeat heavily armoured vehicles: Explosively Formed Penetrators (EFPs).

EFPs were generally cylindrical, commonly formed using a metal pipe with the forward end closed by a concave copper or steel liner. When detonated, explosives in the pipe behind the liner caused a lethal shaped charge to be formed, travelling at up to a mile per second and able to penetrate armoured vehicles. If placed at choke points like intersections and junctions, the slowed vehicles gave the attackers maximum time to judge when to fire the EFP. Use of PIR sensors could automate the detonation so it activated when the vehicle tripped the sensor beam. By facing the EFP back towards the vehicle at an angle, the attack would even succeed when vehicles tried to use countermeasures to activate the PIR beams a few metres ahead of them. Scary stuff.

'How many of these attacks are actually taking place? I know the casualties are increasing, but it's not at Baghdad levels down here is it?'

The information about the security situation and the IED/EFP threat had taken the shine off my initial enthusiasm for the area.

Ian paused before he answered.

'All I can tell you is the capability has been detected and the threat is growing. We've started to see more advanced IED technology deployed in attacks against us in recent days and it's only going to get worse. Another problem for us down here is most of our fleet isn't even armoured. Widespread EFPs would be disastrous.'

I chewed that over for a few seconds. 'Okay, so that's the bad news. How about the ports, are they secure?'

'Yes, the ports are a success story although there's still plenty of development needed, such as dredging Umm Qasr. I'll give you the grand tour tomorrow. And don't worry too much about the threat. It's always doom and gloom from the green slime *(Intelligence Corps)*, but it's been a good tour for us and I'm sure it's still a lot easier working down here than up in Baghdad.'

Ian's responsibilities included the ports in the Basra area, so over the next few days I visited them all and made my assessments of capacities, processing times, security, and the other elements needed for my report. Because of the requirement for special authorisation to enter the city, I was picked up at the ports by local contacts Ian had made during his tour, usually with his translator Hassan alongside. This avoided arousing suspicion with his guys, who would have assumed I remained at the port until they collected me later in the day.

The locals took me into areas where Ian couldn't justify going or which would have required special authorisation. I encouraged Ian to continue his daily patrol activities as if I wasn't there. The only time we drove into the city together was for a task requiring a passenger drop-off at the Basra Palace, an island of British military presence in the city centre. I wanted to fit into his schedule rather than cause additional work and extra exposure on the roads for him and his men.

I felt a lot less vulnerable to the IED/EFP threat when travelling low profile in local cars, but that was a small comfort because instead I faced a much higher threat of kidnap. The apprehension manifested itself physically at times, particularly in the hours before leaving the safety net of the British military. My heart would race as I tried to focus on the imminent task and not on the hollowness spreading in my gut. Like in Baghdad, the more times I went out, the more my anxiety grew that I might end up taking one chance too many.

However, the plan worked well and I visited all the locations needed to collect the information required for my report to Al-Nura without running into any issues. That was until travelling back towards the city from Umm Qasr port one day.

Our local car was stopped at an impromptu police checkpoint. When he saw me in the back of the vehicle, the policeman demanded my passport. As I handed it over I smiled and joked, mentioning the latest football results to try to distract him from checking for my non-existent visa. He flicked through the pages and handed it back with an Arabic comment to the driver. Either he didn't care about the visa or hadn't read the memo about the new requirement. After Ian's warning about the relationship between many of the police and the armed gangs, I'd been ready to hit the panic alarm on the tracker if they'd tried to lift me.

After a week I was no closer to a meeting with Sheikh Mustafa. Although Hassan knew of him, he didn't seem able to get it sorted and the contact details provided in Dubai didn't lead anywhere either. If this guy was as influential as Essam at Al-Nura had indicated, then maybe Hassan felt overawed to some extent. I only got a firm lead when the CO's translator mentioned he knew the Sheikh and informed me of his position as Deputy President of the Basra Trade Chamber. By focusing on the Trade Chamber rather than the Sheikh personally, we managed to get a meeting organised for the following day.

Ian's schedule didn't allow for a drop-off at one of the ports, so instead we agreed I would cross-deck from one of his vehicles to a local escort car down the road and out of sight of the base. With the involvement of the Trade Chamber, the unorthodox plan could be explained to the team as a necessity. It was far from usual practise, but they already thought I might be a spook, so it shouldn't raise too many eyebrows.

If meeting with the Sheikh and giving him the message hadn't been so important to Al-Nura, then I probably wouldn't have bothered with it. Although on the flip side there was the extra thousand dollars available to courier a reply and the opportunity to meet with the Trade Chamber could prove useful on the business front.

The night before the meeting, me, Ian, Hassan, and 'Ax', the CO's translator, convened in Ian's room to confirm the arrangements.

Ian recapped the details. 'As I mentioned earlier, we've got a full day tomorrow and the Trade Chamber offices are in central Basra, so we have to cross-deck you to an escort car outside the city. Hassan will bring the car and get them to park at the side of the road between two berms within a few minutes of the base. He'll have some of the Trade Chamber guys with him who can give you some security for the drive into the city.'

'Do we know what sort of car they'll be in?' I asked.

'Yes, it's a black BMW saloon, registration number 190100. In Arabic numerals of course.'

I nodded. 'That's fine, the numbers are the only things I can read.'

'For the pickup, we've got a long day and you probably don't know how long you'll be, so I want us to RV at Khor Az Zubayr port by sixteen hundred hours at the very latest. That should give us, and you, plenty of time to get done what's needed. It's a safe haven – you've seen the detachment there – so if you're early you can wait for us without any problem. But if you're going to be late, then you need to let me know ASAP. I really need you to be there by sixteen hundred though. Is that all right?'

'Thanks, that's great.' I turned to Ax. 'Is Sheikh Mustafa definitely going to be there? He's my primary reason for the meeting and I really need to meet with him.'

'Yes, he'll be there. The president is away, so as the deputy president he's hosting you.'

'Good. Any idea how many others will be there?'

'I don't know, Mr John. There hasn't been much time. Maybe not so many.'

'Right. And these guys coming to pick me up with Hassan, you know them?'

'No. I had a contact to the Sheikh, but I don't know who else will be there or who they will send.'

'But you're sure everything's ready? The arrangements are definitely agreed?'

Ax assured me everything was ready and agreed, but then sauntered out the door at the end with the warning that most of the Trade Chamber members were responsible for the upsurge in violence. I assumed that didn't include the Sheikh, considering Ax said he knew the guy and had helped set the meeting up, but either way it wasn't a confidence builder. Despite the warning, everything was now set. I just needed to keep my wits about me while I got this done and then thought about heading home.

★

After returning the next day from the Trade Chamber meeting, my encounter with the Sheikh, and the incident with the balaclava gang down near Khor Az Zubayr, I lay on the top bunk in Ian's cabin and mulled over the afternoon's events. I'd scored a full house in the excitement stakes: interrogation, gunman, pissing off the local dignitaries, rescued from local goons. As days went, it was about as seat of the pants as I wanted to get.

I'd delivered the letter to complete my instructions in Basra and made sure my fees were earned, but the Sheikh's reaction to its contents and the warning about the client in Dubai troubled me. I would be careful in my dealings with those guys in future. But for now, my focus needed to be on the journey back to the UK, starting with the drive to the border in the morning.

CHAPTER 28

EPSOM – LATE NOVEMBER 2004

While I thought it was a job well done in Basra, the impression I was getting from Faris in Baghdad hinted at a very different assessment. After submitting my Basra report by encrypted email, I'd received a curt reply from Faris the following day asking about the meeting with Sheikh Mustafa. The tone of his email annoyed me, but I made allowances for the fact English wasn't his first language, plus emails can come across ruder than intended.

By the time I'd received the third shirty email, it was clear everyone in Baghdad and at Al-Nura was unhappy I'd left Basra so soon after meeting with the Sheikh and without taking back a reply to Dubai. I hadn't included details of the Sheikh's negative response in my report, so they weren't aware it hadn't been quite so straightforward. Anger began to build as I read the email questioning why it took me a week to arrange the meeting when they had specifically and pointedly stressed the message was my priority. I had to walk away from the computer to avoid sending a reply I might regret.

'Fuck you,' I shared with Taz lying at my feet as I closed the laptop. Time for a run on the Downs to blow away some of this rage and the cobwebs from sitting in planes and vehicles for the last couple of weeks.

I was still fuming as I ran hard with the dog in the cold morning air, breath spilling out of both of us like a pair of steam trains. The only difference being that Taz looked like she could carry on all day, but I was blowing out of my arse. Even though it had only been two weeks without running, this would hurt later. As my blossoming relationship with Faris and the Al-Nura boys appeared to have hit a roadblock, I turned my attention away from the stiffness in my legs and back to the looming shadow of the customs prosecution.

It was a case of waiting in limbo for the next court date or, preferably, receiving a letter from Customs and Excise telling me to forget the whole thing. Pete was still raging about losing all his equipment during my occasional visits to his office. I went in the hope he'd have inside information about the case, but all I left with was empty words.

★

Pete started up the moment I entered the office, and John and Sam glowered daggers at me for setting him off again.

'Mate, this isn't on. Dryden told me the office computers, my laptops, the photocopier – it's all evidence that's being studied and he can't say when it might be returned. How am I supposed to run my business for Christ's sake? Even the laminator has gone. The fucking laminator! I mean I ask you? As for the cabinets and the files – strewth.'

'So, what about the cases you had running?'

His eyes took on a wild look. 'Nothing, mate. We've got nothing. None of the records apart from the information in the original enquiries and whatever interim reports Sam has recovered from the emails. They've gutted my business.'

'But you've still got the new business coming in the same. From the Internet and existing clients?'

Pete wasn't looking for rationality and his eyes narrowed as he spat out, 'That's not the point, mate. They've taken everything and they didn't even give a manifest or a receipt for what they took. What sort of country is this?'

I smiled weakly towards Sam on the other side of the room, sat in front of a 'new' PC bought out of the local FreeAds. John appeared through the doorway of his small side office and added, 'That's where they've made a mistake though. They didn't log what they were taking or give us a chance to record it all. Just snaffled it away into the van they brought along.'

He was talking as much to Pete as to me, and I doubt it was the first time he'd tried to explain this to his boss. 'You've got them over a barrel,' he said as he pointed at Pete. 'They've screwed up and they'll know it.'

Pete studied John before shaking his head as he said, 'Doesn't help now though does it? We've got to redo the parts of the investigations Sam can't reconstruct, and I've lost all my accounts information for billing and invoices.' He carried on shaking his head.

Time to probe for any updates. 'You reckon they're going to drop it all, so you should get everything back soon, surely?'

'By the time that happens… who knows when that will be. I need it all now.'

'You haven't heard anything yet then? None of the friendly spooks had a quiet word and got this thing shelved?'

Pete looked up sharply at the mocking way I'd said the last sentence. 'It won't go anywhere,' he said. 'There's no way.'

★

As for work, I needed something meaty that paid out quickly, because in a couple more weeks everyone's thoughts would start turning to Christmas. From the end of November, I doubted there'd be much in the way of new work on the horizon until the lawyers, business owners, and other potential clients dragged themselves back to their offices in the new year.

Sat in my office later, the situation in Iraq and lack of current or future work occupied my mind. The German firm had thanked me for my report about Basra, but my revelation that the export of scrap was controlled by the Governor's son had led them to conclude the idea was a non-starter. They didn't believe they would get any kind of permission to compete with him, and they were most likely right. I pondered whether Iraq was a total bust, or if I should give it another shot and explore options in the supposedly safe and booming northern Kurdish provinces. I'd already mentioned the north to Mohammed, but he didn't sound keen.

The one positive on the horizon was the Football to the Summit project. I'd started running a 'real-time simulation' along the route to assist with planning. My daily reports analysed the weather and local news in the area where the trek team would pass through in precisely twelve months to the day. Localised terrorism from different groups affected many parts of India, so the reports also focused heavily on the security situation. Fingers crossed my efforts, combined with the comprehensive proposals already submitted, would help win the contract sooner rather than later. I wasn't being paid anything yet, but by Easter the reconnaissance trips would need to begin. Four months away which right then felt like an eternity.

Staring out the window at the dismal November afternoon, I contemplated calling it a day when a phone call from a former colleague put a smile on my face. A retired Met Police detective, Doug worked at the investigation company I'd left the year before. He was still there enjoying the corporate side of life after his retirement from the force, and an old contact had approached him with a personal enquiry he wanted to pass my way on the quiet.

'John, it's Doug, how are you?'

'Not bad, mate. Iraq's falling to pieces so could do with some more work at the moment. Apart from that I can't complain.'

'Eddie told me you were over there again recently, but I'm glad you're back. I might have something for you.'

'I'm all ears.'

'My friend with the lap dancing chain is looking for some assistance. An outside audit type of thing. Undercover. Not really suitable for us here because he's looking for a discreet investigator rather than a large firm. But I thought it might be something you'd be up for. Anyway, can you imagine Phil or Ray at a lap dancing club? Their tickers would give out, and if they didn't, the MDs would when they filed their expenses. Those corporate boys know how to rack 'em up.'

A grin broke across my face at the thought of the two ex-coppers he'd mentioned ever finding out that Doug had passed the job over to me instead of them. 'Sounds interesting. Yeah, as I said I'm available to take on new work. I won't be going back to Iraq for a while that's for sure.'

He gave me the client's contact details and wished me luck.

Straight after Doug's call, I called the boss of the lap dancing clubs and arranged to drive over to his office, which he ran out of his large pad in nearby Kingston upon Thames. Over the years I'd visited a few clubs, but I didn't earn the kind of money or mix in the sort of circles where it was anything other than an occasional laugh – usually overseas. In fact, the last time had been the opening of the latest club in the same chain. Doug had invited a load of us from the firm the previous year with complimentary tickets although it was only me and a couple of the younger guys who went along.

Compared with going to a nightclub full of drunks, fights, and late-night desperation, I preferred the transactional nature of the lap dancing places I'd been to in the past. As a happily married man I could only look and not touch anyway, so it suited me. The girls seemed to be in control although I knew that wasn't necessarily the case. Plenty of women in the adult entertainment business were getting exploited and it's not something I'd want my wife or daughters to end up doing. However, I was a typical, hypocritical bloke who enjoyed the sight of pretty, half-naked women. It helped that it didn't take much effort to convince myself the girls chose to talk to me because of my dazzling wit and charm.

★

The tyres gave a satisfying crunch as I pulled to a halt on the large circular driveway in front of the imposing mansion. A convertible silver Mercedes SL65 AMG with its roof up sat next to a black Bentley Continental. I didn't know what else Mr Moore did, but I assumed the lap dancing business was a decent earner.

Ken Moore struck me as a jovial guy and very switched on with it. I admired most people who built their own successful businesses.

It's easy to think it all looks very easy, but behind nearly every success story is a long history of hard work and often struggle. As he walked me into the office, he introduced his pretty wife as the office manager.

'This is Christine, my wife. Chrissy, this is John. He's the chap Doug recommended.'

I shook the unsure hand of a pretty blonde who could have stepped out of the fashion pages of an upmarket clothing catalogue. 'Hi Christine, John Pierce.'

She was one of those women who could have been any age from late twenties to early forties. I suspected nearer the latter, partly because of her husband's age, but she looked damn good for it. I might have been a little too obvious in calculating how much of her might be plastic because she appraised me with a challenging look in return.

'For the mystery shopper work,' Ken added.

'Of course. Hi, call me Chris. It's nice to meet you. I don't think I've met a PI before. Oh, apart from Doug. That's what he does now isn't it?' she asked Ken.

'Yes. And John here worked with him until recently I believe. But now you're freelance?'

'That's right. I worked with Doug. Well we were actually in different sections, but I left about a year ago and work for myself now.'

I was trying to keep focused on the conversation, but across the room two stunning girls in their early to mid-twenties had stopped working and were listening to our conversation with interest. Ken followed the direction of my glances. 'Oh, and here we have our two lovely assistants Rachel and Astrid.'

Hollywood smiles followed as we exchanged pleasantries. The attention of three very attractive women had me questioning my life choices to date. Ken Moore had clearly made some very good ones – better than mine. I tried to keep my jaw from hanging open like a cartoon character before it occurred to me that the girls might be family and I got my game face back on.

Like many other similar businesses, their clubs were monitored closely by Trading Standards, who regularly sent officers to the premises in their respective areas to check the regulations were being followed. Especially the strict no-touching rule between the lap dancers and customers.

'We need to check the clubs are all operating in full compliance with the law and the council regulations. Trading Standards are sending in their people undercover, so I want to know for myself what they'll find and what they'll be reporting back. As well as checking the girls are behaving, it also gives us an opportunity to check if there's any evidence of pilfering from the bar staff or reception.'

To achieve this, they intended to have a mystery shopper go to their seven clubs, put plenty of £50 notes through the tills, buy plenty of lap dances, and try to entice the girls into offering drugs and sexual services. In practical terms, it translated to blowing loads of cash on champagne and lap dances, chatting to as many pretty girls as possible, and then getting whisked home through the late-night London streets by a car and driver. All while earning a tidy hourly rate. They were talking to the right guy.

CHAPTER 29

LONDON – EARLY DECEMBER 2004

With her pixie-like face and delicious curves, impressively set off by a perfect-fitting black basque, stockings and suspenders, the girl in the spotlight was stunning, I'd give her that. So too, no doubt, would the owners of the dozens of other eyes feasting on her. It was a shame her perfunctory style didn't do her justice. She didn't own the pole like some of the others, although her captivating presence was enough to mesmerise most of the audience. Not that she had relished the thought of the fifteen-minute slot all the girls were required to perform on the central stage. I knew because she'd told me after the House Mother interrupted our conversation to say she was up next.

She'd rolled her eyes and told me it was the part of the job she hated most, but I tried to encourage her.

'You'll probably do better than I would.'

'Hmm, thanks for that,' she said, as she stood before making her way to the stage. 'Wish me luck,' she voiced over her shoulder as I watched her immaculate rear view gliding away.

'Break a leg,' I replied, a little louder than intended. A hot flash deep inside when she speared me with smouldering eyes and a coquettish smile. That was real, surely?

While Monique writhed with the music, I surveyed the flattering shadows of the Hammersmith club as scantily clad women circled their prey. I saw glamour where many others saw seediness, but only if I didn't think about it too hard.

Monique was her stage name and she hadn't given me the hard sell like the previous two vampires who polished off a bottle of my overpriced champagne amidst repeated demands they dance for me. Their layers of make-up, darting tongues, and thrusting breasts had been well over the top, and that was just sat at the table. Always the gentleman, I concurred of course. Their double act had been mechanical rather than sexy, but by God it was X-rated stuff.

Once the vampires had sucked all the champagne from the table, Monique had drifted into an empty seat and raised an eyebrow at me. 'I bet you enjoyed that,' she said with a teasing smile.

'Not bad. Not the greatest dancers though and their make-up was applied with a shovel.'

She tried to hold it in, but a giggle escaped. 'So, what are *you* doing here?'

'I know. Good-looking guy. Could get his pick of the girls. Just what am I doing here, surrounded by gorgeous women and talking to the prettiest girl in London?'

Monique let another laugh slip out as she shook her head in mock despair.

'Tell you what, a bottle of champagne for the lady?' I asked in a terrible approximation of Sean Connery's James Bond.

I found sliding into my playboy character easy; helped by a bountiful supply of someone else's fifty-pound notes. I'd only had half a glass from the first bottle, so I had some leeway for a drink yet. Too many and it would end up a fuzzy recollection of cleavage, legs and lust, like a previous night at the Tower Bridge club. Lucky my small dictaphone rescued me that time, but even those whispered utterings in the privacy of a toilet cubicle had been difficult to decipher into a full report. Especially the later stuff when the alcohol had impaired my speech. I wouldn't make that mistake again.

Three weeks in and I regarded myself as a bit of a connoisseur of lap dancing clubs and girls. My nights at the other six clubs had been varied. Some I'd visited on my own like tonight, others I'd invited various friends and contacts to mix up the experience and see if the girls might react differently to a couple of guys playing off each other.

There had been a few highlights: falling instantly for a dancer in the Holborn club, who promptly got the sack after I reported the details of her tactile lap dances; similarly being smitten with a gorgeous Spanish girl at the club in Euston who gave me more than one memorable lap dance I didn't report in full; Jim coming up from Poole and being solicited by one of the girls desperate to go home with him; Mohammed paying for two statuesque Russian blondes to give me an XXX-rated five minutes using the spending money I'd given him; and dozens of conversations with beautiful young women in various states of undress.

The best part of the job, chatting to the girls, could also be the worst. They sashayed amongst the tables, waiting for an opening to sidle in and extract cash from the welcoming punters. Great if a girl with some personality dropped in on you, and many of them came across as smart and funny, but a real drag trying to get rid of others who were all show and no substance.

'How about you let me dance for you first?' cooed Monique, with an expression that dared me to say no.

She needn't have worried. I was hooked and had no intention of turning her down. It would also keep the House Mother happy; important because she watched her girls like a hawk to make sure they worked the room efficiently and kept to the strict no touching rules. The girls were self-employed sales people, selling themselves. I couldn't begrudge them that and a momentary prickle of regret as the reality of the situation encroached on our flirting soon dissolved.

I made a show of thinking about it. 'I've just had a great dance and I doubt you'll live up to such a high standard. But okay, I'll give you a try-out.'

A smile creased her lips as she raised her sculptured eyebrows in a look that said, 'We'll see about that,' before she took my hand and led me to an empty booth. If making women laugh was the secret, then I seemed to be on fire tonight. Claire wouldn't have seen the funny side though, as Monique proceeded to reward me with a highly erotic lap dance which straddled the border to the wrong side of acceptable, before finishing with a kiss on the cheek.

'I never kiss customers, but that's for making me laugh,' she said, as she located her basque and sought to pour herself back into it.

'Do you mind?' she said, turning and indicating I should assist with the countless hooks on the back.

What a job.

★

Monique was in high demand after her stint on the pole, so maybe I'd been harsh with my critique. A good job I'd kept that to myself. I didn't see her again for a long time as I went through the motions with a couple more girls. Until the last hour, the big push for the dancers was to lure the customers into £250 per hour private table time. This occurred in a separate VIP area I didn't have the budget to access.

The place was bursting at the seams with customers and dancers. Pretty girls adorned every booth and table, laughing, hustling, drinking, and dancing for mesmerised punters. I caught myself scanning the room for Monique even though she would almost certainly have bagged a VIP client. Twice I thought I saw her looking in my direction through the crowd, but when I checked there was no sign of her. Pointless wishful thinking on my part.

At the end of the night she slid back into the seat next to me.

'This job drives me mad. I've just spent an hour earning loads of money with a table full of idiot bankers, but times like that make me want to give it up.'

'Is this the part where we go all "Pretty Woman" and I make an honest woman of you?' It was an unwelcome attempt to break her introspection and her eyes flashed with venom.

'I'm not a hooker,' she hissed.

'That's not what I meant... sorry.' My size nines had gone right in it as usual.

'Ignore me, I'm just tired. I need to get going now. If I don't give it all up soon, then maybe I'll see you again one night.' But this was said in a matter-of-fact, friendly manner, rather than a flirty and suggestive tone.

I tried to laugh off my regret. After all, I was just another punter overpaying for drinks and handing over cash to watch gyrating, skimpily clad women getting naked. Not exactly something that would enhance my CV.

'Yeah, I need to get going as well. Have you got the number for a taxi driver who won't rip me off going south of the river?' I might struggle to convince a black cab to go south all the way to Epsom and the firm I'd been using had no-one available that Friday night.

Monique fished a card out of her small black purse. 'These are the guys me and most of the girls use. They're only round the corner. Mention my name and they should sort you out okay.'

Another reminder that for Monique this was her working environment. I didn't even know her real name. It would just go down as one of those moments in time shared with a stranger, although in this case a beautiful stranger, both in and out of her expensive lingerie.

★

'So where are you from?' I asked the taxi driver as we cruised across Putney Bridge with the lights of late-night London illuminating the river. With his black hair and a hint of the Middle East in his features, we might have something in common to chat about. His hairline was receding, but he must have been my age or younger.

'Kensington,' came the reply in accented English.

'I mean originally.'

'Kurdistan. North of Iraq.'

That piqued my interest. 'Really? I'm thinking of heading there soon. I'm John by the way. What was your name again?'

With communications now dried up from Faris in Baghdad and Essam at Al-Nura, prospects for Baghdad and Basra didn't look promising. Mohammed was pessimistic about the situation throughout Iraq, but I had read several reports saying the northern Kurdish provinces were a safe and booming environment. Until now I had no links with anyone from that region and hadn't made any efforts to establish any. This was my first conversation with someone who might be able to shed some light on the situation up there.

'Ali. I'm British now, but I was born in Sulaimaniyah and lived there until '91. You know, the war and the uprising. Soon I'm going back to check on our house.'

I'd read Sulaimaniyah was the second main city in the semi-autonomous three-province region run by the Kurds. Although there was a Kurdistan Regional Government (KRG) based in the 'capital' of Erbil, a Kurdish political faction called the PUK ruled the Sulaimaniyah province. They had their own government based in the city of the same name, including a prime minister and all the various ministries. Other than that, and various reports describing the region as the safest part of Iraq, I knew little else.

For the next forty minutes as Ali drove me home, we chatted about Kurdistan, Iraq, London, Chelsea Football Club and family. Ali told me about the route through Turkey that British-based Iraqi Kurds used to travel back and forth to their homeland. It entailed a flight to Istanbul, a further flight to the south-eastern Turkish city of Diyarbakir, before a five-hour drive south and then eastwards along the Syrian border to the Habur customs post at the border with Iraq. Exactly the kind of information I was after. However, it was late, and I needed to keep my focus on completing the final report for the mystery shopper project, so we didn't get into any discussions about future plans. I took a card from Ali with his number scribbled on the back, along with a wad of blank receipts for expenses, and assured him I'd be in touch soon.

CHAPTER 30

EPSOM – LATE DECEMBER 2004

Christmas was fast approaching and the financial situation was miserable. The lap dancing job had been completed with the happy client now lighter by a couple of dishonest staff and unlucky girls. However, the seven visits and accompanying reports had been my only work since returning from Basra. They hadn't generated enough profit to make for a relaxing festive break.

The empty diary for the new year concerned me, but we always made sure our girls had a good Christmas one way or the other, and we had just enough cash to cover it this year. It was the one time of the year I did everything I could to be home with the family. Even in the military, I'd missed birthdays, anniversaries, and family get-togethers, but somehow never Christmas.

The diary also indicated an unmistakable truth: Christmas Day fell on a Saturday that year; the day I attended the police station due to my bail conditions. On the last Saturday before Christmas, I checked whether they really expected me to report at 10.00am on both Christmas Day and New Year's Day.

'Yes sir. Those are your bail conditions and that's when you must report.' With a look and a tone that said, *Unlucky – you've only got yourself to blame.*

Great. Claire still knew nothing of the customs decision to charge me or the bail reporting requirements, so I'd have to sneak off for half an hour when everyone would be in the middle of opening presents. The saving grace might be Claire's parents and brother arranging to pop round in the morning to wish the girls a merry Christmas before we drove to my mum's place for lunch with all the trimmings. I hoped it would cause enough of a diversion to enable me to enjoy the festive cheer from our local constabulary and get back before anyone noticed I was gone.

With Pete still certain Customs and Excise would drop the case once it became clear it wasn't part of an organised crime plot, I hadn't seen much point in worrying Claire with the details of the charges and bail conditions. She knew something dodgy had occurred that night but hadn't tried to delve into the possible repercussions. That suited me.

★

My extracurricular activities on Christmas Day passed without a hitch. The copper behind the counter unable to hide his smirk at my having to report that morning. Twat.

'Merry Christmas, sir,' he said without any festive cheer as I turned to leave.

'And you, mate. What time are you finished?'

Suspicion crossed his face as he answered, 'I'll be home by this evening.'

'Well you have a great day. I'll have a drink for you over Christmas lunch. Laters,' I said with OTT cheerfulness topped off with a mock salute before I nipped out the door, the copper scowling as I left.

The police station had been empty, so I'd been processed immediately and snuck back into the festivities at home less than twenty minutes after leaving. A short enough time that my disappearance went unnoticed.

Christmas itself passed with the usual mayhem of wrapping paper, turkey, alcohol, and the mixture of laughter and tears from the children in the family. Along with our two girls, my sister had a young son and my brother three young kids. It was good to play games, goof around, and forget about Iraq, business, and Customs and Excise.

When I switched on the TV late on Boxing Day, the channels were filled with news that a tsunami had devastated various countries bordering the Indian Ocean. A large part of the southern Indian coastline had been hit hard, including the proposed start location and initial routes for Football to the Summit. I knew right away this terrible tragedy would kill the project. Charity and aid funding now had far more pressing causes to resolve.

The following day I received confirmation all activity was suspended and to be prepared for the project to be cancelled. After everything that had happened during the year, it was sod's law my big hope for getting things back on track money-wise had been wiped out by a natural disaster. My problems paled into insignificance compared to the hundreds of thousands killed, injured and left homeless by the disaster, but I still had an overwhelming urge to commiserate my bad fortune with alcohol.

★

It was late, so I opened the front door quietly when I returned from a few beers with my youngest brother at the nearby pub. Maybe more than a few. The dog looked up and went back to sleep as I fished out my wallet and went in the first door on the left to leave it with my keys on the computer desk in the corner. I was surprised by the sight of Claire sat at the pine table which dominated the centre of the dining room. I wasn't drunk, but I wasn't sober either. She had a fierce look on her face that had me urgently checking through the memory banks to remember what I might have done wrong.

'I was looking for some stamps in the bureau and I came across this.' An escort agency business card from the summer job skittered across the table in my direction.

Thank God for that. Just a simple misunderstanding. 'Honestly that was work...'

Claire cut me off and her voice climbed an octave. 'And this was work as well was it?'

The lap dancing club membership ID followed hard on the tail of the other card. I paused to get my alcohol-slowed thoughts in order and an image of Monique appeared from nowhere in my head. It might as well have been projected onto the wall behind me because Claire must have seen something she took for guilt.

'You bastard.' Said with a look of bitterness.

'I can explain…'

'And don't think I didn't notice you disappeared on Christmas morning. Where did you go?'

'What, you think I nipped out to my other family down the road?' I said with a laugh I would immediately regret.

'Don't you laugh at me. Where were you and what the hell are these?' She pointed at the two cards.

I tried to explain, but I wasn't sharp enough to avoid falling into pitfalls that made everything sound worse than it should. Caught by surprise and unable to conjure up a plausible alternative to explain my Christmas Day disappearance, I revealed the Customs amd Excise saga hanging over me. Claire began crying and looked at me with a disappointment I'd only seen once before: when I was stupidly arrested for drink-driving while on terminal leave from the Corps seven years earlier.

'I can't deal with all of this now. You can stay down here tonight, but I want you to go in the morning and give me some space while I get my head round it,' she said with a weary sadness which lay heavily on the room.

I knew I wasn't in a fit state to start arguing, so I simply said, 'Okay, if that's what you want,' and watched as Claire left the room. Taz joined me in the living room as I bedded down on the sofa and she made herself comfortable on the floor underneath me.

'I'm in the doghouse now, Taz.'

★

If anything, the atmosphere felt even worse in the morning. Claire was working an early shift at the hospital and she stomped around the house hardly speaking before she left, apart from telling me her mother would be collecting Becky at nine, and I should be gone before she returned from work after three. Claire's mum was her normal cheery self, so it didn't seem like reports of my crimes had made the rounds. After she left, I rang an old bootneck mate of mine who lived down in Weymouth. I didn't keep in touch with too many of the lads, but Rob and I went way back.

'I fucked up mate, although more on a technicality than anything serious. Is it okay if I come down and we hit the spicers while I regale you with my latest highlights?'

'Of course, mate. Come on down. You know you're welcome anytime. I'll get Sally to make up a bed for you.'

Rob and I had known each other for years and still got together occasionally to drink spiced rum and talk shit till the early hours. We both had daughters rather than sons and our two families got on well when we all met up. As the drinks flowed, Claire and especially Rob's wife Sally, an ex-Wren, usually made disparaging remarks about our current drinking prowess and general capabilities. Compared that is to the alcohol-boldened tales we spun of commando derring-do, huge quantities of ale quaffed, and fist-fights won.

★

Sally opened the door. 'What have you done?'

'Hi Sally. Honestly, it wasn't my fault.'

'Yeah, I'm sure. He's in the kitchen champing at the bit to start on the beer. Don't you go taking advantage of my good nature and leading him astray tonight. The pair of you can't drink any more like you think you can.'

'Don't worry. We'll take it easy.' But my grin said we wouldn't.

Sally expressed her clear disapproval after overhearing my lurid tales of escort girls and especially some of the lap dancing nights.

'I'll leave you both to it.' Warning Rob with, 'Don't wake me up when you come to bed,' she left the kitchen with a glass of water and a pantomime scowl in my direction.

'So, things are okay between you and Claire then?' asked Rob.

'They should be, mate. It all sounds much worse than it is. A couple of days and I'm sure Claire will calm down.'

I didn't think it was anything too serious, but sometimes things have a way of escalating out of control in a way no-one intended.

'Well you're welcome to stay as long as you like. You know it's my birthday on New Year, and we're having a fancy-dress party again on New Year's Eve like the rest of Weymouth.'

I called Claire each day and we engaged in awkward, lukewarm conversations. I told her I was staying down for Rob's birthday bash and would drive back on New Year's Day. She was non-committal about my likely reception, but then she might have remembered I had to be back in Epsom that day to report for bail.

★

The fancy-dress party on New Year's Eve turned out to be an absolute riot and just the kind of hilarious, crazy night I needed. But waking up bleary-eyed on New Year's Day I knew I'd fucked up. Epsom was nearly three hours away and I would be in no fit state to drive until later that afternoon at the earliest. I had to report for bail in an hour. Shit.

I got through to the duty sergeant at Epsom police station after a lengthy wait on hold. My panic subsided when he thanked me for phoning in and said I could report the next day instead. The Alka-Seltzer was probably doing the rounds at the station that morning and they sounded grateful for one less visitor to process.

CHAPTER 31

EPSOM – EARLY JANUARY 2005

'Will you be back in time for Becky's birthday?'

Did I detect a hint of hope in Claire's voice; perhaps a sign our frosty relations might be warming? Not the moment to admit I'd forgotten about Becky's second birthday later in the month.

'I'm going to try, but her birthday is only a few weeks away and the details of the trip aren't fully agreed yet. It's not even a hundred per cent we'll be going. I'm meeting Ali tomorrow and it'll all be clearer then.'

'Okay.' In a quiet voice, impossible to decode.

I smiled and searched her face for a sign she understood I wanted to make amends. And just maybe I caught an encouraging crinkle at the corner of her mouth as she turned away and began sorting the dishwasher.

★

Ali had been very enthusiastic when I'd called him the previous afternoon. 'Yes John, we must meet. We should travel straight away.'

'Okay. Let's meet tomorrow at Victoria Station. By WH Smith.'

If he was late, it would give me a chance to browse for a new read with the book token I'd received for Christmas from Claire's mum.

Our only previous meeting had been the forty-five-minute taxi ride home from the Hammersmith lap dancing club, but Ali greeted me like a long-lost brother when he finally turned up. The cheeky git even looked at me as I walked out of WH Smith with a new book in hand and grinned broadly as he said, 'A bit late. Not English time then.'

I held up my carrier bag. 'I've been here half an hour already, mate. I just nipped back in to grab this when I thought you weren't turning up.'

Instead of just a quick meeting, we spent the whole day together. First at his older brother's flat in Victoria, then driving over to his place in Kensington, shared with another (younger) brother, or two. I outlined what I'd been doing business-wise down in Baghdad and Basra. My efforts in the simmering cauldron of Iraq seemed to be regarded by the Kurdish audience as validation of my suitability as a travelling companion for one of their own.

The discussion soon moved to practical arrangements regarding flights and dates. I agreed to take care of our flight bookings to get us as far as Diyarbakir in south-eastern Turkey, and Ali said he would arrange everything for our travel by land from Diyarbakir across the Turkish-Iraqi border to Sulaimaniyah in Iraq's Kurdistan Region.

Over the previous twenty years, more than 30,000 people had been killed in south-eastern Turkey during a guerrilla war fought by the PKK, a Kurdish separatist movement. Ali's plan to overnight in Diyarbakir and punch out in the morning by taxi for the Iraqi border, 300 kilometres and five hours away, made my spidey senses tingle like mad.

'What's the security situation for that route?'

He hadn't been in the region since the nineties, but I hoped he'd been able to acquire plenty of useful and current inside information.

'Don't worry. People do it all the time. It's not a problem.'

He spoke with a reassuring confidence and his face displayed a certainty that I wanted to believe, despite suspecting it might be based on blind hope and naivety.

'We have friends, so it's not a problem. And once we reach Kurdistan... then you will see.'

I sought clarification. 'So, we get a taxi to the border and once we get through, there will be people waiting?'

'Not people, *Peshmerga*,' said with a flourish and reciprocal smiles all around the room.

'Peshmerga are the fierce Kurdish fighters who have fought Saddam, Ansar al-Sunna, and now al-Qaeda. They are the reason Kurdistan is safe.'

I knew about the Peshmerga reputation so that sounded promising. Peshmerga literally stood for 'those that face death' and, operating as guerrillas from the mountains against Saddam's forces over the years, many Peshmerga had died fighting against the oppressive Baghdad military – as had many more of their enemies. The only fly in the ointment was the armed Turkish-Kurds, the PKK, who were also called Peshmerga, but with a Marxist agenda and a different set of objectives focused on their struggles with the Turkish government. I needed to be careful not to become mixed up with those guys.

'It sounds like you've got transport and security arranged. Can we get a visa on entry at the border?'

'No. We must go to the Iraqi Consulate tomorrow morning. *Early.*'

He stressed the last word as though it hadn't been him who was late that morning.

'Good. What do we need for the visa process and how much are they?'

The plans for the Turkish side of the border were underwhelming but mixing with the Peshmerga once inside Kurdistan appealed to my sense of adventure. Yet again events were moving forward in a seemingly unstoppable current. I hardly knew them, but I liked these Kurdish guys and their attitude. All the brothers lived in London, held British passports, spoke good English, and came across as easy-going and friendly. It was as though I'd been accepted into a small fraternity.

It took a painful few days of shocking queues, intransigent officials, and finally some assistance from an insider at the consulate to get our Iraqi visas. The trick was a secret knock on the door in the afternoon when the office was closed to the general public. This was when all the press organisations and diplomats had their applications processed. As I walked through the quiet room on my way to the visa interview, I could see the crush of the mornings was for amateurs.

I was waiting to hear back from Ali to confirm our travel dates when I received a call from Pete. He didn't want to speak on the phone and asked me to come over to the office instead. What with the festive period and preparations for the trip to northern Iraq, I hadn't seen him since before Christmas. I agreed to go over that afternoon.

As ever, Pete was still supremely confident that customs were going to drop the case. Then, after a few minutes of mundane talk, he told me why he'd asked to meet.

'I saw George yesterday up at the club and he asked me to pass on a message to you. There are some people who want to meet with you to discuss Iraq. Tomorrow.'

Pete was referring to his contact at the Special Forces Club in London. Earlier in the summer we'd all met with an executive from an oil company with a concession in Kurdistan. That meeting hadn't resulted in any business, but it showed me the club might be an avenue to meet serious players involved in business in Iraq.

'Sounds interesting. What time are we going up?'

No need to check my diary; it was still mostly empty apart from a small due diligence job that was waiting on an agent report before I could finish my own final report.

'I'm not going to be there. They want to meet with you only.' Pete's tone was flat.

'Okay, so what time?'

If anything, that was better for me. Pete wasn't involved in my Iraq business in any way and I'd be able to prevent the discussion from deviating and losing focus on my key objective: to secure a revenue-generating agreement by hook or by crook.

After a brief, nondescript call to George, Pete confirmed the meeting was set for 3.00pm the following afternoon. Good job I hadn't packed for Iraq yet. Either of my two decent suits would still be okay to wear without needing a press at the dry cleaners.

CHAPTER 32

NEAR HARRODS, LONDON – JANUARY 2005

The Special Forces Club was located behind Harrods in London's Knightsbridge. Although I'd served as an attached rank at a British special forces unit (SBS) for a couple of years whilst in the Corps, that didn't qualify me to be a member. I had never attempted selection, let alone become a 'badged' rank as those who succeeded were known. In the SBS they were also known as 'frogs', with the unit emblem at that time displaying a parachuting frog.

In the summer I had been told that there might be a way in, but I had no desire to be a member of a club I wasn't entitled to join. The chance for occasional meetings with members and their guests as opportunities arose was good enough for me.

'John, it's great to see you. I hope you and the family had a good Christmas and New Year.'

George always seemed to be the life and soul of the place. Today, the tables in the small bar area sat empty apart from one elderly couple sipping glasses of wine. No one else was evident other than the barman, although other rooms and facilities up and down the stairways and dotted along the narrow corridors might have been occupied.

George pointed at his glass of wine with an unspoken question.

'No thanks, I'll have an orange juice and lemonade please.'

He frowned as I continued.

'I'd prefer not to drink if we're going to talk about business. I've had more than my fair share over the holidays.' Then in answer to his original greeting. 'Yes, all good at home. Happy New Year to you. I trust your family are well and you had a good Christmas.'

As we exchanged general chit-chat, I considered how to ask him about getting the customs issue quashed. I guessed he'd been involved in Pete's dealings with the British establishment the previous year, so he might be keen to maintain a healthy distance from the ongoing prosecutions. Although he must know the whole thing was a shambles that should never get to court, I decided to wait until after the business meeting. No sense in risking any upset before I'd had the chance to review this new, unspecified opportunity.

'Ah, George, so this is our man Mr Pierce,' said a tall, expensively-tailored gentleman who had entered the bar area from the far doorway rather than the entrance nearest the stairs.

'Mr Pierce, my name is Chapman. Please, we are waiting in a private meeting room through here.'

I looked at George, who made no move to get up from his chair.

'Of course, Sandy. John is raring to go. Perhaps I'll see you in the bar for a drink later?'

'Might be a little busy with office work,' said the grey-haired Chapman, casting a glance in my direction.

So, George wasn't coming into the meeting. That was a surprise.

I assumed the invitation for a drink included me, so before standing up to shake hands and introduce myself to Chapman, I replied to George, 'Sure, I'll see you later.'

George frowned again. Maybe I wasn't invited.

★

There was one other man in the meeting room. Shorter than Chapman, he had more of a bulldog look about him. If Chapman might be a retired ex-Guards officer, this chap had me visualising a current or recent special forces operator who had seen a few bullets and fists flying in his time. Whatever their backgrounds, we were meeting in a private room at the SF Club and everyone else was excluded. This was going to be interesting.

'This is my colleague, Mr Roper,' said Chapman. 'Tea, coffee? I noticed that you hadn't joined George for an afternoon tipple. Wise choice I think.'

'Hi.'

Roper nodded in acknowledgement.

'I'll have a coffee. Thank you,' I added.

Roper poured the coffee and an enquiring eyebrow lifted as he placed the pot down.

'Just milk please.' It had been a long time since I took the NATO standard milk and two sugars.

Roper had also poured a cup of tea for Chapman. An indication of the likely hierarchy here. It was an unusual atmosphere for a business meeting. No cards exchanged, job roles indicated, or other preliminary business small talk.

'Mr Pierce, I work with the Foreign & Commonwealth Office of Her Majesty's Government and there is a matter of some importance I need to discuss with you.' Chapman's hands were lightly clasped in front of him as he spoke in an emphatic, assured manner.

My first thought: we're finally getting to the nitty-gritty of the customs issue. Fingers crossed my involvement would end here and now.

He continued. 'To put it bluntly, it has been decided that your assistance is required to help resolve a matter in Iraq.' The disdain with which he spoke indicated Chapman was not a fan of the idea. I didn't know yet if I was a fan either.

'Although your ready compliance in the matter would be welcomed, I should stress that this is a request for which your refusal to cooperate would have consequences. Consequences that would be detrimental to your business and your liberty.'

That got my back up straight away. 'Hang on a minute, I'm not guilty of that customs nonsense...' He held his hands up and I stopped in mid flow.

'While we are aware of your involvement in a conspiracy plot being investigated by our colleagues in Customs and Excise, there is another, far more serious aspect to consider.'

What the hell was this guy on about? My mind raced and soon the incident in the Baghdad bazaar when I'd careered through the crowds loomed large. Shit. Perhaps I'd seriously hurt or killed somebody and now they'd caught up with me.

While he sipped at his tea and watched, I fidgeted and rubbed my jaw before looking at the ceiling, closing my eyes briefly, and letting out a sigh. I doubt I could have appeared guiltier – but of what?

'You posed as a British intelligence officer to courier a message from terrorists demanding the handover of Iranian IED know-how and technology from militants operating in Basra. Your involvement in the incident at the Churchill Hotel involved similar deception. Taken together, these events cast severe doubt on your character and decision-making at the very least, and quite possibly evidence of your involvement with serious criminal and terrorist organisations.'

What the fuck! If I thought my mind was racing before, it was on steroids now.

'The only reason you aren't already being interviewed under caution is a brief appearance in our files regarding your creditable conduct during an operation in Bosnia in the early nineties, and references from George next door and your former commanding officer at SBS. Your previous Developed Vetting status whilst serving at Poole has also counted in your favour, although I suspect a repeat of that process might throw up some road bumps if it was ever tried again.

'Personally, I counselled against it, but others have suggested you might be given the benefit of the doubt in order that you can provide us with some related assistance. However, that benefit of the doubt is contingent on my assessment regarding your culpability for your activity in Basra, the details of which I would like you to explain to me now please.'

I hung on his every word with a morbid fascination. His reference to 'courier' had caused an icy hand to clasp my insides. I might have really fucked up here. Surely Essam and the Al-Nura people weren't terrorists. I had no idea if any of this was true, but I was already focusing on the 'benefit of the doubt' and how to ensure it came my way.

I felt very hot under the collar, literally, and interrupted him.

'Do you mind?' I reached for the top button of my shirt.

Chapman looked at me like I'd just walked dog shit across his living room carpet, but he nodded and picked up his cup of tea again. That was enough for me; I needed to get comfortable. I loosened my tie, took my jacket off, and hung it on the chair. It wasn't particularly warm in the room, but I'd always had a high tolerance to the cold since my first few winters of Arctic warfare training. A glug of hot coffee did little to remedy my dry throat.

Before he could resume, I had a couple of questions and points to make.

'Mr Chapman, firstly I delivered a message to a respectable member of the Basra Trade Chamber on behalf of business contacts in Dubai, but I had no knowledge of the contents of the private message. I have *never* posed as an intelligence officer and a postman doesn't get prosecuted for the contents of the letters he delivers.'

As Chapman opened his mouth to speak again, I slipped in another point.

'And secondly, the customs incident at the Churchill was a protective surveillance job. A favour in fact. I did nothing wrong. I didn't impersonate anyone, and it *will* be dropped when they realise the facts.'

I looked from Chapman to Roper and back again. Both impassive, although Roper appeared to have an underlying smile on his face. Not necessarily a friendly one.

He had let me speak, but as soon as I finished Chapman continued as a teacher might after ignoring the desperate arguments of a guilty pupil. His face said as much.

'Mr Pierce, the letter you hand-delivered in Basra was purportedly from the office of the Iraqi Prime Minister and declared you to be a

British intelligence officer. The demands the Sheikh provide you with all necessary means and assistance to obtain the Iranian IED know-how were supposedly part of a joint intelligence initiative involving us, the Americans, and the Iraqi National Intelligence Service. Were it not for the fact that the Sheikh already worked with us, the subterfuge might even have worked. That's despite the amateur nature of the forged letterhead, the factual inaccuracies contained within the letter, and the ridiculous use of terminology more at home in a James Bond film.'

He could have finished the last sentence with more contempt, but only if he'd really worked hard at it. I'd love to think they'd given me a '00' number.

The nagging feeling this might spiral out of control sent adrenaline coursing through my veins. My hands pulsed with an energy that made them quiver. Looking down at them, I couldn't figure out if they were actually shaking or my blood was just boiling with stimulants.

'I never even saw the letter. I received the envelope in Dubai as part of a business project looking at viability in Basra.'

An eyebrow had taken leave of Chapman's controlled demeanour and shot up in almost comical reaction, although it was quickly brought under control.

'Dubai. Hmm… continue.'

He clearly hadn't expected that. Hopefully this was a chance to show cooperation which might help calm things down.

'Yes, a company in Dubai, Al-Nura Engineering. I was given the sealed letter by them to hand-deliver to the Sheikh. They claimed it was vital for obtaining business support in the Basra region.'

Chapman looked at Roper and back to me. Was that a good sign?

I threw out another piece of information. 'I was directed to those guys through a businessman in Baghdad, Abu Saif al-Tikriti.'

Chapman had been calmness and reserve personified until that moment. At the mention of the name, he just couldn't help the obvious interest from illuminating his face. If we'd been playing poker, it would have been a clear 'tell'.

I was on a roll and sensed a way out of this mess. After all, I had nothing to hide.

'I only met him a couple of times in Baghdad, but it was Abu Saif who introduced me to the Al-Nura guys as his business associates.'

A different set of stimulants streamed through my veins now. It felt more like endorphins as my mood soared. This could turn out all right.

'You say you only met Abu Saif a couple of times. Would you recognise him if you saw him again?' Chapman's eyes shone with a fierce intensity.

A mental image of Abu Saif's face and large frame sprung into my head.

'Yes, I would.'

'And do you have the details of the addresses you visited in Baghdad and Dubai? Would you also recognise the men you met in Dubai?'

Now I recalled Essam and his sidekick Ibrahim.

'Definitely. I'd recognise the main two men from Dubai, yes. Possibly a couple of the people in the side office as well, including a woman, although I can't remember her name off the top of my head. I have the address details for the office in Dubai and could identify one of the addresses in Mansour, in Baghdad. I don't know the location of the first meeting with Abu Saif, but I can tell you it was in the Al-Adhamiya district of Baghdad.'

He rose out of his chair. 'Very good, Mr Pierce. You'll need to excuse me while I make a telephone call. Mr Roper will arrange for more tea and coffee. And perhaps some sandwiches?' The last comment was thrown as a question towards Roper who nodded.

'I'll be back shortly,' said Chapman as he left the room.

I let out a sigh and the energy drained from my body like water from a bath when the plug is pulled. Weariness sprung out from my bones and, at the mention of food, a ravenous hunger had taken hold. Roper's bulky frame was disappearing through the door after Chapman as I called out, 'Chicken salad would be good, or tuna mayonnaise.'

Surprisingly, Roper's face popped back round the door. 'I'll see what I can do.'

That was the first time I'd heard him speak.

Chapman remained absent for a good twenty minutes. Long enough for me and Roper to making serious headway into the collection of sandwiches which now sat in the middle of the table. I still felt weary, but drinking plenty of water, polishing off three decent sandwiches, and making myself a strong coffee had helped regulate my body's natural fight, flight, and panic modes. Mentally, I was coming to terms with the evolving situation. It's not like being aggressively interviewed was a new experience for me. I needed to stop making a habit of it though.

Chapman came back into the room, closed the door behind him, and took his seat. After pouring himself a cup of tea and taking a first sip, he set the cup down and turned towards me.

'Right, I've discussed our conversation with my colleagues and it has been decided we should explore the possibility of you providing us with assistance in Iraq. I am unable to tell you any more about this aspect until you have provided a full statement regarding the events you described in Baghdad and Dubai, the people involved, and the addresses concerned. Only then will a decision be taken as to how we should proceed.'

So, they wanted me to do some work for them in Iraq. I needed the money, but I also wanted to know how much.

'Okay, that's fine. Do you want me to do that now, or perhaps tomorrow?'

'We're going to do it now, Mr Pierce.'

I'd thought as much. 'And I assume I'll be paid for this work?'

The silence and that look again on Chapman's face made me think I assumed wrong, but I blundered on, nonetheless.

'Or is the intention just to give me something in writing to say I won't be prosecuted for Basra… and the customs thing?'

If we'd been practising the iconic scene from *Oliver Twist*, I don't think he could have pulled off a better look as though he was Mr Bumble and I'd just asked for 'more.'

'This isn't Hollywood. We're not making a deal. I'm going to make the position crystal clear for you. While it is accepted you might have unwittingly acted as a courier for a terrorist organisation attempting to procure a capability that would have a detrimental impact on Coalition forces throughout Iraq, ignorance is no defence as far as us and our American cousins are concerned. You are being offered the opportunity to redeem yourself and this matter can be swept away. However, if you do not agree, today, to provide us with the assistance we seek at the appropriate time, then we will share everything we know about your terrorist-related activities with our American friends. Rest assured, they will deal with you far more harshly than us. They have a tendency to act first and eventually start asking questions a long time later.'

With no real idea of what they were asking me to do, it was difficult to assess whether to agree to help these guys, who I assumed were spooks. MI6 or one of the closely linked departments that operated in the shadows. It wasn't going to be much of an assessment though. I'd have to say yes. The alternative sounded untenable. I could only hope this 'assistance' they sought was something a) I could actually accomplish and b) wouldn't get me killed or otherwise fucked up.

Chapman replaced his now empty teacup on the saucer after polishing off the rest of his drink and giving his words time to air.

'So, what is it you are asking me to do?'

★

Two hours later, the young officer who had appeared with a laptop, printer, and bundles of papers finally indicated to Chapman he'd finished. Chapman himself had asked questions and directed the wording of my statement, while the younger guy, Williams, did the work on the laptop. I assumed Roper wasn't a dab hand at typing and shorthand.

Despite maintaining a posture like he had a rod up his arse, Chapman became noticeably more amenable during the evening. He was especially pleased on hearing I had been a Terrorist Recognition Instructor during my time in the Corps. At the time in 1990, the course in Folkestone was interesting and put to good use during my tours of Northern Ireland. I could never have foreseen that fifteen years later it would help swing a decision which kept me from being whisked into a hell of accusations and jail time if I was lucky, hoods and waterboarding if I wasn't.

'Before I can reveal any further details regarding the potential task, you are required to sign this,' said Chapman as he presented a wad of papers.

As I looked through, he continued.

'You'll see the Confidentiality Agreement you signed in 1997 at SBS, plus an addendum that reinforces your previous undertakings under the Official Secrets Act and some additional clauses related to any information to which you might become privy as a result of our new relationship.'

It wasn't that I didn't trust them, I just didn't trust anyone when it came to signing documents pushed under my nose.

'I should really take legal advice before signing anything.'

It would be kind to call them blank stares from the other three men sat round the table, but suffice to say the message was obvious and received loud and clear.

'But this is pretty straightforward, so I'll take a few minutes to read through.'

We might have been getting on better than our original, frosty exchanges, but I wasn't going to try pushing my luck.

With the laptop and signed documents stowed away in a locked case, we had finally reached the moment of truth. Time to hear what crazy shit I had signed up to. I'd been forced to agree they could intercept my phone and email communications, which really pissed me off. Even while I signed the form, I considered ways to circumvent it. I didn't have anything to hide, but I didn't like the idea of these clowns snooping on everything I did. My use of encrypted Hushmail was likely to upset the apple cart, although no need to mention it there and then.

Even after all this time, Chapman still looked immaculate in his three-piece suit and Windsor-knotted tie. His house master at Eton or Harrow would no doubt be proud.

'Abu Saif al-Tikriti is the *nom de guerre* of a man believed to be a senior lieutenant to Abu Musab al-Zarqawi, head of al-Qaeda Iraq. It is understood he is the Shadow Emir, effectively the second-in-command to Zarqawi and potentially the next leader of AQI once Zarqawi has been eliminated. Unfortunately, the identity of Abu Saif has not been confirmed and there are no clear photographs from which we can identify him. It is therefore our intention you will accompany our people when appropriate to positively identify Abu Saif and allow us to take it from there. A simple and straightforward task, for which you will avoid a great deal of unpleasantness.'

It might have sounded simple and straightforward, but I started picturing scenarios where I might be sent in to PID (positively identify) Abu Saif on my own, up front and centre. I'd met the guy before, fine. But I didn't know he was some kind of ninja bad-ass back then. If all this was compromised – and the whole Sheikh Mustafa working with British intelligence hadn't escaped my notice – then I might well end up walking into a fitting for an orange jumpsuit and a neck shave that would involve my head and body becoming two distinct entities on Al Jazeera. Fuck.

I assumed my misgivings weren't stretched all over my face because Chapman and Roper shook hands with me as we bade our farewells. Chapman reminded me I wasn't to discuss our meeting with anyone. Not George in the bar next door, my wife, former colleagues, or anyone else. He also told me I had to report any contact from Faris or the guys at Al-Nura immediately. When I said I planned to travel to Kurdistan in the next few days, he thought for a moment and quickly warmed to the idea.

'Very good. Let's hope an opportunity arises to acquire our target while you are already in Iraq. It would make the logistics much easier.'

As for the next steps, they told me it depended on unfolding events. An email or a phone call from my contacts in Baghdad or Dubai might prompt action, or Chapman and his colleagues might engineer a chance to target Abu Saif by their own efforts. If they needed me to meet with them, a message would be left as a draft at an email account for which they provided the password. Rather bleakly, the message would say:

Your father is ill and I am going to the hospital to visit him tomorrow.

Which meant a meeting was set for 6.00pm local time the following day at one of the meeting locations. If in the UK, I was to make my way to the taxi rank at London's Waterloo Station. After a flurry of phone calls and deliberation, it was decided if I was in Kurdistan there were two possible meeting locations. In Erbil it was the newly opened Erbil International Hotel; 200 kilometres away in Sulaimaniyah it was the Sulaimaniyah Palace Hotel. I had to confirm my attendance at the meeting by adding the following line to the draft message:

Please keep me informed.

'How about if I'm unable to make the meeting?'

Chapman's eyes narrowed. 'Make sure you do. If your confirmation has not been seen by nine am local time on the day of the meeting, you will receive an SMS from a UK number with the same message, with the timing changed to *today* indicating the meeting will be at 6.00pm that day. Reply with the same confirmation. If the opportunity arises, it is vital we take it. We may not get a second chance. Do not make us have to come and find you.'

And I thought we had been getting along nicely.

'We'll be monitoring the location of your phone, so keep it switched on and get to the nearest meeting location at the designated time. If you see Roper or Williams, then the validity of any instructions they provide will be immediately clear. If you are approached by anyone else who mentions my name, then you must call this number immediately to establish their credentials. It is doubtful we will meet again until after your involvement, so I will wish you Godspeed now, although you can be certain you'll be in the safest of hands whenever the operation does materialise.'

The London number I needed to memorise was based on my old Corps service number to assist me – very clever.

I didn't know if George was still at the club when I left because Roper guided me out of the building via a route that avoided the bar.

Heading home I reflected on the events of the last few hours. The final months of 2004 had seen the customs debacle, problems between me and Claire, and now this fallout from Baghdad and Basra. I sincerely hoped things would improve in 2005.

CHAPTER 33

SOUTHWARK CROWN COURT,
LONDON – JANUARY 2005

At the end of January, I arrived suited and booted outside Southwark Crown Court for the latest instalment in the battle with Customs and Excise.

In an unusual move, a joint motion had been filed by all our barristers to dismiss the whole thing by arguing we had no case to answer. Apparently, this was rarely a successful tactic, but they believed it had a chance in these unusual circumstances.

Because Pete's client had a QC (Queen's Counsel – a silk), all the other barristers, including mine, let him take the lead. That was all very well, but unlike the others I hadn't been involved in the impersonation nonsense or the dry run-through. My barrister didn't seem to care though, and neither did he seem to have much idea about my role in the alleged crime.

After taking the stairs up to the designated floor, I could see the other defendants and their families sitting outside the courtroom. Like me, Pete attended on his own. We were both keeping our wives well away from this depressing bullshit.

I hadn't told Pete anything about my interaction with Chapman and the intelligence guys. When he'd asked me about the meeting at the club, I simply told him it involved my business in Iraq and a highly confidential matter. Even now, Pete remained optimistic someone would rock up and tell us the case had been dropped. That probably wouldn't happen, but I hoped Chapman had found a way to snuff it out, for me at least.

During the hearing, the judge heard arguments for and against dismissing the case. The customs barrister outlined the Crown's case that a crime had clearly been committed and only a jury could decide if the defendants were guilty. Our defence barristers, led by the client's silk, argued it was all simply horseplay between business associates which had been misconstrued. At one point, the customs barrister started making a big deal about the dry run-through in Berkeley Square being crucial evidence. I called my barrister over.

'I wasn't even at the dry run-through. If that's the crucial part, then you need to tell them I wasn't there.'

Tentatively, he got to his feet when the judge allowed and tried to repeat the point I'd made. But he stumbled over the facts and got quickly shot down by the prosecution. He turned to give me a 'well I tried' look. Fucking useless. It felt like these big-time Charlies were playing a debating game with people's lives at stake.

I simmered with anger as I sensed the hearing slipping away from us, which would mean a jury trial in the coming weeks. Finally, both sides rested, and the judge said he would consider the arguments and reconvene the proceedings the following Monday to deliver his verdict. It was a surprise when he said the defendants were not required to attend. Fine. No way I'd be coming back to this circus if I didn't have to.

★

Monday afternoon I got the phone call from my solicitor Denis.

'The case has been dismissed. It doesn't mean you've been acquitted, and customs could still prosecute with new evidence. As it stands though, the court case is over.'

I had no idea whether Chapman had been involved in this decision or not. Regardless, it felt like an immense weight had been lifted from my shoulders. Now all I needed to do was patch things up with Claire and make a success of the business. Neither of those would be easy, but I'd be trying my damnedest to make both work out right.

CHAPTER 34

APPROACHING TURKEY/IRAQ BORDER
EARLY FEBRUARY 2005

'What do you mean we'll see him at the border? Where's my fucking passport?'

My third land crossing of an Iraqi border in twelve months wasn't running smoothly even though I was still some way from the Turkey-Iraq border crossing itself. Practice clearly didn't make perfect.

I was angry. Repeatedly demanding to see my passport every couple of minutes after handing it over to Ali, he'd kept promising me it wouldn't be going anywhere. Now apparently someone I didn't know was God knows where making the photocopies required for the border crossing. For some reason, this plan I hadn't agreed to entailed us meeting near the border some thirty minutes away before the return of our passports and the necessary copies.

'No, I want it back right now.'

Of all the ridiculous bullshit I had experienced recently, there was no way I intended to risk losing my passport like this. But it was too late; we were now committed to this course of action because we couldn't get hold of our mystery fixer on the phone.

'He'd better fucking be there!' I slammed the door shut harder than intended after jumping back into the car.

Although I was clearly furious, Ali seemed to take it all in his stride. He appeared confident we'd both see our passports again in Silopi, even though he admitted he'd never met this fixer before.

'He'll be there, don't worry. The taxi driver knows him very well.'

I wasn't reassured, but it was done now. Against my express wishes, but it was done.

Nearly an hour later my passport was back in my hands as promised and Ali had the bundle of copies needed to get us through both the Habur Gate on the Turkish side and the Ibrahim Khalil border crossing on the Iraqi/Kurdish side. To his credit, he didn't have an 'I told you so' look on his face when he handed my passport back as we made our way the last mile or so to the border.

Perhaps it was because we'd upset their mid-morning coffee break that the Turkish border officials were sloth-like in the processing of our passports and forms. It took over two hours of to-ing and fro-ing between the various offices within the Habur Gate complex before we finally had Turkish exit visa stamps in our passports and the surly officials allowed us to proceed to the Iraqi side.

After the frustrations of our progress up to then, I had little hope the Iraqi officials at Ibrahim Khalil would be an improvement. Ali had shrugged it off and practically bounced with excitement as he got closer to setting foot on his home soil again.

We filed into the visa office behind the taxi driver and handed over our passports with the Iraqi visas we had spent so much effort acquiring in London.

The officer behind the desk took one look at them, smiled, and said in perfectly understandable English, 'You don't need this. Everyone is welcome to Kurdistan.' He then spoke to Ali in increasingly faster and boisterous Kurdish until eventually he called for glasses of chai all round.

Whilst I was keen to get going, Ali became the life and soul of the visa office as he engaged in animated exchanges with all the officers and guards. I heard the mention of 'Israeli' and queried Ali about it.

'He asked if you were an Israeli.'

'Why an Israeli? My British passport is over there.'

'In Iraq, they think every foreigner is working for the Israelis. Up here they don't care though. The Israelis are like the Kurds, surrounded by enemies and hated by Arabs.'

That finally explained what the guys in the car had been on about in Basra. Even here, with my British passport being processed in front of me, I was still asked about links with Israel.

After a glass of chai and ten minutes of Ali and the border officials joking together like old friends, we were back in the taxi and driving to the passenger pick-up and drop-off point, marked by a low white building in amongst the fences.

A few minutes later, the taxi was already on its way back across the border with new passengers as Ali bear-hugged a laughing, bald man in his late twenties. They kissed opposite cheeks at least four times, speaking over each other in Kurdish as they did so. Then they broke apart and slapped each other on the back. The shaven-headed guy's smiling eyes turned to me and he spoke Kurdish in my direction.

'This is Dara, my brother. He says welcome to Kurdistan.'

'Tell him it's great to be here. So, another brother?'

Ali looked back at Dara and put his arm round his waist. 'Not my actual brother, but my *brother*, you get me?' – and without waiting for my reply – 'He's my cousin and we grew up together in Suli. Now he is Peshmerga.'

Dara wore casual trousers and a shirt rather than a military uniform although he did have a sidearm in a holster on his belt. The two other men with him were more clearly soldiers; both wearing khaki military-style clothing, topped with chest webbing and carrying AK-47s. The younger man with dark hair greeted me in English with a 'Hello' as I looked over at them. The older of the two men had sandy-coloured hair and blue eyes. He smiled at me and spoke something in Kurdish I didn't understand. I nodded and said hello in response.

'Hamza is from a village where they all have hair and eyes like you.' Ali laughed and repeated his comment in Kurdish for the benefit of the others. 'His daughters have blondie hair and blue eyes. From Alexander time. You know, Alexander the Great.'

I launched into a round of handshakes.

'I'm John, it's really good to meet you all. Thank you for coming to pick me up.'

Neither Dara nor Hamza spoke any English and the other guy only a few words, so Ali switched effortlessly between English and Kurdish to keep the conversation flowing. We climbed into a top of the range Toyota Land Cruiser. The dark-haired guy driving, Dara in the front passenger seat, and Ali next to me in the back. Hamza jumped into the rear of the SUV and positioned himself on one of the bench seats.

Dara looked at me, circled his finger, and said, 'Monica.'

'Monica?' I turned to Ali. 'What does that mean?'

He and Dara spoke briefly in Kurdish before Ali reverted to English.

'Monica is the name for the car. All these types of Land Cruisers are called Monica here. After Monica Lewinsky. You know, with Bill Clinton. They like her and they think the car is beautiful like she is.'

I nodded. 'Okay, Monica. That's going to be easy to remember.'

'Monica,' repeated Dara smiling, and he turned back to face the front, spoke to the driver, said 'Mr John' quietly to himself and we set off south.

The topography in northern Iraq was a continuation of the terrain we'd passed through as we'd driven south from Diyarbakir; snow-capped mountain peaks, craggy gorges, and large hills in the border area, which eventually rolled into smaller hills and undulating terrain as we travelled further south. The mountains always stretched away on our left as we drove; an epic landscape which merged into Turkey to the north and then Iran to the east as we progressed in an arc through the northern reaches of Kurdistan Region territory near Zakho and Duhok, down to the east of the regional capital Erbil, and onwards towards our destination, the city of Sulaimaniyah.

In the late afternoon we descended along a winding road from yet another craggy peak and arrived at a small collection of restaurants and shops. A kilometre away, behind a large dam, sunlight glistened off the surface of a large expanse of blue water.

'That's Dukan Lake,' said Ali. 'The dam provides electricity for Suli, so everyone is happy when the lake is full. We'll have something to eat here and then drive the last forty-five minutes. Do you want to wash your hands?'

After using the sink in the outside bathroom, we joined the others in a glass-fronted restaurant. The plastic tablecloth and functional chairs gave it the feel of a school canteen. Even before we ordered, a waiter laid out several starters, dips, and portions of hot flatbread across the table. I'd already viewed the grisly toilet block, so I opted for the safe bet of chicken, rice and beans. Unsure of what facilities would be available at our destination, I intended to stick to foods that minimised the chances of a stomach upset.

As we ate, I caught fellow diners and the waiters looking in my direction. I hadn't seen any other Westerners since leaving Istanbul on the flight to Diyarbakir the previous day and I gathered foreigners were a rare sight. But everyone seemed friendly enough. Conversations flowed readily across the tables between seemingly unrelated groups of customers, including ours.

On the drive from Dukan Lake towards Sulaimaniyah, the high ground loomed large and menacing to our left. Snowbound peaks lined the route, appearing to guard the city as we reached the outskirts. We joined a three-lane ring road, but instead of heading into the city we drove up the slopes to the east.

Snow covered the hillside as we turned into a largely empty parking area near the top and I realised they had brought me to see the view. Sulaimaniyah lay spread out on the floor of the valley down below us as though it were a giant's map. The city itself had no high-rise buildings, apart from one tall, dark smudge in the centre, at the end of a scar of a road cutting through the city's heart.

'What's that tall building there, in the centre?'

After conferring with Dara, Ali replied, 'The Sulaimaniyah Palace Hotel. The best hotel in the city. It's where foreigners usually stay although he says it's not very nice. Don't worry though, you'll be staying at our family house. Come on, it's cold, let's go.'

I stole a few more moments looking across the untainted peaks and valleys. As I thought of Hamza and his village of Alexander the Great's descendants, the wind whispered with the distant tramp of marching feet from the armies of ancient empires. I'd never been here before, but a sense of belonging emerged when I turned and saw my eager new Kurdish comrades waiting on my return to the car.

CHAPTER 35

SULAIMANIYAH, IRAQ – FEBRUARY 2005

Ali hadn't been back to the family home since 1991. It stood on a large plot in the Rzgari district of Sulaimaniyah City, just off the ring road, or 'North Circular' as Ali called it after the similar road in North London. An old couple lodged as tenants in a self-contained section of rooms on the upper floor. The rest of the two-storey house and upstairs balcony remained unoccupied and unused. There wasn't any furniture or appliances, but Dara and the boys went off to collect some basics to get us through the night.

With no electricity due to one of the frequent power cuts, we warmed ourselves from an oil heater stood in the middle of an old rug, the heater doubling as our light source. And we now had a gas hob with a refilled gas canister for the kitchen. We didn't need to fire it up though because our friends had also returned with bread and hot food made by the wife of Dara's brother, a Peshmerga general.

Despite our meagre surroundings, the food tasted great and laughter bounced off the walls of the empty house as we all dug in with our fingers. The teapot simmered on top of the heater as we finally settled down for the night with a couple of blankets each on top of the rug. It wasn't the Ritz, but I soon fell into a deep, contented sleep.

★

General Rashid was revered by his brother Dara and by the men who served under him. His reputation as a fearsome warrior commander had been honed during many skirmishes with Saddam's forces, most recently alongside US military advisors during the 2003 war. In a series of swift engagements, they'd defeated the Iraqi army units based in the vicinity and eradicated the Islamic jihadists Ansar al-Sunna from their nearby border enclave.

He stood only 5'6" in his stockinged feet yet projected a commanding presence and radiated confidence. His eyes were alive with intelligence and a playful smile flickered under his thick, black moustache. Wearing traditional Kurdish clothes, consisting of baggy grey-green trousers, topped off with a matching martial-type jacket and cummerbund, this man epitomised how I'd imagined a Peshmerga general would look. He didn't speak a word of English, but his friendly manner transmitted genuine warmth.

'The General welcomes you into his home,' translated Ali.

'Please thank him for his hospitality and tell him I'm honoured to meet him and be a guest in his house.'

After some conferring in Kurdish and a smiling nod my way from the General, Ali replied on his behalf, 'He says you're welcome. His home is your home.'

After leaving my shoes outside the front door beside everyone else's, the General showed me and Ali into a large sitting room with five sofas arranged round the edges to provide comfortable seating for a dozen people. A large flat screen television showed a local Kurdish news channel with the sound turned down low.

Four men including Dara were sat in the room and all stood up as we entered. I gathered the youngest person in the room was the General's eldest teenage son and the two older gentlemen in Kurdish dress were lunch guests. One of the older guests greeted me in broken English and I took the opportunity to engage him in conversation. Unfortunately, we couldn't get much further than the weather, my nationality, and how great it was to meet each other.

The General's son and Dara both disappeared for a few minutes before returning with bottled water and glasses of chai for all the guests. Dara was noticeably quieter than he had been when play-fighting and joking with Ali the previous day.

'It's because he respects his brother so much,' answered Ali matter-of-factly when I asked about it.

Before long, we were sat cross-legged on the deep rug around a large plastic picnic blanket covered in bowls and plates of food, cans of Coca-Cola and 7 Up, and a large steaming central dish of rice bedecked with chicken legs and wings. I had to be careful not to eat too much of the moreish bread in case I became full up and unable to eat the volume of food my hosts deemed satisfactory. The bread in Kurdistan was thinner than in Baghdad and southern Iraq, so a little more forgiving. I paced myself as the General frequently offered me plates and bowls across the blanket, eventually taking it upon himself to place food onto my plate. Perhaps he thought I was just being polite by not digging in, but in fact I was already stuffed.

After attracting Ali's attention, I told him, 'Tell the General the food is great, but honestly I'm already full and can only finish what's on my plate. It's absolutely delicious though. Thank him very much.'

It didn't hurt to praise the food and, by implication, his wife's cooking skills. Although the General's young sons flitted into the room at various times, the only sign of his wife and daughters was the occasional sound of female voices and laughter drifting from another room in the house. Probably the kitchen from the amount of food being served.

Once dinner was finished and cleared away, and I was on about my fifteenth glass of chai for the day, the talk centred on the General and his various wounds. I'd forgotten Ali wouldn't have seen the General in over ten years. They had plenty to catch up on.

'I've told him about the doctors in Harley Street. You can get him a visa, so he can get a full check-up. He still has bullets inside and he was at Halabja when the gas came,' explained Ali.

Even though I'd been very clear with Ali about my background and the minimalist nature of the finances currently available, he spoke as though I'd be waving some big company wand to get visas issued and doctors' appointments arranged. I tried to appear positive while being as non-committal as possible.

'I'm sure if the General could get a British visa, then I could assist with making an appointment with a Harley Street doctor or a private hospital. I really don't know the current situation regarding visas though. I'll check and see what the process involves.'

If I thought that was the end of it, I was wrong. Two minutes later Dara came into the room carrying a large brown envelope and handed it to the General. He pulled out a series of X-rays and began pointing at white marks in the shoulders, arms, and chest.

'Those are the bullets,' said Ali from over my shoulder. 'Saddam's men they tried hard, but they couldn't kill him.'

After being handed the X-rays, I studied each one briefly while gently nodding my head. I didn't know what everyone expected me to say as they waited for my pronouncement.

'Okay. Yes, Harley Street is a good idea.'

It meant nothing, but the General and the other guests wore big smiles as I handed the envelope back.

After an afternoon tour of the city which included a drive past the Sulaimaniyah Palace Hotel at my prompting, we returned to the General's house in the evening.

'The General doesn't drink, doesn't swear, doesn't smoke, and doesn't look at women apart from his wife, but he does like to play cards,' announced Ali as a deck of playing cards appeared.

After teaching me the basics of Kurdish blackjack, we began playing with bets of 1,000 dinar notes – about two-thirds of a dollar. The hours flashed by as the money flowed back and forth between us. I'd only had a few dinars, so Ali had bulked up my stake money. As the game broke up and we departed for home, the smiling General spoke to Ali.

'He asks if we can play tomorrow night. Only this time you bring some money.'

I'm not a great gambler or card player, but I laughed as I told them it was game on.

Conscious I hadn't checked the email account on my first night, I set up the BGAN on the balcony wall, adjusting it to the direction and angle of the nearest satellite. At the other end of a six-foot cable, me and my laptop were positioned on a white patio table and chairs. Once the Internet connected, I checked the account the spooks had set up: nothing. After checking my own emails, I packed everything up and returned downstairs.

CHAPTER 36

The next couple of weeks passed by with visits to various of the great and the good of Sulaimaniyah and trips to places of interest such as the Azmar Mountain which towered over the city, the museum at Saddam's old intelligence headquarters, left unchanged since the day the Kurds rose up and took the city back in 1991, and a visit to the museum in Halabja commemorating the victims of the 1988 gas attack.

Dara and Hamza were ever-present alongside a revolving selection of drivers. We'd meet for a late breakfast and then head out for the day. The first time we'd called in at one of the basic little outlets serving breakfast, I'd enjoyed a white, crusty, cream-type dish along with my warm bread and hot chai.

'What's this stuff called?' I asked Ali, as I shovelled in another mouthful.

'Err, it's... I don't know the right name. It's the... fat stuff.'

'Fat stuff. Okay, well I love it.'

So, the 'fat stuff' became our breakfast staple and we never tried to find out any other name for it.

Alongside the cultural visits and trips to prominent buildings and landmarks, I engaged in several meetings with business people and politicians, trying to assess the opportunities available for international companies. Hotels, housing, power, banking, water networks, transport infrastructure – the list encompassed nearly everything needed to develop a city.

But did they have any money available to fund new projects or were the local and regional governments both hoping international investment would provide the crucial funding? Unfortunately, it appeared to be very much the latter. Investment opportunities were readily identifiable but paid contracts nowhere near as much. Turkish, Iranian, and Lebanese companies were investing in strength but trying to convince a British or other Western company to risk money in northern Iraq would be a stiff challenge.

★

There had been a few blackjack games at both Ali's and the General's house, culminating in a wild night that saw me lose nearly $1,000 on a sure thing.

'All, all,' I said with a theatrical wave of my hand. Every dollar I'd brought along now piled in the middle of the rug as we sat on the floor at the General's place after an evening of balanced wins and losses.

The General spoke to Ali who then translated. 'He says you shouldn't bet like that. He has good cards, so don't risk all your money.'

He'd tried that once before and been bluffing. It wouldn't work a second time. 'Mate, tell him I advise he doesn't bet any more either. I have a great hand and don't want to upset him.'

Ali communicated my answer, and the General looked at me, matched my bet, and turned over his cards. Fuck. He hadn't been bluffing this time. Over $950 of my money sat in a large pot in the middle, along with more than another $1,000 from the other two. Ali had wisely folded early.

Not that he had, but I considered making a joke about the General cheating before deciding it might not translate well. I'd got carried away and bet funds I couldn't afford to lose. As we prepared to leave I was still shell-shocked by my stupidity. I put my shoes back on outside the front door and nodded at the armed Peshmerga guarding the gate. He snapped to attention. The General walked in front of me with a bundle of notes in his hand.

'He says he can't take your money from you under his own roof,' said Ali following behind him.

The other times we'd played it had been for pin money, but clearly winning big in his own house made the General feel uncomfortable.

'So next time he says we play at our house,' Ali said as we all laughed and shook hands and bid *kwarfis* (goodbye). My laugh was both embarrassed and grateful. I'd tried to refuse the lost money, but the General had insisted.

Even though we hardly spoke a word of each other's language, thanks to Ali, the General and I were getting on famously.

★

Apart from one night when the BGAN refused to connect to the satellite, I checked the spooks' email account every night. No message in the drafts. It might be weeks, months, years or never, before a chance arose for them to get Abu Saif – if he was indeed this 'Shadow Emir' Chapman had mentioned. And I'd received no further contact from Faris in Baghdad or Al-Nura in Dubai.

★

Claire had been disappointed when I told her I wouldn't make it home for Becky's birthday.

'I'm sorry. This might be my last chance to make things work in Iraq. It's going well if slowly. Although I'm starting to get some important meetings lined up.'

The truth: I was thoroughly enjoying my time in Kurdistan.

'It's like Surrey, but with mountains,' I said, trying to reassure her that security wasn't an issue.

The local government and security forces were absolutely committed to keeping the region secure, especially for visitors. No foreigner had been killed by violence since the 2003 war and they were determined to keep it that way. I still hadn't seen another Westerner

247

since I'd arrived, apart from a flash of a well-fed face in a passing vehicle, so my safety was probably a high priority for the security forces and their street level agents on every road.

'They won't let anything happen to you,' Ali said. 'Of course, they are watching all the time. It's very safe here. You've seen it for yourself.'

It helped we were always accompanied on our travels by three Peshmerga and had two AK-47s back at the house and a 9mm handgun in the glove compartment, all supplied by General Rashid. Truth be told, I had few accurate details of the current threat environment in the region. It was low-level compared to the rest of Iraq, but the locals appeared to feel any admission of credible threats revealed a slight on their capabilities. They kept up the mantra all was safe and well – even while Ali boasted about arrests of suspected militants and the seizure of suspect vehicles. An element of active threat clearly existed, so I elected to maintain vigilance against the likely indicators of hostile surveillance and targeting. Not easy when people already watched me everywhere I went.

I was fairly satisfied we were equipped to respond to an armed attack, although it took a lot of persuasion for my hosts to maintain measures to counter the threat that concerned me most: our vehicles being left unattended and booby-trapped. Either the driver or Hamza had to stay monitoring the vehicle while the rest of us conducted our business, drank chai in cafes, or ate in restaurants. After three or four days, it became a set routine and the pout on the face of whoever got stuck with the vehicle disappeared.

On Thursday morning at the end of the third week, after tucking into my new favourite breakfast of fat stuff, bread, and chai, we all climbed into the Monica and headed for a meeting with the Director of Sulaimaniyah Municipality, referred to by Ali as the mayor. His offices stood on the main Salim Street in the centre of the city, a kilometre down the road from the Palace Hotel. With my best suit deployed, I hoped the meeting would herald a discussion about funded and available city contracts requiring international expertise, and for which they might accept the higher fees that would entail.

Dara, Hamza, and the driver stayed with the car as Ali and I checked in our phones at the security reception. Receipt tickets in hand, we climbed the stairs and joined a horde of locals waiting to get an audience with the mayor or one of his minions. Having a suit, fair hair, and blue eyes got me an automatic fast-pass to the front of the queue, seemingly with the acquiescence of the locals who parted like the Red Sea and ushered me through.

Ali introduced me, and we shook hands with the mayor as they traded Kurdish greetings.

'Welcome, welcome. Please, take a seat. I'm sorry but my English is not so strong,' said the mayor.

'Your English is very good. Much better than my Kurdish or Arabic.'

'You speak Arabic?'

'Only a few words. I must work harder to learn both Kurdish and Arabic.'

Although I thought he spoke English quite well, the mayor preferred to have our conversation translated by Ali.

He expressed his thanks for my visit, and I got the impression I might be the only independent British businessman without regional roots to have visited in recent times. However, our discussion never ranged into any specifics regarding contracts and business. This was a 'getting to know you' type meeting.

The sense that Western businessmen were a rare sight was reinforced by the sudden appearance of a television camera and reporter in the middle of our conversation. There went the low profile. They didn't request a filmed interview, but I answered a few questions from the reporter after they'd filmed the visual footage for that night's piece on the Kurdsat news channel.

After collecting our phones as we left the mayor's office, I noticed neither my UK mobile nor my local AsiaCell Nokia had any signal. Reception was usually reliable in the city, so I didn't expect to wait long for it to reappear. Dara and the boys were waiting outside to give us a lift down the road to the under-construction Salim Shopping

Centre, where we were due to meet with the owner to view some offices on the second and third floors.

'It's a nice day, so I think I'll walk down,' I announced, conscious I wasn't getting enough decent exercise and glad of the fresh air after spending all morning in cigarette smoke-filled rooms. It was only a few hundred metres down to the new building and I'd have to cross the busy road, but better than nothing.

Ali's face projected confusion. 'You can't walk,' he said.

'Why not?'

'Well, what will everyone think? They expect you to be driven in a nice car. You're a businessman. This isn't London.'

Ali was more sensitive about all that than the locals. I very much doubted they gave a monkey's how I rocked up to meetings or left afterwards.

'I don't care. I'm going to walk. You coming?' I turned away from the car and set off towards the gate.

Ali caught up twenty metres down the road, slightly out of breath. He tried to light a cigarette on the move and complained about my lack of cultural awareness.

'You shouldn't do things like this. It confuses them.'

He wasn't happy, but it might have been more to do with the fact he had to walk with me. I don't know why – the sun in the clear blue winter sky had reduced the early chill to a pleasant and refreshing nip.

'Well they'd better get used to it, mate. I'm sure they couldn't care less anyway.'

I waved away a young lad trying to sell me chewing gum. The stuff I'd tried the day before tasted like they made it from old car tyres.

The new office building looked old and tired already, and it wasn't even finished yet. However, it stood in a decent location on the main city road, with shops on the ground floor and basement levels, plus a row of shops, restaurants, and food carts on the opposite side of the road, including a pizza place and a beer shop. A secure underground car park with resident car wash was also mooted. The offices would have Internet twenty-four hours per day, apart from an hour at lunchtime for some reason. Maintenance perhaps. And the rent would be reasonable. This was one for the shortlist if I decided to set up shop out here.

It was after midday when we finished looking round and Ali was already suggesting we should go for lunch. I checked my phones again and saw an SMS had arrived on my UK number.

Your father is ill – going to the hospital to visit him TODAY at 2.00pm.

I'd checked the email draft folder late the previous night, so I hadn't missed anything. The content surprised me: today at 2.00pm. Maybe events had moved so quickly it needed a fastball. I considered calling the contact number Chapman had provided in London.

All phone calls on the regular GSM mobile network could be easily monitored by all and sundry, but I did have the sat phone in my daysack. Monitoring satellite phone calls required sophisticated interception equipment most countries didn't possess, which made them inherently more secure. But rather than faffing about, I judged it easier to turn up to the nearby RV location at 2.00pm and see what happened.

'Ali, I need to go to a meeting at the Palace Hotel at one-thirty.'

Ali briefly considered my statement. 'No, we don't have a meeting there. The next one is at Nawroz Park at four o'clock.'

Mr Nawroz was a leading local businessman who also owned a park with some animals and a few children's rides. We'd met the previous day and he was keen to show me his plans for redevelopment and expansion of the park.

'You're probably going to have to cancel Mr Nawroz. I've just received the message about an urgent meeting at the Palace and I have to go.'

I lifted my head and gave him a thin smile after pressing send on my confirmation reply.

Please keep me informed.

Ali started grumbling about cancelled appointments and mysterious meetings.

I tapped my watch: 'One-thirty, mate. British time.'

He brightened up when I then pointed out that meant we needed to get lunch now.

By telling him it was 1.30pm I had a fighting chance of getting there by 1.45pm. I wanted to be early to scout the location and make myself comfortable. On my previous visit I'd been surprised to find the coffee tasted quite decent. The 'Nescafe' might even have been the real thing.

CHAPTER 37

It was 1.40pm by my watch as the guard rolled back the wheeled security spikes at the vehicle entrance to the Sulaimaniyah Palace Hotel and our driver nosed the vehicle down the narrow passageway and into the car park.

As the primary hotel used by international visitors and regional politicians, the Palace would likely feature on any terrorist target list for the city. Concrete T-walls surrounded the front of the building facing the main road and the only vehicular access was the way we'd arrived.

The car park was shared with the adjacent two-storey office building which housed Nokan, the ruling political party's commercial arm. It was no surprise they took the cream of the local contracts and I'd therefore already met with the Nokan head of operations during my previous visit to the hotel site a few days earlier.

'I come in with you?' asked Ali.

'No mate. I need to go to this one on my own. It's sensitive and they won't allow you to join in.'

I was trying to be diplomatic; I knew Ali would be unhappy because he didn't have an invite. It might have been easier if he and the guys left me there to get on with it, but I preferred them to stick around at first, until I knew who I was dealing with.

'I don't know how long it will take but once I get an idea, I'll let you know. If I can't see you, I'll call you. I'm sure you won't mind going to grab a chai somewhere if it drags on.'

Considering the amount of time spent waiting for other people in this city, I was irritated by Ali's obvious impatience about the one meeting I'd arranged in all the weeks we'd been here.

Once inside the rear hotel entrance, I passed through a metal detector, which beeped due to the kit in my daysack. The security guard made as though to look interested but slumped back into his chair after I issued a brisk 'Hello' and kept walking. I nodded a greeting to the male receptionist and scanned the lobby as I approached, checking for any likely contact from the spooks.

A couple of Middle Eastern gentlemen in smart suits sat on decorated, stiff-backed, wooden sofas and a Westerner waited near the lifts on the other side of an open archway. Apart from them the lobby appeared empty. From the front of the reception desk, I cast my eyes around again just in case. I couldn't help smiling when I spotted a familiar face observing my arrival, sat in the far corner with his back to the wall. He already had a cup in front of him, so I ordered myself a Nescafe and made my way over to where Roper was sitting.

★

Roper told me a meeting involving the Shadow Emir was believed to be imminent in the northern city of Hawija, about sixty kilometres west of Kirkuk. Other than that, he was scant on details.

'We'll both get a more complete brief once we get to the base,' he said, checking his watch, 'and we need to get on our way there now.'

He looked frazzled compared to the previous time we'd met but his eyes were alive, clearly more at home with fieldwork and a chance to ditch his London suit for trail boots, cargo trousers, and a polo shirt.

I glanced down at my suit and tie. 'Well I need to change out of this before I'm going anywhere, especially somewhere like Kirkuk. If we cut down to the North Circular, we can swing a right and our place is on the way. If you follow our car, we can go from there. How many of you are there?'

'Just me, a driver, and an English-speaking Peshmerga officer,' he said with a rueful look. 'I only landed in Kirkuk three hours ago, so not much time to get organised yet.'

That explained the frazzled look. Kirkuk Air Base was approximately 100 kilometres to the west. Most of the route was under the secure control of the Peshmerga but closer to Kirkuk the threat level rose significantly.

I digested that for a moment.

'I've got Peshmerga with me. Why don't we take both vehicles to Kirkuk? It shouldn't be a problem.'

Roper looked surprised and perhaps even impressed. 'Okay, let me see who you've got with you and we'll take it from there.'

He started to rise just as my coffee arrived but quickly smiled and sat back down.

'You've got time for that coffee though,' he said, as his hand reached over and grabbed the little chocolate that came with it. 'I haven't had time to eat and I'm starving.'

★

The reception desk conjured up a tired-looking chicken salad sandwich which Roper munched on heartily as we walked to the vehicle. Ali, Dara, and Hamza chatted as they leant on it, and the driver sat inside singing along to the strains of a Kurdish ballad being piped out of the car stereo. When Roper signalled with his hand, a uniformed guy climbed out of a similar Land Cruiser a few spaces down and came over to join us. The driver cut the music as I made the introductions.

'This is Ali and this is Dara, a Peshmerga captain. His commander is also his brother, General Rashid.'

There was no recognition on Roper's face when I mentioned the General's name, but his accompanying Peshmerga officer nodded as I spoke. Ali moved straight in with an enthusiastic handshake and a gushing introduction in English, while Roper's Peshmerga officer spoke with Dara in Kurdish. It was clear from the off they knew each other.

'Ali, I need to go to Kirkuk. Can you guys come along so we have two vehicles for the journey?'

'Kirkuk? No, that's not a good idea.'

'Mate, I have to go to Kirkuk.' This wasn't up for debate.

Dara cut in with an injection of Kurdish that left Ali with a thoughtful look on his face. He grinned at me as he lifted a phone to his ear.

'So, what did he say?' I asked Ali.

'He says we're taking you to Kirkuk. He's already agreed it with the major there. It's his friend.' Ali didn't look particularly comfortable with the turn of events. 'What do you have to do in Kirkuk?'

'Don't worry about that. We just need to go to FOB Warrior. We might be there for a while though, so we're going to call into the house on the way now and pick up some gear. You need to take some overnight stuff and spare clothes.'

Ali's mode changed to despair. 'But how long? Tomorrow's Friday and we have a lunch invitation with the mayor. Dara needs to check with General Rashid first as well.'

Dara called over excitedly from his phone call and Ali's shoulders slumped. Despite his protests we were going to Kirkuk.

And it was the first I'd heard of lunch with the mayor.

'Look mate, this is something I have to do. Just call up and cancel anything you've arranged for the next couple of days.'

I had no idea what other treats might be in store, but they'd just have to wait.

★

Despite the busy road to Kirkuk we made decent time. Roper had insisted I travel in his vehicle, so Ali and the gang were right behind us as we cut through any hold-ups and checkpoints with our siren and flashing blue lights occasionally sweeping cars from our path. On a Thursday afternoon, people finished work early and hurried home for the Friday/Saturday weekend. We bypassed the checkpoint queues via the military lanes and arrived at Forward Operating Base (FOB) Warrior by four o'clock.

Once inside the base with temporary ID badges issued to me and my guys, we stopped in a parking area filled with military Humvees and a range of unmarked SUVs. While the Kurds and I stayed with the vehicles, Roper disappeared into a building 200 metres away that was a hive of activity. Numerous soldiers and airmen, mainly American, moved themselves and various bits of kit with a sense of urgency.

When he reappeared, Roper was accompanied by a mature, broad-shouldered, square-jawed man wearing chinos and an untucked, short-sleeve shirt. The unmistakable bulge of a holstered sidearm visible under the shirt.

'Has your guy got clearance?' the big man asked with an American accent as they drew closer.

'Developed Vetting to TS *(Top Secret)* level,' replied Roper as we met at the edge of the car park.

I'd been through the Developed Vetting process back in the late 90s, so knew how deep they checked your personal and financial background. It included interviews with personal referees to identify potential weaknesses and flaws.

My oppo Rob had been one of those interviewed for my DV and had caused some consternation when he said, 'Yes, John sometimes wears women's clothes,' in reply to a question. Apparently, his explanation that it was 'a bootneck thing' had required some further clarification before they moved on. He was referring to the occasional wild run ashore (night out), where dozens of burly marines would dress in the skimpiest of women's clothing, at least until some joker yelled 'naked bar' or similar.

It had been mentioned in my final interview with a smile, but there was no way I would have passed the DV clearance these days with my recent history – both my dealings with the criminal justice system and my financial situation would have put paid to that.

Judging by Roper's conspiratorial glance, I suspected either a few corners had been cut and rules bent, or the shiny new DV certificate didn't even exist.

The American stuck out a big hand. 'Joe Holmes, Task Force 145.'

'John Pierce.' I turned my head towards Roper and indicated in his direction. 'On temporary attachment with these guys.'

'Well let's get you up to speed. We only have a couple of hours until we need to be set. This way.' The American led the way into the building he and Roper had exited a short while before.

Roper called over to his guys and told them they could go to the DFAC (Dining Facility) provided they were back at the cars in thirty minutes.

'And take these guys with you.' He motioned towards Ali and the boys. 'But make sure one of you stays with the vehicles at all times, okay?'

We left the Kurds debating who should stay with the vehicles as we walked over to the temporary operational headquarters of Task Force 145 and its attached assets. Joe led us into a briefing room adorned with maps of Iraq, particularly the area of northern Iraq in the vicinity of Kirkuk. He drew our attention to a map of the area west of Kirkuk and said that multi-sourced intelligence indicated a meeting of high-level insurgent leaders would take place either tonight or tomorrow night in northern Iraq.

Although the meeting location wasn't 100% confirmed, there was every indication it would be in the insurgent stronghold city of Hawija, approximately sixty kilometres west of Kirkuk. Hawija and its rural environs was a hotbed of Sunni militancy and a very difficult area in which to operate successfully.

'Due to the extremely hostile nature of nearly all the local inhabitants, it's too dangerous for *you* to move forward into the AO *(Area of Operations)*,' said Holmes, nodding towards me.

'We also need to keep the footprint on the ground as light as possible. The risk of compromise in this area is very high, but the target is considered important enough that we already have the green light to take a shot at him. Last night a TF145 team infiltrated the city and set up an OP *(Observation Post)* in the industrial sector of the city which gives them "eyes on" the anticipated meeting location.'

Holmes used a pointer to indicate the location on the map. 'The team has set up two cameras on separate satellite relays which are transmitting clear images back to the TOC *(Tactical Operations Centre)* here.'

He then spoke directly to me.

'Your role is to positively ID the key target known as the Shadow Emir, Abu Saif al-Tikriti. Alongside you will be two people from our intelligence team. Unless you identify your boy, or they identify another comparable High Value Target, the operation will be stood down. We cannot afford to risk compromising our covert sources by using such highly sensitive intelligence in this direct way unless the pay-off is deemed acceptable. If you see Abu Saif, you need to be one hundred per cent sure it's him. Understood?'

No pressure then. I just hoped these transmitted images would be clear enough for me to be certain one way or the other.

'Yep, understood.' I tried to sound more confident than I felt.

Holmes then went on to provide an overview of the assets being deployed on the mission, including a dedicated surveillance drone and a squadron of Black Hawk helicopters ready to transport the support and extraction teams into the target area, before whisking everyone and their hooded prisoners back here to FOB Warrior. The higher value targets could probably expect a plane ride to years of incarceration with Uncle Sam.

'Although you'll have PID'd Abu Saif by video image, it would behoove us to have you confirm his ID face-to-face as soon as he's back here.'

I wasn't impressed with the thought that Abu Saif would know it was me who had identified him. I'd be looking over my shoulder for the rest of my life, which might prove to be a lot shorter with that plan.

'Abu Saif knows who I am. I'm happy to do anything that's needed to help get this guy, but he knows too much for me to do it face-to-face like this.' I gestured between us. 'Will it be a two-way mirror or something?'

Holmes considered my question.

'Sure. Makes sense. When I say face-to-face, it might be via close video link anyway. If it needs to be in the flesh, then we'll be using the suites with mirrors. If not here, then somewhere else.'

Thank fuck for that. I liked this guy already.

The American continued. 'We're on standby from eighteen hundred hours. You and the intel guys need to have camp beds near the live feed screens in the TOC. Although we'll have video playback capability, time will be of the essence once the targets appear. The helos will take twenty minutes from a firm 'GO' to get the extraction team on the ground. We need those targets identified ASAP to make this work.'

As Roper and I went back to the cars to grab our kit and let the Kurds know they needed to scavenge for a place to sleep tonight, I tried to find out some more about Holmes and his people.

'So, what's the deal with this TF145? Is it an American special forces unit? How come we're involved with them?'

Roper looked across at me. 'It's actually a combined US and British special forces and intelligence group, tasked with hunting down high value insurgent targets. The team on the ground in Hawija are from Hereford *(SAS)*. There are a few Brits knocking about, we just haven't bumped into them yet.'

I pressed further. 'How about Holmes? Delta, SF, Agency or what?'

Roper stopped and turned towards me. 'Does it matter? I'm sure you can imagine the various units and agencies involved in this kind of set-up. British and American. Whatever their backgrounds, they're part of this Task Force right now.'

'Yeah sure, I just wondered.'

I was intrigued, but Roper was right. It didn't make any difference which three-letter outfit the people in this Task Force came from. For these guys, it was all about completing the mission successfully.

CHAPTER 38

The TOC was busy but surprisingly quiet, as though a fierce librarian prowled ready to pounce on anything livelier than muted conversations and the hum of electronic equipment. The peace occasionally broken by the crackle of radio transmissions – the latest from the support and extraction teams as they checked comms between themselves and the 'Night Stalkers' Black Hawk squadron who would be their ride for the mission.

My eyes nearly popped out of my head when I met the two intelligence personnel from TF145. Dexter struck me as a smart, funny guy right from the off, but it was his colleague, Katie, who took my breath away. She was stunningly attractive, with long blonde hair tied up in a messy ponytail and the most entrancing light-blue eyes I'd ever seen. She looked as though she was modelling her combat uniform with curves that could be politely termed 'distracting' to say the least. To go with it, she came across as down-to-earth, funny, and intelligent.

'I think you have a new fan,' Dexter said. My face must have betrayed my thoughts.

As Katie's eyes flicked over to mine and a mischievous smile played on her lips, my cheeks warmed up.

'Sorry, I was just surprised. You're…'

'What?' asked Katie, clearly revelling in my discomfort. My reaction probably similar to many other dumb-asses in these male-dominated environments.

'You're not quite what I was expecting. You're just very pretty for someone stuck in the dark here.'

Now it was her turn to blush, but she quickly countered with 'Shucks' in a syrupy voice and fluttered her eyelashes.

We all laughed to the disapproving glares of two operations officers stood nearby.

Dexter pulled me back on track. 'Let me take you through the equipment here and show you how to replay and refine the captured images.'

★

The tension was mounting in the TOC. Nearly 21:00 and no sign of any movement had been reported at the suspected meeting location. Joe and Roper were talking with an army major when Joe was summoned to a secure call. He looked thoughtful on his return.

'Update. Latest source intelligence reports the meeting will take place tomorrow night, but the location won't be Hawija, it will be Mosul. Exact location will probably be unknown until tomorrow, but anywhere in that city is going to be challenging.'

All this said calmly, but he seethed with frustration when he stopped by the Intel Section on his way out.

'We've got a goddamn team out there in Indian territory and now we're going to get zero time to prepare anything but a hasty plan for Mosul. And if this is a goddamn trap, then I'm going to personally string up the son of a bitch who set it.'

Rather than the previous excited tension, a more nervous atmosphere settled over the TOC; everyone concerned the original intelligence may have been falsely sown and the team on the ground in Hawija might face attack or ambush at any time. The decision was taken for the team to remain in situ at the OP until the early hours of the morning. It couldn't be discounted that the new intelligence might be wrong and the meeting could still take place in Hawija at any time. It was getting late, but Joe encouraged everyone to stay vigilant.

'Okay people, nothing's changed as far as the mission is concerned until the team move into the extraction phase. Let's keep concentrated on the task at hand.'

Despite the fears the Hawija meeting might be an elaborate misinformation ploy, the TF145 team extracted themselves successfully without compromise. Once the drone feed and Blue Force Tracker confirmed they'd moved out of the OP and cleared the industrial zone, I climbed into my lightweight sleeping bag on a camp bed and fell into a deep sleep. The last thing I saw before I closed my eyes was the tousled hair and serene face of Katie on the cot next door, but I was thinking about Claire.

★

I'd caught the tail end of breakfast at the DFAC and bumped into a bleary-eyed Ali and the rest of our ad-hoc Kurdish team. Everyone else looked bright-eyed and bushy-tailed, but Ali wasn't a morning person.

'So, can we go back to Suli now?' he asked.

'No mate. Things didn't work out last night. It sounds like we'll probably be trying again tonight.'

'Really?' Ali emitted a loud sigh as he dropped his head. Although when he raised his eyes again and spotted the copious breakfast selections, he perked up. 'Right, I'm getting some eggs.' He wasn't fat by any stretch, but he wore both his heart and his stomach on his sleeve.

Looking up from my piled plate, I saw Roper and signalled to him. After collecting his own pile of hot food, he came over and sat down.

'We need to be ready to move up to Mosul. A Chinook up to the airbase at FOB Marez. No move before twelve hundred hours. No final decision has been taken, but it looks as though we're going to try again tonight.'

'Okay. What about the guys?' I indicated Ali and the gang.

'Nabil will come with me for liaison with Peshmerga elements up there, but your guys can head back home.'

'I know someone who'll be happy with that.' I threw my eyes in Ali's direction.

Apprised of the plan, Nabil and Dara were soon deeply engaged in conversation.

Nabil said, 'Mr Tom, you should bring Dara with us. Him and General Rashid have important contacts with the Peshmerga in Eastern Mosul.'

'Can't you deal with that?' asked Roper.

'It's Friday and there's not much time. It would be much better if Dara is with me.' Dara whispered a message before Nabil added, 'Dara and Hamza.'

Friday is the holy day and the main day of the weekend in Iraq. Most people spend it with their families, so Nabil might have trouble raising any potential assistance in the short time frame available. Roper didn't need that explained to him. He understood the situation and the difficulties.

'Is it okay with him?' he asked Nabil.

'Yes, he's ready. And he's never been in a helicopter before.'

And judging by the excited look on Dara's face, he didn't want to miss the opportunity for a helo ride across the Nineveh plains to Mosul. I'm sure Roper realised he'd make a friend for life if he allowed him along.

'But what about me?' Ali had changed from wanting to go home to concern at missing out.

'You and the driver can head back home once you're finished here,' said Roper.

Ali looked at me for support, but I had no intention of trying to squeeze him into the plan. With Nabil able to translate, there was no requirement for him or the driver.

'Get back to Suli, mate, and I'll be in touch when we're all finished, okay?'

Ali expressed regret he'd miss the helicopter ride, but I'm sure he felt secretly glad to be going home. He didn't seem comfortable in the military environment, probably because he had little idea what was going on.

CHAPTER 39

MOSUL – FEBRUARY 2005

The TF145 TOC was being hastily reassembled at FOB Marez in Mosul when we arrived by Chinook in the early afternoon. Joe spotted us and came over as we entered the new temporary home in an aircraft hangar. I scoured the frantic activity and spotted Katie, who flashed me a smile as Joe took us into one of the offices, the walls filled with maps of Mosul city.

Joe partially extended a telescopic metal pointer with an embossed handle.

'We're working on the assumption we'll get the green light, but it's by no means definite. Given the lack of planning and preparation time, this is going to be far more hazardous than any of us would like. The one good aspect is the terrain and location are much more in our favour up here compared to Hawija.

'As you can see from the map, we're on the southern edge of the city and the Old City area here' – the pointer circled an area on the west bank of the river – 'is only three kilometres north of our current location. We have a lot of assets available which can quickly assist with the extraction and any clear-up that might be required.

'The difficulty is we might not know the exact meeting location until very late. It's not going to give us much time to conduct recon and move into position. We do already have local assets and surveillance teams on the ground in the city, but what I'm building up to is,' – Joe turned and chopped a meaty hand in my direction – 'I want you to deploy out into a forward staging location, and possibly even a direct OP, depending on how this thing rolls out.

'Our hasty plan involves you and the OP team moving to an RV point here.' The stick indicated a position on the southern outskirts of the Old City. 'The Baghdad bus station. From here it should be no more than one and a half klicks to any potential meeting location.'

Roper moved closer to the map and I followed suit.

'Dexter will be with you to identify other High Value Targets and Kate will remain at the TOC observing whatever live feeds we're able to get set up.

'Tom, I understand you've got two well-connected Kurds with you. Can you see if you can raise any support from that angle in the eastern part of the city and in the Old City itself if possible? Nothing too heavy, just friendly forces available on standby if required. Anything they can do on that side will be highly appreciated. And if you can get us any safe havens in the Old City then I'll get you a goddamn medal.'

'Roger that,' replied Roper. 'The guys are already setting up meetings with Peshmerga commanders. I'm trying to get them to come to us, but can we get a couple of vehicles in case we need to head out?'

'Sure, speak with Chris Collins after this and tell him what you need. If you have to go, then John here needs to remain. He's no good to us if you get stuck somewhere out in Mosul having tea with the locals as the meeting goes down.'

Chris Collins was Joe's number two and seemed like a guy who wasn't easily fazed. He listened to Roper's request. 'Sure, let me make a call.'

Before long, two battered twin-cab Toyota Hilux trucks arrived at Roper's disposal, along with a four-man escort team. Once the vehicles arrived, Roper, Nabil, Dara, Hamza, and the security escort jumped into them and disappeared into the city to meet with senior figures who weren't going to interrupt their Friday afternoon to come calling on us.

Because I was going out on the ground, they issued me with various kit and equipment: body armour, Kevlar helmet, medical kit including field dressings, morphine and QuickClot, and a Heckler &

Koch MK23 handgun and holster. I hadn't seen the .45 calibre HK handgun before, but I'd used plenty of other HK weapons in my time. Having a .45 rather than a 9mm provided better stopping power. If I did end up having to use the weapon, it would help make sure the targets stayed down if I hit them. I said nothing as I signed it out with the other kit, along with four 12-round magazines. If I was going to end up in the heart of Mosul, then a decent .45 was top of my list after being told I couldn't have an M4 rifle.

'We can't have too many people waving their dicks in the air if the shooting starts,' Joe had said as justification why I couldn't have the M4. 'But I've okayed a sidearm. Can't have you going in there naked.' He laughed as he patted me on the back.

Just after 1600 hours, a briefing convened in the middle of the horseshoe of containerised offices housing the TOC nerve centre. Joe issued a warning order to everyone that we were now all on fifteen minutes notice to move, with no move before 1630 hours.

'The meeting location is confirmed, and we have the green light to proceed. The target location is grid 38SLF330230, the Mosul Museum. Timings for the meeting are as yet unknown, but the intention is to move into our positions by eighteen hundred hours. Scratch all the hasty plan RV details. Covert teams are already identifying OP and surveillance locations although expect a requirement for vehicle-based surveillance posts. The target location is outside the Old City, which is to our benefit, but this is still a nasty neighbourhood.

'Everyone needs to be ready to abort the mission if the abort code is signalled. We don't have time to verify the intel to the degree we'd like, so let's all be careful out there and ready to notify the TOC at any sign of suspicious activity. And I mean anything. We don't have "pattern of life" knowledge in this area to work from, but you are the best of the best and we all need to be on our "A" game tonight.

'I don't like this kind of fastball any more than the rest of you, but we have a chance here to capture one or more serious al-Qaeda commanders and we have to take it. Team leaders, surveillance coordinators, and air liaison officers to my office for a planning meeting immediately on completion here. A set of orders will be issued by sixteen-thirty hours, but be advised that for some of you it may be a "bonnet brief". Time is against us.'

Joe and the assorted planners headed into the central TOC office as the briefing broke up. I walked back to my kit and checked it again, just to be sure I was ready for anything. Even before Joe had spoken, I'd known this might prove a difficult evening.

After the American assault against Falluja in November 2004, scores of displaced insurgent fighters had regrouped with the strong al-Qaeda Iraq (AQI) presence already in Mosul. The city had soon been rocked by a serious insurgent offensive which overran police stations and seized most of the western part of the city. Although the US 25th Infantry Division had counterattacked alongside Kurdish Peshmerga and regained control, most of the local police units had dissolved and the end state was more of a stalemate than a victory.

Mosul was AQI territory and this was going to be a difficult mission to complete without stirring up a hornets' nest. I don't know if anyone else thought the same, but images of the movie *Black Hawk Down* about the Battle of Mogadishu were running in my head. This was a different situation to the one the Americans had faced in Somalia in 1993, but there were enough parallels to make me really want that M4 rifle.

Bang on 16:30, I joined Dexter and a six-man US Special Forces team wearing bedraggled winter clothes for a mission briefing. The SF guys were all dark-haired and either sported beards or were heavily unshaven. Each man bulky to the point of looking fat due to the body armour, kit, and weapons under their locally sourced winter jackets. At least two appeared to have Middle Eastern heritage and chat passed back and forth in Arabic as I entered and sat down next to Dexter.

Like me, Dexter didn't fit the local profile as far as looks, but Mosul was more forgiving than further south because of the common sight of people with fairer hair and light-coloured eyes. I didn't want to go through a replay of Mohammed's 'mute cousin from Mosul' plan like in Baghdad the previous year, but that was pretty much how Dexter and I were going to have to play things. We both had shemaghs at the ready and wore local jackets over our equipment and body armour. Only carrying sidearms, our weapons were easily hidden compared to the rifles and M249 machine gun of the SF team.

Roper, Nabil, Dara, and Hamza were all still out on the ground enlisting the support of the local Peshmerga, so, for now at least, this was our team.

A map of the target area flashed up on the screen at the front of the room. A big, scruffy-looking man with wild hair and a full beard cut away from his conversation and stood up.

'Gentlemen, my name is Greg Summers and I'll be commanding Team BLUE 5 for today's mission. Due to time pressures, this will be an abbreviated set of mission orders. Prepare to move on completion of this briefing and no later than seventeen hundred hours. The attached intelligence personnel are John, there, from the UK, call sign GRAIL 1, and Dexter here, who we all know, call sign GRAIL 2.'

Greg outlined the mission. First, he used the map to describe the target area, which was less than three kilometres from where we were sitting. The main Mosul Museum building was rectangular-shaped, with the two shorter sides facing east and west. Its entrance on the eastern side faced a complex mess of a traffic junction. The western side had a car park leading to an access road which marked the edge of the museum property. On the north side was Al-Jamhuriya Street, a main thoroughfare with a central reservation and shops lining the opposite side. To the south was a square with park space containing unknown levels of trees and foliage. The Hurriya Bridge leading to East Mosul was only 400 metres east along Al-Jamhuriya Street. The immediate area was spacious when compared to the tight-knotted streets of the Old City, which began just a few hundred metres to the north and west.

Three four-man TF145 teams were already inserting in proximity to the target.

Team VIPER 1 would be in buildings fifty metres west of the museum across the access road, giving them eyes on the car park, the western side of the buildings, and down Al-Jamhuriya Street running along the northern side.

VIPER 2 would be in the rear of specially modified vehicles parked up between 100 and 200 metres to the east, with eyes on the entrance and the open ground in the square to the south.

The third team, VIPER 3, including me and Dexter, would be positioned in an apartment above a grocery shop across the road to the north, with eyes on the east-facing entrance less than seventy metres away.

Four further teams, designated BLUE 1 through 4, would cover four junctions which made up a square encompassing the target area, with each side of the square approximately 350 metres. These teams provided an outer cordon to ensure any insurgent movement in or out of the target area was monitored and curtailed if necessary. Any indications of compromise or an unfavourable tactical situation and the abort code could be issued. That code was 'FUMBLE'.

Finally, the assault force stood by, ready to pounce from the air in Black Hawk helicopters once they received the confirmation code Abu Saif and/or other High Value Targets were in the target building. The GO code word was 'TOUCHDOWN.' Once the TOC transmitted the code, it would be a matter of minutes before the assault teams would be landing outside the main entrance and abseiling onto the roof of the museum, dealing with any resistance and securing prisoners.

In support of all this activity were surveillance planes and drones, fast air (fighter bombers), green army units on standby, and an as yet unconfirmed level of Peshmerga support, ready if needed in the eastern half of the city, across the River Tigris.

Greg and his team would not be part of our OP team though. That team, VIPER 3, was already inserting into the apartment overlooking the museum entrance. Instead, Greg's BLUE 5 team were tasked with escorting me and Dexter to the OP, before they would take up position as a support team within the square cordon area.

Roper and our Kurds were at a Peshmerga command post on the other side of the river, deployed as a liaison team. Their TF145 escort team on the way back to take up a role as the second support team in the cordon area, call sign BLUE 6.

The Commander's intent was for everyone to be in position by 1800 hours, before the daily Islamic prayers of Maghrib due at that time and those of Isha just over an hour later. A hypnotic call to prayer would resonate at slightly different times from every mosque, summoning thousands of worshippers who would pour through the streets. The resulting noise and movement were expected to help conceal the presence of the TF145 forces.

It was vital the motley crew of TF145 operators blended into the city, monitoring for suspicious activity and ready to react if things went off kilter. But it was intended the assault teams would have extracted the prisoners and we'd all be returning to base before the insurgents knew what had hit them.

CHAPTER 40

Our two taxis moved smoothly in concert in the late afternoon traffic as we headed north into the heart of Mosul. They were being driven by the two Middle Eastern-born American SF soldiers, mine by Ricky (Tariq) and the other taxi with Dexter on board by Jordanian-born Moose (Mustafa). Greg sat in the commander's seat in front of me and another of his men, Neil, alongside me in the back. Dexter had a similar arrangement in the vehicle behind us, commanded by Greg's 2IC, Russ, otherwise known as 'Wolfman' on account of the thick hair covering his forearms and sprouting from under his shirt. The grey cloak of the late afternoon was drawing in and the Tigris over on our right flowed alongside with a murky malevolence.

Plenty of other taxis were in amongst the blaring horns and shouting drivers jostling their way into the city centre. Dexter's taxi overtook us at times and dropped back at others, our elastic connection hopefully invisible to those around us. My HK MK23 was made ready with the safety catch on. This was a completely different scenario to my recent trips to Iraq. Despite the exceptional professionalism of the TF145 guys, they operated in a dangerous world where many factors of risk and chance were outside their control, the potential for compromise a fact of life. How it was dealt with when it happened marked out the best guys from the rest.

Greg broke the silence in the vehicle. 'Target building entrance will come into sight one hundred metres to our left in… one hundred… fifty… target building left.'

We moved through the junction with the museum entrance visible over to our left. As we continued north to circle round to the drop-off point, I glanced over to the shop buildings on the opposite side of Al-Jamhuriya Street where VIPER 3 was already deployed. Soon after, we needed to force a left turn through the river of opposing traffic; our driver Ricky traded angry gestures and shouts with the other drivers as we edged our way through. After both vehicles had made the turn and closed up again, Greg gave the warning order.

'Drop-off three hundred and fifty metres, prepare to deploy.'

The city bus depot was a mass of people, buses, and interloping vehicles, somehow all managing to avoid colliding with each other.

'This junction is the Emergency RV,' Greg said before we turned left to head south down a narrow road towards the target area.

One hundred and fifty metres later we turned left at a crossroads and the taxi pulled over. 'This is the RV,' said Greg, opening the door and letting the initial swell of the call to prayer flood in, first from our left, then from distance ahead of us. I joined Greg and Neil on the broken pavement.

The streets were narrow with two and three-storey buildings left and right, although there was a main road just over a hundred metres immediately ahead – the same road we'd been driving north along three minutes ago before cutting left through the traffic and past the ERV. However, the three of us turned right down an empty side street after only forty metres, with Dexter and his two escorts spaced out and following. Ricky and Moose in the modified taxis had taken off to position themselves as rear cover and prepare to pick up the team and move to their support position once we were handed over to VIPER 3.

The soporific crescendo of the call to prayer from multiple mosques began to recede as a figure emerged from the shadows on the left. Adrenaline shot through my body as I anticipated more figures to emerge or flashes of gunfire to erupt, but Greg and the figure exchanged Arabic greetings before Greg urged me over.

'This is Shaun from VIPER 3. He'll take you into the OP. Good luck and see you at the RV once we're done.'

I nodded, and Shaun swept me through a small gate, with Dexter following quickly in my wake. We carefully navigated a rubbish-strewn yard where I spotted a broken bottle of Johnnie Walker Black Label whisky. Not their most expensive label, but a surprise to see it here in Central Mosul. I didn't imagine drink-fuelled get-togethers were encouraged. As we entered through a doorway into the building, we passed a figure with an M4 in his shoulder – another member of the team. Then up a flight of stairs and into a dark hallway. Shaun motioned for us to get down low as he opened a door and moved inside.

Considering the team only had minimal notice, the set-up and location was impressive. The front entrance of the museum visible right in front of us across the road about seventy metres away, with the building itself stretching away to the right, down Al-Jamhuriya Street.

Dexter checked the left-hand optic before moving aside so I could take a look. Fixed to a tripod, it was trained on the large museum entrance and gave an incredible close-up view of the door and the immediate surrounding area. As I lifted my head away from the scope, Dexter passed me a set of binoculars which I used to check the target area again. Not magnified to the same level, but still very good. Dexter tested the second optic on the right and gave a thumbs up. A high-resolution camera was also fixed on the same view, beaming pictures back by satellite uplink to the TOC although it appeared the link had a technical issue.

'Fucking piece of shit isn't connecting,' the soldier muttered to Dexter, who didn't seem to get much joy out of it either.

The gravity of the situation bore down on me heavily. Until then, I'd been concentrating on getting to the OP. Now the success of the mission relied to a large extent on the ability of me or Dexter to correctly identify one or more of Abu Saif and other High Value Targets. The two other VIPER teams in the vicinity of the target had digital photofit prints from the description of Abu Saif I'd provided in London and images of other key targets, but they'd been poor quality and I doubted anyone would find it easy to make a positive ID from them. I hoped their satellite feeds were transmitting images back to Katie at the TOC more successfully than ours.

In the fading light, my biggest fear was the illumination wouldn't be sufficient to make an identification. A large sodium light shone above the museum door, but the fragility of the electricity supply meant no guarantees it would stay on. All that assumed the intelligence was accurate and we weren't on another wild goose chase or, even worse, being lured into a trap.

★

I checked my watch: 20:43. Both the prayers of Maghrib and Isha had come and gone and we'd spent most of the last three hours straining to detect movement towards and around the museum entrance, with nothing seen so far. The VIPER 3 commander, Shaun, had kept us updated as he received various tactical messages from the other teams, and the 18E SF communications sergeant, Danny, received longer range encrypted traffic from the TOC.

Roper, Nabil, Dara and Hamza seemed to be doing a useful liaison job over on the other side of the river. I assumed that was how we obtained information apparently originating from Kurdish intelligence. The first message, not long after 18:00, had confirmed a high-level meeting was taking place in Mosul tonight, along with a cryptic warning the insurgents were discussing 'American spies' in the city. There was no clarification whether it meant our presence had been compromised in any way, or it should be construed as a more general warning. However, it prompted instructions from the TOC to be on high alert for signs of insurgent surveillance efforts or gatherings of armed men in potential attack positions.

Shortly afterwards, a further message excited Dexter, who whispered across to me, 'The Kurds are reporting Zarqawi is in the city for the meeting. This could be the jackpot.'

By 20:43 it had been two-and-a-half hours since the message about Zarqawi. Units from the 25th Infantry had been moved into blocking positions, ready to cut off escape routes out of the city, so now hundreds of men watched and waited, knowing each minute that passed could be a minute closer to a trap being sprung which could deal a serious blow to AQI and the Iraq insurgency.

I caught the sound of distant gunfire to the right and turned my ear towards it. It was faint, probably a kilometre or more away, but sustained and growing in intensity. We all exchanged glances as the gunfire was augmented by explosions. It sounded a long way outside our target area and cordon, but then a second, louder firefight erupted much nearer.

I heard Shaun transmit, 'VIPER 3, roger, out,' before he gave us an update. 'BLUE 1 on the north-west corner of the cordon is reporting heavy presence of armed men north of their position and down Al-Jamhuriya Street to the south-west.'

As sporadic shooting joined in behind us to the north, Danny cut in. 'TOC reports insurgents have attacked two police stations west of the Old City. Could be a diversionary tactic to cover key movements. All teams stand by for instructions. Be prepared for immediate exfil if required.'

I caught Dexter's eye and we both shook our heads. Surely the insurgents knew these attacks would stir up the security forces, so it seemed unlikely they would initiate an operation immediately prior to a meeting of their highest-level commanders. A diversion perhaps, but that too struck me as doubtful. The thought grew in my head – we might be watching the wrong location.

Although it wasn't impossible the AQI leaders were already in the museum at that moment, it was improbable. The three VIPER teams had monitored all the approaches since late afternoon. We needed to remain on standby in case Zarqawi, Abu Saif, and their gang suddenly appeared, but deep down I think everyone suspected this was a bust.

We'd finished packing away all the kit except one of the optics, when four pickup trucks sped through the junction fifty metres to our left and swung towards the museum entrance.

'VIPER 3, hostile vehicles on the goal line. Stand by, Stand by.'

I had my eye to the scope watching a dozen armed men spill out of the trucks as Shaun gave a quick update.

'Guys, BLUE 2 reports no additional hostiles in view. Dexter, John, you got PID on any of our targets?'

It might be unlikely, but none of us had given up on the possibility the meeting could still happen here.

There was a pause as Dexter scanned with the binos and I concentrated hard on the armed figures in front of me. They had jumped out with intent, but after a cursory check of the door and a glimpse down the sides of the building, half of the men seemed to relax. The other half jumped into two of the pickups and drove out of sight past the far southern corner of the museum.

'Negative PID,' reported Dexter.

Much as I willed it, Abu Saif wasn't one of them. 'Negative PID.'

'Roger,' acknowledged Shaun. 'Could be an advance party,' he said to us before speaking into his mike. 'VIPER 3, negative PID.'

These guys might be an advance party, but with the sound of gunfire reverberating across the city, surely the AQI leaders wouldn't be settling down for a cosy chat now.

'VIPER 3, roger, out,' said Shaun into his radio in answer to a message I hadn't heard.

'VIPER 1 has the two trucks at the rear of the building on the western side. Looks like they're checking it's secure but making no attempt to enter.' Shaun paused then added, 'I don't think this is going to be our night.'

Danny's voice broke in: 'VIPER 3 acknowledged.' Then to us: 'TOC reports from Kurdish intel that the meeting has already taken place at the Hunchback. 25th Infantry has engaged a large force heading north on Tampa. Possibly AQI command elements. Codeword: FUMBLE. All teams are ordered to extract immediately.'

Danny had already moved to the last remaining scope as he spoke and began packing it away.

The Hunchback was the name of the leaning minaret of the Al Nuri Mosque in the Old City. Setting up this operation around that target would have been very difficult if not impossible. A check of the map showed it was less than one and a half kilometres away, but it may as well have been in a different country.

Everything wasn't lost though. If 25th Infantry had intercepted a leadership convoy, then maybe the night could still end on a high. My concern was our current location. Where did the bad intel come from about the museum as the meeting location? Compromise? Disinformation? A decoy? A trap? Judging by the posture of the armed guys currently lounging outside the museum, it didn't appear we'd been compromised or it was much of a trap. They weren't acting as though they knew teams of special forces were watching their every move.

'What do you reckon, Dex?' I asked.

'I reckon we need to be very careful getting the hell out of here,' replied Dexter.

'Roger that gentlemen. Come on, let's haul ass,' said Shaun, moving low towards the doorway.

CHAPTER 41

Now an intricate dance was required to extract all the TF145 personnel from the city and back to the airbase without compromise. The three VIPER teams would move first and, once they were all mobile, the remaining four BLUE teams at the corners of the cordon would melt away.

VIPER 2, who had been deployed in scruffy local vans to the east of the museum all night, were already on their way towards us to pick up Shaun and VIPER 3.

VIPER 1 in the buildings to the west were being extracted by the BLUE 6 support team which had earlier escorted Roper and the Kurds to the Peshmerga Command Centre in the battered pickup trucks.

Greg and the BLUE 5 team were manoeuvring their taxis to the RV location by the crossroads where they'd dropped us off.

As we left the OP building, the night felt alive with an electric energy stirred by the crackle of small arms in the distance. The tension of the situation alone would have been enough to keep me on edge, but the snarling clamour of the city amplified the foreboding.

But there was no time to worry about it as we moved out onto the street and away from the OP. Engine noises and lights drew closer and turned into the road ahead of us. I waited for a steer from Shaun and the team and a thumbs-up allowed me to release the breath I'd been holding. This was VIPER 2, here to extract Shaun and the guys. While the other two team members climbed into the vans with the kit, Shaun and Danny took me and Dexter up to the road junction and went firm. Forty metres to my left I could see two taxis parked near the crossroads facing towards us, with two figures heading our way.

'Good luck,' whispered Shaun before he and Danny made their way back to join the rest of the team at the VIPER 2 vans.

Dexter and I closed on the approaching figures of Greg and his BLUE 5 second-in-command, Russ.

'All good?' asked Greg.

'Good to go,' I replied as Dexter signalled the same.

Russ and Dexter peeled off into the first taxi driven by Moose as Greg led me towards the second. Behind us I heard Moose's taxi pull away and further down the street tyres screeched as a vehicle turned the corner from the main road, its lights sweeping towards us. Our taxi was dead ahead with Ricky in the driver's seat. I fought the urge to turn and see what was coming our way. As we climbed into the taxi and closed the doors, a pickup skidded to a halt on the driver's side and we were challenged with fierce Arabic. Shit, we'd just hit our first slice of bad luck.

Ricky responded with a heated torrent of Arabic as I caught sight of at least four armed men hanging off the back of the pickup. There was only a second or two for the team to assess if we could talk our way out or it was destined to go noisy. If the armed men got out of the truck and started aiming their weapons it would be too late to do anything. I heard Greg flick off his M4 safety catch.

'Ricky take the cab, I'll take the rear,' said Greg.

With the decision made, I followed suit and clicked off the safety catch of my HK. It was almost a relief. The cloying tension of potential compromise exchanged for the instant adrenaline spike from knowing we were about to engage the enemy.

As Ricky jumped out of his door in apparent outrage, Greg sprang out of his side and brought the M4 up on aim. As the weapon barked out its lethal report, Ricky raised his sidearm and engaged the pickup driver. The windscreen and driver's head exploded in a splash of red and he slumped over the wheel. Ricky switched to the passenger, putting two rounds into his chest before he could react with anything but an astonished look on his dying face. Meanwhile Greg's eight or nine shots seemed to have put paid to any further activity from the rear of the pickup. It was brutal; they never had a chance.

To my left, Neil held his hand up in a 'wait' signal as the sounds of the sudden violence died away. Ricky and Greg climbed back into the taxi, bringing in the smell of cordite with them.

'GO, GO, GO,' yelled Greg.

Ahead of us, another set of lights from a large vehicle swung around the corner from the main road and now approached at speed. Had they seen the mayhem inflicted on the first vehicle? The rear lights of Moose's taxi had already passed the new threat without interference – they were clear. The VIPER 2 vans were also nowhere to be seen, so it was only our vehicle left.

Greg spoke quickly into his mike as we accelerated away. 'BLUE 5 ALPHA Contact! 5 BRAVO continue extraction. 5 ALPHA following right behind you, out.'

The new headlights switched to full beam and pulled over into our lane as they bore down on us.

'Fuck. Right, right, right,' yelled Greg.

The taxi lurched to the left as Ricky jerked the wheel to whip through the right-hand corner that led back towards the OP and the museum at the bottom of the road. The taxi had a meaty engine under the bonnet, but none of the vehicle was armoured. We wouldn't last long unless we kept moving and escaped the area before the insurgents could get themselves organised.

Greg informed all other call signs we would break out of the city centre to the south at speed, with no immediate assistance required. Every team had a deployable Blue Force Tracker unit which should transmit its position to the TOC – potentially very useful for a team requiring support – but it was a new deployable version without an external aerial and as yet unproven when it mattered. Most of the teams were dubious about its capabilities and range.

'Incoming,' yelled Ricky. He must have seen muzzle flashes in his mirrors from the pickup behind us.

Nothing hit us though and we barrelled out of the road past the front of our former OP building and slew to the left a short distance from the museum entrance path. Another taxi blared its horn as it swerved to avoid us, but a sickening crunch from behind seconds later indicated its driver's luck had run out.

The road was busy with evening traffic as we headed into the main junction next to the museum, ready to turn right and head south for the airbase. I'd juggled my Kevlar helmet on like the other guys, apart from Ricky who was too busy driving. The covert approach was out of the window now and just one raking burst from a machine gun could cause carnage in the close confines of the taxi.

At the museum entrance, insurgents were jumping into their two pickups. If they hadn't recognised our initial contact with their comrades, the sight of a car chase thundering out of a side road on to Al-Jamhuriya Street shortly afterwards would have given the game away. Provided we maintained our momentum, we had a good chance to get clear before they could do much about it.

The cacophony of horns, led by ours, was eclipsed by an almighty bang as a gas-tank truck broadsided us with a glancing blow. For a moment it seemed we would brush it off and keep going, but the taxi came to a sudden and spine-shuddering halt in a knot of vehicles, steam, and screams. The shock of the impact seemed to gouge out a silent space around us, but the city chaos poured back in almost instantly.

My head had rebounded hard off the car door, but fortunately I'd got my helmet on in time. Neil was already climbing out on my left and Greg was stirring in front of me, as evidenced by his heartfelt, 'Fuck.'

Ricky didn't look so good in the driver's seat. He hadn't had his seat belt on or his helmet.

'Debus and watch for hostiles,' Greg ordered as he undid his seat belt and forced his door open.

My door opened with a wrenching sound and I had to kick it to allow myself out. I couldn't feel any specific pain, but every movement was in slow motion and my head had a heavy, unbalanced feel to it. I tried to shake off the shock of the impact. No good. The sensation of bricks in my head wasn't going anywhere. Taking in the scene, I could see the taxi we'd missed earlier had slammed into the truck pursuing us, leaving a terrible mangle of metal and broken bodies.

With those guys out of action, I checked towards the museum and saw an insurgent pickup snaking its way towards us. A second pickup approached from a different angle, slowed by the mess of broken cars that had rippled out from our crash in the middle of the junction.

Behind the gas-tank truck, I briefly spotted two armed guys less than fifty metres away and closing as they made their way on foot towards us. At that moment, an old guy wearing a keffiyeh jumped down from the cab of the truck and gave me a 'what the fuck?' look. I shrugged my shoulders in reply and felt pain in my neck.

The momentary calm was broken when Neil opened up with his M4 at a target out of my view on the other side of the truck. 'We need to keep them off while Greg gets Ricky out,' he shouted over to me.

The driver's side was wedged into the smash of vehicles, so no way Ricky's door could be opened. I could see Greg stowing away the Blue Force Tracker unit before working to bring him out through the front passenger door. When I turned back in the direction of the museum, a figure appeared behind the truck driver with an AK-47 in his shoulder. I brought my HK into a firing position with both hands and double-tapped two shots into the centre mass of the target. Apart from the shocking explosion of noise caused by the .45, the target went down without making a sound. Provided he wasn't wearing body armour, I didn't expect to see him again.

Greg was sending a situation report and outlining the status of our casualty, Ricky. Apparently, he remained conscious but unable to walk unaided. After a pause, Greg responded to an inbound message with 'Roger, out.'

'Okay guys, prepare to move. Neil, grab hold of Ricky. John, you take his M4. Roger that?'

'Roger that.'

The clatter of shots pinging off the metal around us indicated we didn't have much time. Yelling and shrieking peppered the air from the various car collisions and no doubt the added realisation a determined gunfight was kicking off. As Saturday evenings in Mosul went, I didn't know if this was unusual or just a regular night downtown.

Greg covered me and Neil as we moved back to the taxi although he didn't take any shots. The limited visibility from the weak street lighting made target acquisition tricky and there were still plenty of people running both towards and away from the recent carnage.

Neil grabbed hold of Ricky round his shoulders and stood him up, while I relieved him of his M4 and three spare, full magazines of thirty rounds. The semi-transparent mag in the weapon was also full, so I had 120 rounds total, plus the now holstered HK for closer range. It would be better if we could get away without becoming involved in a serious firefight though. Sheer weight of numbers would be against us very quickly.

Ricky had blood on his face from a cut above his left eye, but he was trying to get himself back into working order, even as the pain etched on his face gave away how much he was hurting. As he put weight on his left leg, he let out a rasp of furious Arabic before hobbling through the broken cars and towards the south-east corner of the junction, Neil variously pushing and dragging him along. Ricky had his own HK sidearm in his hand as they moved off, so he hadn't been rendered completely ineffective.

We'd all ditched or stowed our Kevlar helmets. Now we were on the street, the recognisable shape would make it easier for the insurgents to pick us out amongst the locals. As Neil and Ricky got into the swing of their joint movement efforts, Greg and I moved alternately behind them in short tactical bounds, taking up fire positions to target any chasing insurgents.

CHAPTER 42

With the crash site thirty metres behind us the traffic was moving more freely, although numerous pedestrians radiating out from the mess, including us, prompted constant braking, the incessant blast of car horns, and an accompanying uproar of total hysteria.

When I turned to adopt a ready fire position there were plenty of figures in our wake, but none I could pick out as bad guys. More importantly, none shooting in our direction. I'd already hit one and Neil had hit at least one more, so hopefully those initial deadly exchanges had bought us some time.

'Contact right,' shouted Greg from behind me.

Stooped low, I ran back towards him as he fired three short bursts from the M4 while a truck racing in from the left emitted a light show of muzzle flashes in return. The windscreen shattered open from Greg's accurate fire and the truck ground to a halt forty metres away with the occupants spilling out into the surrounding shadows.

Greg directed me after Neil and Ricky who had reached the buildings at the corner of the junction. The air became quickly alive with the crack and thump of incoming rounds very close. Two punches to my kidneys threw me forward, stumbling to the ground. The slung M4 bounced off the tarmac and smashed into my face as I landed. My right eye immediately started to swell and there was wetness on my cheek as I fought for breath after being winded by the various impacts.

After a loud explosion in the direction of the new truck, Greg hauled me up. 'Come on, keep moving.'

As we reached Neil and Ricky, each nestled behind a stone pillar outside an electronics shop, Neil was firing his M4 in short bursts before he then reached for a fresh magazine. Ricky had his handgun in a firing position, but the insurgents were outside his effective range. I almost felt guilty I had Ricky's rifle. Almost. I tried to blink away the stars in my vision and rubbed at the wetness on my face with a sleeve. It came away bloody.

Greg shouted an update. 'There's a Kurdish force on the way, but we've got to get off this street.'

On cue, salvos of larger calibre ammunition slammed into the building behind us and a stream of AK-47 rounds impacted to our right. Greg shook his head. 'That grenade didn't hold 'em up for long. Right, deploying smoke. Neil, pitch another grenade at that fucking Dushka.'

Greg threw a red smoke grenade to our front, quickly obscuring the already murky scene like an old-fashioned London pea-souper, while Neil threw a frag grenade in the direction of the truck-mounted 12.7mm DShk anti-aircraft gun threatening to ruin our evening. Unfortunately, the resulting explosion didn't stop the giant bullets smashing into the masonry close by.

'Prepare to move. MOVE.'

On Greg's order we all ran south down the left-hand side of the road, before Neil turned Ricky a hard left and they disappeared into a narrow alleyway between two houses. I darted after them and Greg took up a kneeling firing position at the alleyway entrance.

'Can you get through?' Greg shouted, sounding less controlled than he'd been until now.

'There's a locked door, but we'll get through it,' replied Neil.

I stopped in the middle of the passageway, my back howling in discomfort as I tried to wipe more blood off my cheek and away from my eye. My face was tightening up with the swelling and my back stiffening.

Greg opened fire from his position at the entrance. 'You need to hurry up.'

Alongside the metallic taste of blood in my mouth, there was a vibration coming from my jacket pocket. My local Nokia. I didn't recognise the number. 'Hello?'

'Mr John? Is that you?'

'Yeah, who's that?'

'Mr John, this is Nabil. I'm with Captain Dara and local Peshmerga. We're looking for you now. Where are you?'

I shouted out. 'Greg, I've got the Kurds on the phone. They need an RV to pick us up.'

But Greg was tied up changing a magazine and then bringing his weapon back into the shoulder and firing at our pursuers. When dust erupted from accurate shots hitting the brickwork just above his head, he leapt along the passage. The sound of splintering wood at the other end accompanied a cry from Neil, 'We're through.'

I charged out past the broken door with Greg close behind me. We were on a narrow road to the rear of a row of houses and buildings, with a noticeable breeze coming from the River Tigris sloshing about 200 metres away across dark, open land. The Hurriya Bridge was 250 metres to our north, which meant another bridge lay 750 metres to the south.

'Greg, the Kurds are looking for us. Where shall we RV?' I shouted through panted breaths, indicating the phone in my hand.

Greg motioned for me to go firm and we knelt in firing positions covering the rear arcs while Ricky and Neil lumbered forward a tactical bound. 'They're not on our net, so tell them we'll be five hundred metres south of the bridge if they can get here in the next five minutes. Halfway between the bridges.'

I passed the message on to Nabil although I wasn't convinced he understood the directions through my laboured breathing.

The darkness swallowed us as we moved into the scrub and light foliage nearer to the river. We were all breathing hard and every intake of breath was hurting my ribs as the pain spread out from my back. Ricky and Neil had slowed considerably, but they were still moving forward.

My vision was blurry, so I couldn't see if the insurgents had followed us. 'How close are they behind us?'

Greg was already facing back on aim towards the broken door at the end of the alley a hundred metres away. 'Nothing yet. Hang on… yep, here they come.'

A pickup truck nosed itself onto the road at the back of the houses from an access road close to the alleyway we'd used. I couldn't make out any large gun fitted in the truck bed, but there were a group of armed men either side of the crawling truck, moving carefully.

'Hold your fire,' hissed Greg. It didn't appear they could see us, although it wouldn't take them long to figure out where we must have gone. Hopefully the Kurds were close by.

An unwelcome wave of exhaustion flooded over me and I physically sagged.

'Are you okay?' asked Greg.

'Yeah, but I'm seizing up.'

'Just keep it going and we'll get out of here. There's a helo extraction getting ready now, as well as the Kurds. We'll be okay.'

Whether he believed it or not, he sounded confident.

Bursts of AK-47 fire sounded from the road back to our right. Nothing was landing near us, so they might have been firing into likely positions trying to elicit a response. That wasn't going to work with us. As we handrailed the river on our left, I looked behind to the road and saw a lot of figures over there. Some were running behind us into the scrubland. We'd slowed down, and the insurgents were less than seventy metres behind.

Their truck was on the road to our right almost parallel with our position. A second truck rumbled down another access road to join the first and the lights of two more SUVs appeared to our front right by a corner building 200 metres ahead. The situation was looking bleaker by the moment.

'Come on, one more push,' Greg shouted.

But it was difficult to see how we were going to evade the blocking force now deploying in front of us. A flash of light and a rumble of noise erupted from near the two vehicles up ahead as an RPG streaked out like an arrow towards the insurgent trucks on the road. My spirits leapt as I realised it must be the Kurds. There was an eerie calm as we watched the RPG close on its target and disappointment when the warhead missed the trucks and exploded harmlessly behind them. Now intense small arms fire ignited between the two opposing groups of men and vehicles.

We closed to a hundred metres or so from the river and wheeled right to move parallel to the road through the grass, bushes, and occasional trees. The men behind us in the scrub were shooting at the two SUVs up ahead, prompting streaks of return fire.

'John, confirm that's your Kurds up there and tell them we're coming in from their right,' Greg yelled above the bedlam.

As I fumbled for the Nokia to call Nabil, the sudden sound of helicopters in the air overhead added a new, welcome dimension to the proceedings. I couldn't hear Greg over all the noise, but I hoped he was talking directly to the pilots. A dark shape swooped overhead, and a light show of liquid death rained down into the area behind us, indicating the right guys knew where the bad guys were.

'Nabil? Nabil?' The phone showed we were connected, but nothing from the other end.

'If you can hear me, four of us are coming in from your right-hand side. From the river.' Silence. I caught my breath and yelled over to Greg on my right. 'Can't get through.'

Greg's mouth was moving but I couldn't make out his words, so I ran closer. Ricky and Neil had been doing well, until they both suddenly disappeared from my view with painful shouts. I dropped down next to them.

'Ricky's leg gave way. We'll have to carry him,' panted Neil.

Greg slid in next to us. 'They're almost on top of us. We've gotta hold 'em here. Wolfman's taxi turned back and is up there with the Kurds now, so I've got comms and they know we're here. The chopper will keep us covered.'

I peered into the darkness behind us but could only see the occasional muzzle flash. Excited shouts drew closer. I brought the

M4 up on aim and fired into the vicinity of the nearest flash twenty metres away. Greg and Neil also opened up and an anguished cry rang out from one of our targets. A heavier machine gun, probably a PKM, unleashed a barrage with a mix of tracer rounds in our direction from the road 200 metres away. The fire unerringly accurate, I pressed myself into the dirt as the 7.62mm bullets whacked into the ground close by.

It wasn't all bad news though; cannon fire from the helicopter above slammed into one of the insurgent pickups, causing it to jerk to a stop at an awkward angle. Then the PKM blasted another salvo, forcing us to keep our heads down. We needed that gun silenced or at least one of us would get hit. Greg was calling the helicopter to hit the machine gun, but they were receiving incoming fire themselves and had been forced to pull away.

With the PKM pinning us down, the insurgents were moving closer and engaging us with accurate fire. The crack and whine of bullets filled the air. More lights from vehicles up on the road indicated the situation was only getting worse.

A second helicopter came in for a strafing run on the insurgents behind us, while staying noticeably higher than the first. 'Helo says we have a dozen armed men approaching our position,' shouted Greg, just as a loud explosion sounded a few metres ahead of me.

'Grenade,' I shouted, although too late for anyone to do anything about it. I fired two quick shots at a blurry figure ten metres out to my right and then changed mag: 'MAGAZINE.'

To my left, Neil was firing regular aimed shots. 'Keep your eyes on the right,' he said as he squeezed off another round.

I crawled further to the right and noticed movement from the direction of the river. Insurgents trying to circle round behind us.

'Enemy right,' I yelled, and fired three bursts on automatic in their direction.

Another fusillade from the PKM, spitting its fury into the ground all round us.

A shout from my left. 'RPG!'

The earth exploded, and I was temporarily airborne, although strangely without pain. After landing in a tangled heap, I could make out vague nearby figures amid the crescendo of gunfire, shouting, and explosions. Underneath the external clamour, my ears vibrated and rang as though cymbals crashed inside my head. I opened my mouth to shout a warning about the insurgents behind us but nothing came out. When I tried to lift my M4, it felt as though my arms were on back to front. I stopped, closed my eyes for a couple of seconds, and then reopened them.

'John, it's Russ. Where are you hurt?'

Russ. The other half of the team must have reached us.

'I think I'm okay. Just a bit fucked up,' I replied slowly.

He nodded. 'Okay good. We've got to get out of here now. Can you walk?'

'I'll try,' I said as I nodded back to him.

Russ hauled me to my feet as volleys of small arms fire swept out from our now enlarged perimeter and overhead a helicopter poured a devastating bombardment towards the river.

A familiar bald head appeared in front of me. Dara. 'Mr John, Yella *(Come on)*.'

Dara and Hamza pushed and dragged me the 100 metres or so up to the Kurdish armoured SUVs and bundled me inside. I saw Dexter in the taxi alongside and raised a hand in his direction before collapsing into a seat. A bottle of water nuzzled my lips, Hamza encouraging me to drink. From the concern on his face, I assumed I looked in bad shape.

I felt banged up but relieved all my limbs seemed to be in working order. My hand dipped into my pocket for a boiled sweet to give me some energy and pulled out my ever-present lucky eyeball instead. This odd little link back to my girls in Epsom overwhelmed me for a moment. I wasn't sure how much of the right kind of luck we'd had today.

I raised my head at the sound of yelling near the vehicle and saw Greg pointing at the other SUV as he and Neil supported Ricky by his shoulders and half dragged him towards it. Ricky looked barely conscious and blood soaked his jacket and shirt. The doors slammed, and we drove off fast with a helicopter escort hovering above us, shooting sporadically at nearby threats as we evaded the insurgents' grasp.

Back at FOB Marez we were all taken straight to the infirmary. I'd stiffened up all over but had got away without any serious injury; it looked a lot worse because my face had taken a battering. Without doubt the Kevlar vest had saved me from the shots to my back and most of the shrapnel from the RPG explosion. My right leg had a small chunk of metal sticking out of the thigh which looked bad. However, the medics reassured me it was only superficial and quickly removed it.

A couple of the Kurds had minor wounds and both Neil and Greg were being treated for lacerations, but it was Ricky who had sustained by far the worst of it. At some point he'd been badly hit by a couple of 7.62mm rounds and a large slice of shrapnel. Hard as they tried, the doctors couldn't save him. Ricky was dead.

CHAPTER 43

BRIZE NORTON, UK – LATE FEBRUARY 2005

I woke and lifted my head as Roper gently shook my shoulder and said, 'We're starting the descent into Brize.'

My neck hurt, but then so did everything else. I'd been patched up and given a party pack of painkillers, which might have explained the lucid dreams already sliding out of my memory as I glanced gingerly around the sparsely occupied cabin. During a 'rip' changeover between units in Iraq, the RAF VC10s would be chock-a-block, but this plane only had a smattering of British soldiers on board.

We'd boarded at Ali Al Salem Air Base in Kuwait after a bumpy flight on a packed American C130 Hercules from Mosul via Baghdad. The mood on the Herc had been sombre following the death of Ricky and the failure of the mission to capture any insurgent targets.

Joe Holmes had shaken my hand before we'd left Mosul and Katie had popped into the infirmary to wish me well, but the sense of loss and frustration hung heavily in the air and stilted the conversations. At least the chit-chat on this flight sounded breezy with occasional laughter amongst the small groups. Most, if not all, of those on board were heading home from deployment, which always lifted the spirits.

'When we land, there'll be a debriefing at the base,' said Roper.

Great, just what I needed. Seeing the expression on my face, Roper tried to soften the blow. 'You did everything that was asked. Sometimes these things just don't go the way we want them to. Plenty of times in fact. The debriefing won't take long. It's more of a formality.'

I buckled up my seat belt and tried to muster some enthusiasm, but all I wanted was to get home to Claire and the girls.

★

After being disembarked first, Roper and I were escorted through arrivals by RAF Military Police and driven in a Land Rover to the officers' mess. Once inside we were led up to a room where I shouldn't have been surprised to see Chapman sat with another of his suited henchmen. He made no acknowledgement of the butterfly stitches on my cheek and above my brow or the angry-looking black eye I sported.

'Mr Pierce, welcome back to the UK. I don't intend to take up too much of your time, but it's important we understand exactly what transpired in Mosul. We have been briefed by our military colleagues of course. However, it will take a little while yet before they can provide us with a full understanding of events. In the meantime, your assistance is gratefully received.'

He made it sound as though I had a choice about all this.

'I don't know how much help I can be. I only know a small part of what happened and at no time did I identify anyone even remotely similar to Abu Saif. You'll be aware that one of the Americans from my team was killed during the mission. I'm really not feeling up to this right now. Can we do it some other time?'

Chapman eyed me over the cup of tea he was drinking. 'I'm afraid that will not be possible. But we will complete the debrief today and then you'll be free to go.'

I'd thought it would be a rigmarole and I was right. For over two hours they fired questions at me about the initial aborted Hawija mission and then the operation in Mosul. Roper joined in at times to steer the timeline and add observations and inside knowledge from his viewpoint. It wasn't an interrogation, but the way I was feeling it might as well have been.

'Let's break for some sandwiches,' announced Chapman, just as I was about to declare I was finished.

As we waited for the sandwiches to arrive, Chapman began to reveal some new information.

'You might be interested to learn the meeting that took place in Mosul on Friday involved the entire AQI command including Zarqawi and Abu Saif. There's even unconfirmed reports Zarqawi was injured during the various skirmishes. We were very close to dealing these people a serious blow. Unfortunately, they implement a strict 'need to know' policy regarding these meetings, which is why it is so hard for us to interdict them. Our inside source was clearly only privy to a decoy location and not the actual meeting place. He hasn't been heard from since and we therefore currently assume he is blown, which probably means dead given the organisation he works for.'

'You don't think we were lured into a trap?' I asked, before casting my eyes towards Roper to gauge his reaction.

'There is no indication the TF145 presence was detected, apart from some low-level warnings from the Kurds. If the whole mission had been compromised the loss of life would likely have been far worse. Instead, it appears your team were simply unlucky to run into an insurgent patrol, and you actually managed to extricate yourselves quickly and effectively from what could have been a very sticky situation.'

I interrupted and said flatly, 'Apart from Ricky getting killed.'

Chapman paused. 'Very unfortunate, but these occurrences go with the territory for special forces.'

The anger flared up in me at this pompous git, but as I searched for a reply, the fight left me just as quickly to be replaced by a surge of sadness mixed with frustration.

Chapman continued, clearly sensing my irritation. 'That's not to demean the death of a brave soldier. Simply a realistic appraisal of the difficult environment in which we operate.'

I looked at Roper. I didn't imagine Chapman operated anywhere more dangerous than late-night London on his way back from the opera, although I had no way of knowing his background. For all I knew he could be a war hero and spy legend. Roper's face wasn't giving anything away. I turned back to Chapman and asked more in hope than expectation, 'I know. Are we finished here?'

'Let's have some sandwiches and then we can finish off. Shouldn't be long now.'

As he spoke there was a knock at the door and three tray loads of food and fresh drinks were deposited amongst us.

An hour later we were all done. It was dark outside as I considered the long journey home. First, I needed to get to Oxford by taxi or the interminable bus ride, then a train to London, a Tube across the city, and finally another train to Epsom. I seemed to have been travelling forever and really couldn't face it.

Chapman shook my hand at last and thanked me. 'Your help in this matter won't go unnoted.'

I lifted my head. 'Does that mean customs are completely dropping the investigation?'

'As I explained before, this isn't a deal. However, your cooperation has been acknowledged and relevant parties will be made aware of it.'

It was about as good as I was going to get. I grabbed my dusty daysack and turned to shake hands with Roper. Then I addressed them both. 'Can I get a lift? Honestly, I'm shattered, and I don't even know if I've got enough cash for a taxi. If you're going back to London, then you can drop me off anywhere in the centre.'

Chapman's look was priceless, but before he replied, Roper stepped across and they moved to the side of the room to confer.

Chapman looked at me and sounded uncharacteristically like a kindly uncle as he said, 'It's late, so how about we arrange for you and Roper to stay here at the officers' mess tonight and a car will take you home in the morning?'

I expect it sounded ungrateful, but I could only give a begrudging: 'I suppose that's okay, thanks.'

But Chapman wasn't finished yet and steel returned to his voice. 'Mr Pierce, before I go, although you have demonstrated your commitment admirably over these recent days, we may still need to call on you in the future. You remain the only person we have who can identify Abu Saif. If we need you, we will call on you again and you will have to comply. Everything I told you at our last meeting remains relevant and your potential prosecution for terrorism offences remains on the table. Is that understood?'

I stared at him, taking in what he'd said and trying not to show my growing fury. Did this idiot not understand what I'd been through just a couple of days before? I forced myself to remain calm and polite.

'Yes. Understood.' What else could I say?

CHAPTER 44

The following morning, I was glad for the night in the officers' mess and the hearty breakfast which accompanied it. Most of my clothes were still in Sulaimaniyah with Ali, so my casual attire caused some raised eyebrows. However, I think my patched-up face was enough to stop any direct admonishment.

The spooks had sent a black Jaguar up from London to collect us. On the journey down, Roper and I chatted about odds and sods and avoided talk about the mission. The driver probably had higher clearance than me, but the debriefing the previous day had covered everything there was to say.

Roper wished me luck as we shook hands outside my house in Epsom. As I turned away from the car, the front door was already opening, and Claire walked out with a smile on her face which was quickly replaced with a look of concern. She looked past me at the Jaguar pulling away and then turned back and kissed me.

'Ow,' I said and smiled.

'I'm sorry.' Claire stepped back and looked at my face closely. 'What have you done? What have you been doing? And who was that in the black car?'

'Whoa steady. Can we go inside? It's been a long trip.'

As we made our way to the door, Taz suddenly appeared and ran straight at me, half jumping as we collided. She started whining and dancing in circles, demented with joy that I'd returned. That was probably more to do with food, walks, and runs, but I couldn't help laughing as my mood lifted after the black clouds of recent days.

I told Claire my injuries had been caused by a car crash; not too far from the truth. There didn't seem much point trying to explain further, and the Official Secrets Act meant I couldn't anyway. But I did open up about the business in Iraq.

'The business in Baghdad is finished. I don't have anything firm up in the north yet, but I think it could work up there. The Kurds were really good to me. I just don't know if we can afford to take another chance.'

Even as I said it, I think we both knew I'd be going back to Kurdistan. I'd invested too much time and effort trying to get the business off the ground to stop now, even though there was nothing concrete to show for it. Despite only just arriving home, and with no idea how we would afford it, I could already sense the lure of adventure enticing me back to Iraq again.

Being home with my girls was therapeutic. Natalie's concern on seeing my injuries pierced through her teenage exterior and we joked together like the old days. Becky remained her funny, innocent self and accepted my return and injured face with hugs and initial questions. Her look of concern vanished after I said, 'Daddy had a silly accident,' and was replaced instead by her pointing at my face and saying, 'Silly daddy.'

It had always concerned me that I missed so much of my girls growing up, but that came with the life I'd chosen. Even so, although I might be away for weeks at a time, which shocked many of Claire's friends in a town without any nearby military community, on my return I tried to make up for it. It might be uneven, but over the years I'd probably spent more quality time with the family than if I'd been stuck in a City job working sixty to eighty hours a week.

Claire accepted my explanations about the lap dancing and the escort agency being work-related without wanting to know the details. But she made it clear I needed to tell her if I became involved in that sort of project again. The facts wouldn't necessarily break us but hiding them just might. We'd gone from an icy distance before my absence to passionate partners now I'd returned. Time apart achieving what the friction of daily coexistence would never have allowed to the same degree.

★

In late March I travelled the lengthy route back to Sulaimaniyah via Diyarbakir and was reunited with both Ali and my luggage. My superficial wounds had fully healed, and we dived into completing the business meetings that had been under way when Roper had showed up the previous month.

No matter which way I cut it, the budget to run a small business operation for the next twelve months made depressing reading compared to my available funds. Should Claire and I take the high-risk option to remortgage the house? It was a big, crazy step to take, but UK house price inflation had given us an opportunity that could finance the business in northern Iraq. It was tempting. However, we both knew that just because we could, didn't mean we should.

My arrival back in Sulaimaniyah heralded a bout of private celebratory dinners and the odd losing game of blackjack. News of the Mosul operation was on everyone's lips, not least because General Rashid was pleased to promote the pivotal role his brother Dara and the other Peshmerga had played in securing our safe extraction from the city. On each occasion, haunting Kurdish music captured the mood as they remembered both their own fallen from previous battles and the more recent death of Ricky in Mosul.

Ali was larger than life during these gatherings and revelled in describing the action as it had unfolded, despite the fact he was back in Sulaimaniyah at the time. He set the scene and took the audience on a rollercoaster ride of emotion through the events with unerring accuracy, most likely gleaned from conversations with Dara, Hamza and me.

His tale began with the helicopter ride north and included the failed mission he assumed had intended to kill the al-Qaeda leader Zarqawi, our unlucky compromise, the brave entry of the Kurdish rescue force, and the devastating realisation of Ricky's death. Throughout, he weaved in his undisguised admiration for the bravery of all the Peshmerga and Coalition forces fighting the common enemy.

Irrespective of his contribution at the time, the whole episode had bound us all closer with a genuine sense of brotherhood and common purpose as we now sought to work together and set up a successful business in the region.

By early May I was back in the UK, re-energised by my second visit to Kurdistan and encouraged by the opening of new international airports in both Erbil and Sulaimaniyah. For business development, I had my eye on a conference called the Iraq Development Programme Summit, scheduled to take place at the Hyatt Hotel in Amman at the end of June. A stand at the conference could be just the thing to get the company in front of the clients it needed and kick-start some much-needed revenue. It would be costly, but it was now all or nothing.

When it came time to either put up or shut up, I can't say we agonised over the decision. Claire and I looked at each other and smiled with grim acceptance as we quietly agreed to remortgage the house and commit the cash to making the business work.

'I trust you,' said Claire.

What could I say to that? I'd try as hard as I could to make this work, but there were no guarantees it would be enough.

CHAPTER 45

AMMAN – LATE JUNE 2005

I flew into Amman, confident my business concept would interest companies attending the reconstruction conference. Although Erbil was the capital of the KRG, Sulaimaniyah was a sizeable city and province with its own government and no other British companies offered the business development and support services we could provide. The event was being held over a three-day weekend at the pricey Hyatt Hotel; Ali and I were staying at the InterContinental down the road. A bit of a faff, but the cost difference made it worthwhile.

On the first night I thought I saw a former colleague from the Corps; a guy who had passed selection and joined SBS. I had no idea if he was operational or had left the military, but I erred on the side of caution and avoided catching his eye or bumping into him in case I compromised an SF mission which might be under way.

Ali was in his element. Both knowledgeable and amicable, he grabbed delegates with his description of a Western-friendly oasis nestled against the Iranian border. The interest in our set-up and our capabilities grew stronger through the weekend, and I found myself involved in earnest discussions with some large corporations regarding the situation on the ground in Kurdistan. It was unfortunate, as a guy called Tim from leading accountants PWC told me over a drink one night, that we weren't based in Erbil.

'Nobody goes to Sulaimaniyah. You can't get anything done because they're all fighting each other for every contract.'

I tried to reassure him our contacts at the heart of the Sulaimaniyah administration would help avoid those type of issues. Unfortunately, there was a lot of truth in what he said. Kurdish officials there always wanted to talk about the largest contracts, but those projects with big budgets were the deals the locals scrapped over – blocking each other using patronage sprinkled throughout the bureaucratic machinery of state.

I needed a client focused on getting into the region with a clear business objective we could deliver. But for all our impressive talk, the lack of any track record was proving to be a problem. Despite the positive interest in our activities, we hadn't been able to secure that elusive first contract.

This conundrum was running through my head as I absent-mindedly washed my hands in the bathroom at the other end of the hall from our stand. I'd taken a wander around the other company stands to see if anyone else was winning business and to serve up a few more of my own cards amongst the delegates.

'John.'

I turned to my left to see JD, the SBS guy I thought I'd seen the previous day. I didn't want to compromise him, so I checked we were alone before replying, 'Hello mate, are you working?'

'Yes mate. We're watching you, so you might want to be careful.'

'Watching me… why?' My mind reeled, the surprise in my voice palpable.

'You know I can't tell you anything, mate. I just wanted to give you a heads-up, for old times' sake.'

The door began to open and the sound of accented English voices discussing a Baghdad power station spilled in. JD had drawn back into one of the cubicles and locked the door by the time the two well-dressed Arab gentlemen having the conversation appeared. I nodded a greeting at the new arrivals in the mirror as I dried my hands.

I processed JD's news. For the last four months I'd concentrated on the new opportunities beckoning in Kurdistan and heard nothing from the spooks, Faris in Baghdad, Al-Nura in Dubai, or even Mohammed back in London. Why now?

As I opened the door to leave, a frisson of fear fluttered inside. If my role in the Mosul mission had become known to the wrong people, to Abu Saif himself perhaps, then I could be in real trouble. In Kurdistan I was relatively safe in the Peshmerga and security forces bubble, but here in Jordan, homeland of the AQI leader al-Zarqawi, I now felt exposed and vulnerable.

If a threat had emerged, then why hadn't anyone told me? Was Claire in any danger back at home? At least I had good guys watching over me, but the not knowing was going to drive me insane. Much as I was grateful he'd spoken to me, it might have been better if JD hadn't said anything. The feeling of helplessness, of being caught up in events way beyond my control again, was suffocating.

For the rest of the day I remained wary of my surroundings and the appearance of people I didn't know. Utterly ridiculous considering the whole point of being at the conference was to meet new potential clients. Ali sensed something was wrong and tried to lighten the mood as we took a taxi down to the Coronation Street pub for a drink with a business contact of his living in Amman.

'One of the companies today, they were very interested. They are British engineering guys looking at oil by Chemchemal, near Suli. They want to meet with you tomorrow and I think they'll sign a contract with us. Don't worry, we will soon be celebrating.'

'That sounds good, mate. You've done well these last couple of days while I've had a couple of distractions. Now tell me again about this bloke we're meeting.'

★

Ali's contact turned out to be a friend who was a nice enough guy but of no business value for us. After two rounds of drinks I told Ali I'd see him later and headed outside to catch a taxi back to the hotel. As I stood in the embrace of the warm evening breeze, innocent laughter and chatter from the pub rose and fell as the door opened and swung shut. I casually cast my eyes over the nearest buildings, cars and pedestrians. How many were in the surveillance team and did they have eyes on me right now? Shame they couldn't just give me a lift and save me a few dinars.

I sensed something was amiss as soon as I entered my room at the InterContinental. Unlike the last couple of days, the room hadn't been cleaned and yet I could swear my bag and some clothes had been moved. I scoped out the bathroom warily. Empty. That cryptic message from JD really had put the wind up me. The room wasn't particularly untidy or dirty, so I bolted the door with the 'Do Not Disturb' sign displayed, kicked off my shoes, and grabbed a water from the minibar.

The usual horrific images of carnage in Baghdad were rolling across CNN when the doorbell chimed. I took the precaution of checking through the spyhole and sighed at the distorted view of Roper stood outside with a second man. I paused and then opened the door.

'Roper, what a pleasant surprise.'

'John.' Roper nodded and indicated I should let them in.

'I take it this isn't a social call,' I said over my shoulder as I walked over to take a seat at the desk by the window.

'No, Mr Pierce, this isn't a social call,' replied a serious-sounding American voice. 'Your presence is required in Baghdad and I've been ordered to make sure you get there.'

'I'm in the middle of a business conference. I can't just drop everything. When's this trip to Baghdad meant to be happening?'

'Forget the business conference. You'll be picked up here at oh-seven-hundred hours sharp and taken to Queen Alia for the flight into BIAP. This isn't an invitation. Now you know my British colleague Tom here, and he assures me you fully understand the situation. Is that right or do we have a problem?'

What a tosser! I looked at Roper's dispassionate face and then back at the American.

'No, there's no problem. I'm just right in the middle of something important and could really do without being dragged into Baghdad on a whim right now.'

'This is no whim, Mr Pierce. This is a rare opportunity to take down one evil son of a bitch, and unfortunately it appears you are the only person who can positively identify him. My people probably don't want you anywhere near this operation any more than you want to be there, but we both have our instructions and yours will take you to Baghdad tomorrow morning.'

'I'll be flying to Baghdad as well,' interjected Roper. 'We'll be going together.'

Something positive at least. I didn't trust spooks, and I was damn sure the American was one, but I got on well enough with Roper.

It wasn't as though I had any choice in the matter, so I listened to the skimpy briefing which told me little other than the flight to Baghdad would be followed by a helicopter ride to the US base in Balad. Then I considered whether to let Claire know where I was headed. No, better not to.

★

When Ali returned to the hotel later that night, I explained I had to travel at short notice for an urgent meeting, so he needed to man the fort in Amman for the final day of the conference.

'But what about the British engineers? I said you'd meet them tomorrow and I'm sure they will want to sign a contract with us.'

'You're just going to have to deal with them again, mate. Tell them I've been called away on urgent business and I'll be in touch in the next couple of days. Make sure you get their business cards with all their contact details and as much information about their objectives in Suli as possible.'

The meeting was the easy part. Now came the bad news.

'Listen, I haven't paid the organisers the balance owing for the stand yet. The money should be in my account in the next couple of days. Here's a cheque for the outstanding amount but try to delay giving it to them until the last possible moment to buy me some time. They're a British company, so hopefully they won't even bank it until they get back to the UK.'

Ali had a panicked look on his face. 'What about the hotel rooms? Are they paid?'

Bouncing cheques and leaving debts still got you into prison in much of the Middle East, so I couldn't blame him for being concerned.

'The rooms are paid already but there'll be room service and mini-bar charges to pay. Here's $200 to cover it.' As I handed him the cash, a grateful smile replaced the panic on his face.

'Thanks mate,' I said and meant it. 'I'll call you in a couple of days or so to let you know what's happening.'

The latest gloomy reports from CNN about insurgent attacks in Iraq prompted memories of the previous mission in Mosul. When I closed my eyes, I held the image of Abu Saif in my mind and willed the luck to roll our way so we got him this time.

CHAPTER 46

IRAQ

As the South African pilot began the steep descent into Baghdad, I exchanged a couple of quips with Roper about the quality of the flying on this Department of Defense contracted plane compared to a civilian airline. Until then, we'd hardly spoken since his car had picked me up from the hotel dead on 07:00 and we'd gone through an extensive set of checks and searches at the airport before taking off at 09:30.

I think we both felt comfortable enough to get lost in our own thoughts rather than trying to force a conversation – I did anyway. It wasn't as though we could chat about our recent work together or the coming mission in front of other passengers, even if they were primarily US military personnel.

I'm sure Roper was also still smarting after nearly causing a diplomatic incident at the airport scanner when a customs official seized a GPS from his hand luggage. I tried not to show it, but I found the whole incident highly amusing. Roper was furious, and it took a gaggle of senior Jordanian officials to finally placate him and see to it his GPS was returned. So much for us keeping a low profile.

We didn't corkscrew into Baghdad as severely as my last flight out of here a year before, although it wasn't far off. Everyone on board, including me, breathed the obligatory sigh of relief when the wheels touched down and the plane began to slow. Personally, I was more concerned the pilot would miscalculate and slam the aircraft into the deck than an unlikely surface-to-air missile attack. Either way, I was back in Baghdad.

At the bottom of the aircraft steps we were tagged by a beefy American wearing Oakley sunglasses. Suddenly exposed to the blinding sun reflecting off the tarmac, I dug around for my own pair.

'Mr Roper? Mr Pierce? I'm Todd from TF145, can I see your ID please?'

During the minimalist briefing the previous evening, Roper's American spook buddy, Carl, had issued me with a Department of Defense ID Card adorned with my photo. No blue or red stripe to denote a foreign national either – a 'clear' badge. It did the trick here without needing to fish out my passport.

'Outstanding. This way please.'

After identifying our luggage as it emerged off the back of the small jet, Todd handed us each a Kevlar helmet and a pair of yellow ear defenders before pointing towards our destination across the apron: the flight line for the onward Black Hawk ride to LSA Anaconda in Balad, eighty kilometres to the north.

There was already some kit in the back of the SUV as we climbed in, which I assumed belonged to Todd because another soldier sat in the driver's seat. It was therefore no surprise when he said, 'I'll be flying with you to Anaconda, so you don't need to worry about any instructions for arrival. I can escort you to the TOC once we're there.'

Our two-helicopter flight was already fuelled and ready for take-off. I donned the helmet and ear defenders and followed Todd and Roper towards the assigned Black Hawk. After heaving our gear into the helo, where the crew chief secured it with the rest, we clambered in and I tried to nonchalantly fix the four-pronged seat belt without giving away it was my first time in this type of helicopter. When I settled back for the ride after solving the puzzle, none of my fellow passengers were giving me that 'who's this clown' look. Even better, the crew chief went over to a soldier already on board when we arrived and made him refasten his seat belt correctly. I wasn't the only first-timer then.

I lifted my head and took a deep breath of the warm, dry air. Now I'd been sucked into the operational tempo of things again, I was looking forward to getting on with it.

Less than twenty minutes after take-off we touched down at LSA

Anaconda. Directed past the imposing blast walls, I smiled at the 'Catfish Air' sign above the small terminal building. To my mind it had shades of the Vietnam War about it. No sooner had we entered than Todd was greeted by two similarly bulky guys in American uniforms and we were directed out to two waiting SUVs.

'The SF lines are at the other end of the main runway,' said a British voice to my surprise.

'Things are fairly manic right now, so we're taking you to the Ops Room where you'll get a briefing and the head shed will decide what we're doing with you.'

I didn't know if he was aware we were Brits, but he didn't bat an Oakley-clad eye when I replied, 'Cheers mate.'

As I walked into the TOC, my eyes swept the room and pinged Joe Holmes engaged in conversation with a senior British officer. Then I noticed the unmistakable figure and broadening smile of Katie who was walking in my direction while Dexter walked and talked alongside her. There is no doubt the sight of a pretty woman who's pleased to see you is a morale booster of the highest order.

'All fixed up then?' she said on reaching me and Roper, making a show of scanning my face for signs of lasting damage. I hoped for a hug and the chance to breathe in some of the alluring perfume I'd vaguely detected, but this was a special forces operations room not a bar, and I wasn't getting that lucky.

Dexter was smiling as his hand shot out for a vigorous round of handshakes, first with Roper then with me. 'Great to see you guys. This time we'll get the job finished.'

'I hope so. Some of us have got real work to be getting on with.'

Dexter didn't miss a beat. 'Don't worry. You'll soon be able to get back to your nice, comfortable civilian life and leave us to get on with protecting the free world.'

Unlike a lot of the Americans I knew, he took attempts at British sarcasm and irony in his stride.

'Talking of which,' said Roper, 'can you bring us up to speed now or are we due into a formal briefing?'

Katie exchanged nods with Dexter before she replied, 'Sure guys, come with us and we'll update you. FYI, elements of the mission have already launched, and your team will be deploying tonight. You'll get those details in a tactical briefing here at fourteen hundred hours, but we'll focus on the intel situation with you now so you're up to speed.'

★

We sat down in the Intel Section with a strong coffee each, and Katie and Dexter filled us in on the latest developments and a sketchy outline of the mission. After Katie had run through a general situation brief which echoed the doom and gloom from the latest news reports, Dexter took over.

'The NSA and your GCHQ have made a breakthrough in our SIGINT penetration of various aspects of the insurgency. In recent weeks we've been using this new capability to link personalities and better understand the AQI organisation, particularly its command structure and control methodology. Combined with our existing HUMINT sources and intel from counter-insurgency raids and other initiatives, we believe there is a strong likelihood a meeting of senior insurgent leaders is taking place tomorrow at a location north-west of Muqdadiyah in Diyala Province, seventy-five klicks east of here.'

'How strong a likelihood?' I asked. 'Are we talking the same as the Hawija and Mosul intel, which was a bag of bollocks, or is it going to happen for real this time?'

'John, you understand how these things work,' came Roper's admonishing tone from next to me.

'No, it's a fair question,' said Dexter holding up his hands, although his face betrayed that I'd annoyed him.

'We're certain a meeting is taking place tomorrow and we know that a mobile phone belonging to a key AQI Internal Security chief has moved to a farm complex north-west of Muqdadiyah, where two of our British teams have him and his team under surveillance right now. Their situation reports indicate a loose cordon has been set up around the complex and preparations appear to be under way for the arrival of more people.'

Dexter paused.

'Our understanding is the meeting is due to be chaired by Abu Saif al-Tikriti, the Shadow Emir.'

He directed that last comment towards me and took a beat before continuing, letting the information sink in.

'Al-Zarqawi is reportedly still recuperating from his recent, unspecified injuries, probably sustained during the operation in Mosul, and is not expected to be present. The location and terrain are challenging but this is considered, almost unanimously amongst those whose opinions count, as a high-grade opportunity to kill or capture significant AQI personalities and disrupt insurgent operational planning.'

If he thought I'd buy into that without question he was wrong.

'Almost unanimously. So not everyone "whose opinion counts" is on board with this then?'

Dexter sighed. 'John, there's never any guarantees, but everything points to this being our chance to finally get Abu Saif and take down other senior leaders in a single swoop. Even so, opportunities like this must still pass a high bar before any related operation is given the green light. This op has passed that threshold and has the green light. What else is there to say? Everyone here knows we might not get the result we want. Hell, there's been enough false leads and dodgy intel this last two years to last us all a lifetime. When it happens, we just have to suck it up and go again. I realise you've been pulled into this without any choice, but you're here now and you need to get on board with it and focus on your important role in helping us achieve the mission objectives.'

I hadn't meant to be a dick about it, but I was still riled about being press-ganged in Amman to join in with another half-arsed scheme dreamt up by British and American spooks. No point banging on about it though. I'd made my point and probably already gone too far with it.

'I know Dex, I'm on board no problem. I just have a healthy habit of questioning everything. If a plan is good, then it should be able to defend itself against robust questions.'

That didn't necessarily mean I thought this plan passed muster. For these guys all sat here kitted up and itching to take the fight to AQI it was a no-brainer. For me, trying to set up a business with limited resources, it was a huge pain in the arse if I was going to get dragged into every new plan for the foreseeable future until one of them eventually worked or I got fucked up.

'Now that's cleared up…' Roper spoke pointedly at me before switching his attention to Dexter and Katie, '…can you give us some more details of how we're going to be involved?'

Katie answered matter-of-factly. 'You guys and Dexter are deploying with a team tonight to an OP giving you eyes on the target farm complex. Dexter and John will make a positive identification of the High Value Targets when they arrive, and the Task Force will execute the assault once the GO codeword is issued. That's as much as we can tell you now. The rest of the details will be in the fourteen hundred briefing.'

So, there it was. We'd be deployed at the pointy end of the spear again in another insurgent stronghold. My first thought: 'I wish I had better footwear with me.' My Merrell shoes were great, but for padding around the wilds of Diyala my KSB boots back at home would have been better. My second thought: 'Ah ha – Roper's coming along this time.'

CHAPTER 47

1400 HOURS – LSA ANACONDA SF TACTICAL
OPERATIONS CENTRE

A series of mission briefings had already taken place over the previous twenty-four hours, but Roper, me, and three other latecomers assembled by the Intel Section desks in the TOC for our own intimate presentation. Joe Holmes welcomed us to the TOC with a warm handshake and introduced a British SAS colonel, Ben Sheridan. Sheridan was businesslike rather than friendly, probably to be expected considering he had at least two teams out on the ground already for this operation, and no doubt other missions in progress elsewhere. Alternatively, he might just have been a cold fish.

The arrival moments before the briefing of my team leader from Mosul, Greg, was a welcome surprise which made me jump up into a back-slapping embrace without thinking. All very American and unusually demonstrative for me.

Greg smiled as we pulled apart. 'Man, they pulled you in for this show again. They only told me this morning. You look better than the last time I saw you,' which made me laugh.

'It's really good to see you, mate. You've had a shave this time then?'

His appearance was a lot less wild than the last time I'd seen him, and a grin filled Greg's newly revealed, rugged, All-American features. Then a touch of sadness filtered out from my memory and I paused, wanting to say something about Ricky, but unable to find the right words.

Maybe Greg sensed what I was thinking. 'We'll get the job finished this time. For Ricky.'

'Yeah.' I nodded, still stuck for words.

The extra time available to plan and execute this mission compared to Hawija and Mosul was evident in the pre-positioning of assets, contingency planning, and the sense of confidence round the TOC that the Task Force were ahead of the game on this one. Two SAS teams had already deployed in proximity to the target farm complex, with one of them ready to guide us into the OP position that night. Positioned slightly further back from the target to reduce the chance of accidental compromise, the SAS teams would still be within range to provide immediate support if our American-led team got into trouble.

I smiled when I heard our helicopter insertion would be into the safe hands of General Rashid's Peshmerga on the edge of the Kurdish-controlled terrain north of the Hamrin Lake. Rather than having the helicopters drop us closer to the target and risk spooking the AQI security team at the farm, the Kurds would be using their local knowledge to drive us to a drop-off point to the north-east of the target.

From there we would patrol on foot the last few kilometres to a final RV secured by one of the SAS teams, GOLF 20. Clearly coming from an army background rather than Royal Marines, Colonel Sheridan referred to us tabbing to the RV location rather than the bootneck version of 'yomping', giving me a sideways glance as he said it.

The second SAS team, GOLF 21, would maintain eyes on the target as the final Close Target Recce (CTR) was undertaken and we maneuvered into the OP position. Our OP team, designated EAGLE 6, would be commanded by Greg and included guys I already knew from Mosul and a couple of others I hadn't met before.

Provided the AQI leadership showed up, Dexter and I would be key in identifying Abu Saif and other High Value Targets. Katie and the other intel guys in Balad and elsewhere would be hooked in to the live feeds coming from our surveillance cameras on the ground and an overhead drone.

The way I saw it, provided he showed up then either Abu Saif should be neutralised, or the Task Force should get enough high definition snaps of his ugly mug to make me redundant. Just in case those eventualities failed to materialise, I was going to make damn sure Dexter got an eyeful of the big man from Baghdad, so they could rely on his recognition skills instead of mine if Abu Saif did somehow evade capture. Much as I respected these people and their objectives, I was an outsider here and had my own battles to fight elsewhere.

If the mission was completed as planned, then me and the rest of EAGLE 6 would be extracted by helicopter. The contingency plan if the raid was aborted, or otherwise went awry, was for the team to withdraw on foot. Either to an emergency RV to the north with the Kurds, or another to the east at the Hamrin Lake dam where US troops would be located.

A mix of American SF and Delta Force, designated Team SILVER, were ready here at the base to conduct a heliborne assault to kill or capture the AQI leaders and seize laptops, documents, phones, and anything else that might provide useful intel. They hadn't flown forward to the closest US base, FOB Normandy, to avoid raising any suspicion from either the accompanying increased volume of helicopter flights, or their presence being noted by insurgent sympathisers. It meant a longer flight time but I think it suited everyone to keep the preparations close to home at the Special Forces HQ here in Balad, which I'd now heard was nicknamed The Factory.

A platoon of US Army Rangers, Team BRONZE, was already deployed forward to FOB Warhorse near Baquba where it had joined with elements of the Multi-National Division North Central (MND-NC) Quick Reaction Force (QRF) commanded by 42nd Infantry Division HQ. They were ready to bounce up into Muqdadiyah as soon as the assault had been triggered. They would establish a wide cordon and conduct aggressive patrolling to try to deflect the locals from realising the mission's primary target was the farm complex.

It might be unlikely the regular locals would know about the AQI meeting, but a helicopter raid on a single location would quickly become widely known, arousing interest and suspicion. That could result in AQI making immediate contingencies which might lessen the value of any intel obtained. Team BRONZE and the QRF would also act as both a southern and western cut-off should any of the AQI fighters escape the net at the farm and try to make a break towards Baquba or Balad Ruz.

At FOB Normandy, the US military base immediately east of Muqdadiyah, a TF145 team, SILVER 5, had flown in to direct support from elements of the 30th Infantry Division based there. Besides acting as the eastern cut-off, this unit would have men positioned at the Hamrin Lake dam, one of the emergency RVs for our team if we needed to make our way out on foot. I sincerely hoped we'd be enjoying the planned helo extraction back to Balad with the main airborne element of Team SILVER.

The northern cut-off comprised General Rashid's Peshmerga, designated Force KILO. I had no doubt my Kurdish friends Dara and Hamza would be at the heart of their involvement. Force KILO would be stationed ready to extract us from an emergency RV north of the Diyala River if the situation demanded.

Finally, a plethora of fast air, helicopter, and drone assets were allocated in support for surveillance, targeting, logistics, and medevac.

Apart from a weather advisory about possible high winds coming in from the east, the situation was ideally poised in most respects, with everything set. We just needed the AQI boys to come to the party or it would all be a damp squib.

The GO codeword: 'DISNEYLAND'.

The ABORT code that none of us wanted to hear: 'LOCK KNIFE'.

CHAPTER 48

It was shortly after 20:00 when our two-helicopter flight of Black Hawks from the Night Stalkers took off into the warm summer evening. Yet again I'd only been issued with a sidearm, this time a Glock 17 with six magazines of seventeen 9mm calibre rounds. A 9mm weapon didn't have the stopping power of a .45 but it still did the job at close range. Roper and Dexter were both issued the same weapon. The Glocks were for our emergency personal protection only; our requests for rifles turned down flat.

Roper was on the flight, although he'd be remaining with the Kurds of Force KILO as the TF145 liaison officer after his successful performance in Mosul. The communications issues prevalent during that mission had been partly solved by providing the Kurds with equipment and frequencies so they could communicate with the rest of the Task Force units if necessary. Unfortunately, very few of the Kurds spoke decent English so it wouldn't be without its challenges.

I got the impression Roper was envious he wouldn't be getting into the thick of things. Much as I really ought to have been back in Amman negotiating a client contract, if I had to be here then I was glad to be at the business end. Thoughts of danger or fear didn't come into it. I had no doubt everyone involved also wanted to take as active a part as possible, each wanting and willing to step up to help ensure the mission's success and have the backs of their oppos.

Our destination south-west of the Kurdish town of Kifri was about ninety kilometres as the crow flies. We flew a circuitous route and it took nearly forty-five minutes before the helicopter flared for landing. After we disembarked, the birds sped away to the north and their departure left me with a sense of abandonment, as helicopter insertions always had since I was a young marine. A feeling that contact with the world outside your immediate teammates had suddenly been cut.

With the sound of the Black Hawks receding into the distance, our Kurdish welcoming party emerged from the edges of the makeshift LZ to greet us with broad smiles and excited chatter.

'Chonit bashi, Mr John?' *(Hello, how are you?)* Dara had appeared in front of me with a big grin on his face before shaking my hand warmly.

'Bashum, supas,' *(I'm good, thank you)* used up about twenty-five per cent of the Kurdish I knew.

Dara laughed and turned to speak in Kurdish to someone behind him. From the shadows emerged General Rashid with a welcoming smile.

'Mr John, chonit bashi.'

'Bashum, supas.' I repeated to the obvious amusement of the General and the rest of his Peshmerga.

General Rashid laughed and slapped my back before calling Nabil over.

Nabil was straight into the groove. 'Mr Tom, Mr John, the General welcomes you back to Kurdistan and wishes for you the protection of Allah for your mission.'

'Please thank the General,' said Roper. 'Now you recognise Mr Greg here. He and the General need to discuss the next phase of the mission so we can move out on schedule at twenty-one hundred hours.'

Greg's height meant he dwarfed the naturally diminutive Kurds, and his camouflaged face and tactical load-out made him look the epitome of a special forces soldier. 'It's an honour to meet you, sir,' he said to the General with Nabil translating. 'Shall we move to the vehicles and check the route?'

Greg, the General, Nabil, and Roper moved to the lowered tailgate of a Toyota Hilux pickup and spread a map out in front of them. Like the rest of EAGLE 6 I already knew the details of the route, so stayed at a distance with Dexter as the glow of red torchlight illuminated the map.

About thirty Peshmerga were gathered round the vehicles chatting quietly and laughing less quietly, no doubt in the certain knowledge they were in safe surroundings.

Our American team, however, had naturally moved into all-round defence to cover the discussion between their commander and the General. I could see Greg's second-in-command, Wolfman Russ, and Neil, who'd both been with the team in Mosul. Moose was also here on the far side of the cars. The other two members of the team were a hilarious black guy named Morgan who should have been on stage, and a big unit from Texas with an M60 machine gun that looked like a toy in his hands, unsurprisingly called 'Tex'.

We mounted up into the six-vehicle convoy at 20:55 and set off five minutes earlier than scheduled. I noticed the Kurds had removed either the bulbs or the fuses to ensure the interior lights of the vehicles didn't come on when the doors opened. They might have appeared relaxed in their own backyard, but they knew what they were doing and had been doing it for a long time.

One of the Hilux's operated well forward of the convoy as a scout vehicle and the other dropped to the rear as a sweep vehicle, just in case we were approached from behind. Roper and the eight of us from EAGLE 6 were in four Land Cruisers which made their way, using sidelights only, towards the Hamrin Lake. We crested a hill to see the large lake spread before us, glittering faintly under the night sky even without any moonlight.

I travelled in Dara's vehicle with Neil, behind the General's lead vehicle which had Greg, Roper, and Nabil on board. It was impossible to follow the messages in Kurdish coming over the radio from the lead scout and the replies from the General, but we encountered no delays or obvious issues.

West of the lake, the hilly terrain morphed into uncultivated open land. Trees, bushes, and grassland loomed in front and to the sides as we wound our way down narrow roads towards the drop-off point. By my watch it was 21:45 when we finally slowed before coming to a halt; the four SUVs each twenty metres or so apart as the lead scout reported in. After a short while we rolled forward again and pulled up behind the scout vehicle. Dara turned and squeezed my hand briefly before we all debussed into the cooling night air.

The Peshmerga moved like a well-oiled machine, fanning out noiselessly to provide cover as EAGLE 6 assembled and moved off to a flank into a hasty ambush position. As the sound of the Kurdish vehicles driving away merged into the night – another link to the outside world gone – we deployed ready to react to an attack if the drop off had been compromised. Without a rifle, I might as well have been naked. I shook my head as I remembered Mosul and felt the first fingertips of fear crawling over me since I'd arrived back in Iraq.

In the planning and briefing stages, it's easy to focus on objectives, contingencies, assets, and other factors. However, once you're on the ground and the tangible reality of those plans is apparent, it's only natural to feel vulnerable and fearful of what could be out there and what might happen. It was for me anyway, and not having a rifle didn't help. For this mission Dexter and I were important elements, but to our SF comrades in EAGLE 6 we comprised a human cargo to be nurtured and protected. After our experience in Mosul, at least they knew I wasn't completely out of my depth in this environment and could contribute usefully if things went kinetic.

Dexter and I took up prone positions immediately behind the five men facing back towards our approach route. Neil lay prone behind us, guarding against any approach from the rear with a boot over my lower leg and the other across one of Dexter's.

After ten minutes lying in the dry grass, my night vision had improved to reveal a mix of surrounding foliage and trees in greater detail. With no sign of compromise detected, the guys in front rose into kneeling positions and the nearest leant over and tapped me on the shoulder. Time to move out. I passed on the signal by tapping my boot against both Neil's calf and Dexter's foot. After we'd risen, Greg's camouflaged face came close enough for me to recognise him, and he used his hands to indicate the positions for Dexter and me in the order of march. We'd be in the middle of the team as it moved in single file, as per the team briefing earlier that day.

The route to the final RV was just under eight kilometres and the plan had us reaching it by 02:30, in just over four and a half hours. For a regular bimble that would be plenty of time, but we needed to patrol with caution to avoid any risk of compromising our presence. It was perfectly achievable, provided we didn't encounter any unexpected issues.

Although sunrise wasn't until 06:00, the pre-dawn Fajr prayer was scheduled for 04:15 and we knew from the two GOLF teams already on the ground for the last twenty-four hours that most of the AQI security team would be awake at that time to pray. We could also expect some movement between outlying farms and the nearest mosque.

After reaching the final RV, we would still need to carefully advance the final few hundred metres. One of the British teams had performed a Close Target Recce (CTR) of the farm complex and both identified and prepared the closest workable OP position in a nearby treeline. However, the plan still required Greg, Neil, and Morgan to move forward with two of the British team for a final CTR before Greg returned to lead in the rest of EAGLE 6. The preparation work by the British team was intended to ensure the position was suitably hidden from view in daylight, which could be difficult to assess in the darkness.

The team forded the Diyala River (known as the Sirwan River by the Kurds) at a narrow and shallow point previously identified by one of the GOLF teams. We sliced through the night with purpose, boxing around several buildings and farms due to signs of activity and the occasional barking dog. Although our advance was frequently interrupted as Greg stopped to assess potential obstacles and make route adjustments, we made good time.

As the patrol closed towards the RV, we began to encounter more signs of cultivated land and an increasing density of inhabited dwellings. Our tactical movement became more cautious and resulted in slower progress as Greg selected shorter bounds to make best use of the available cover. Regular wooded areas helped conceal our advance, and even in more open terrain we were often cloaked by an abundance of tall grass, bushes, and small pockets of trees. All despite the appearance of the moon adding some unwelcome illumination to the proceedings.

My watch showed 02:15 as we went firm close to the final RV. On schedule, but we'd needed all the time available. After a few tense minutes lying in the swaying grass, straining to hear any signs of suspicious activity above the increasingly strong breeze, I got the signal to move and immediately passed it on to Dexter behind me. I hadn't been able to see what was happening up ahead, but I assumed we had linked up with the GOLF team waiting to guide us into the OP. A couple of minutes later we dropped into all-round defence and a camouflaged face soon appeared to my left and mouthed 'Final RV' in confirmation.

I knew from the mission briefing that the OP was located 200 metres to our front, and soon Greg, Neil, and Morgan would be led to that position by two of the SAS men from GOLF 20. As the five of them slipped away into the night, I shivered from the rising breeze. It was 03:05 when three figures returned. I couldn't be sure who was who in the darkness, but it should have been Greg and the two Brits. According to the mission plan, Neil and Morgan would have remained in position at the OP while Greg came back to lead in the rest of us from EAGLE 6.

The Brits would now patrol to their own OP position set back from the target and watch our flanks and rear, ready to provide support if necessary. The other team in the vicinity, GOLF 21, was deployed on the other side of the farm complex, again set back a few hundred metres from the target.

After picking our way slowly to the treeline only eighty metres from the target location, I was directed into my assigned position inside a prepared hide. I took off my rucksack, checked the time on my watch, 03:29, and felt a flash of exhilaration now we had completed this phase of the mission on time and without compromise. The exhilaration was quickly replaced with the weight of tiredness.

It was crucial that Dexter and I kept sharp for our observation duties later in the day, so we'd been instructed to get our heads down on arrival. Greg and the team would take care of sentry duties. Once we had daylight to work with, then we'd need to set up the optics and cameras and adjust our position as may be needed – hopefully nothing too drastic. Right now, all we could see through the observation slits was a whole load of blackness. I threw a piece of chocolate into my mouth before electing to go through the hassle of finding and then donning a fleece over the top of my body armour.

The wind now whipped through the surrounding trees, but at least Dexter and I were protected from the worst of the elements in the dug-in hide. I shimmied into a comfortable position and felt warm and snug as sleep began to roll over me. Putting on the fleece had been a good call. However, before I dropped off, the bite of a mosquito reminded me it wasn't quite five-star living.

Although I'm a light sleeper in the field, the 4.15am call to prayer from the closest mosques had failed to wake me. Instead, it was Dexter's hand on my shoulder that later roused me to a state of instant alertness. He used hand signals to indicate the optics and cameras laid out in front of him and where they needed to be set up. I peered through the nearest observation slit to orientate myself.

Well done to the Hereford lads; our location was ideal in relation to the target. Not only were we close, but our field of view was excellent. I could already see an armed figure standing by a dusty Land Cruiser near one of the farm buildings. Although I couldn't make out his features clearly, I knew the optics and cameras would capture him and anyone else who moved into our view with impressive clarity. We also had a great view of the road and track leading into the farm which the GOLF teams had reported to be the primary entrance.

This was going to work.

The wind hadn't dropped, and the daylight revealed dust in the air which would reduce the effectiveness of our observation equipment, but not yet to any significant degree. Provided it didn't deteriorate, we should be okay. Dexter and I worked together to assemble the tripods, optics, cameras, and satellite transmitter.

As I'd expected, the optics zoomed in with shocking definition on the armed man and a second who had since joined him carrying two glasses of chai. My confidence I would recognise Abu Saif if he came into view was absolute. I'd need to bide my time though; it was only approaching 06:30 and the meeting wasn't expected until lunchtime or early afternoon. If that intel was accurate, it meant at least six tense hours of watching and waiting and hoping a full-blown dust storm didn't arrive.

By 11:00 only weak sunlight filtered through the swirling dust, although still enough for our equipment to obtain an acceptable level of detail as we observed the AQI security team moving around the buildings and the perimeter. The one positive from the storm: it helped to conceal us and our limited movement. Our position had been well chosen and prepared, but any additional camouflage was welcome.

New arrivals appeared in two white Land Cruisers at 11:30, which excited Dexter. As the cars stopped in our sight line, he recognised one of the men climbing out as a suspected AQI logistics commander. His excitement was infectious and it began to bubble inside me as well. The positive attitude in the hide was dampened when Greg informed us the satellite link for the camera was inoperable due to the weather and the drones could not eyeball the target. The helicopters carrying Team SILVER might not be able to fly if this got worse.

I imagined the TOC in a state of permanent planning revision as the potential ramifications of the worsening weather had to be taken into account. The other pieces on the board – the two GOLF teams, Team BRONZE at Warhorse, TF 1-30 at Normandy, the Kurds of Force KILO and even our own team – might have a bigger part to play than expected.

Greg crawled up to the edge of our hide with an update: 'Team SILVER has been lifted forward to FOB Warhorse, ready to insert by road if the conditions result in Sus Ops *(Suspended Operations)* for the birds.'

Positive news, although it was still a forty-kilometre road move from Warhorse. I bet the Meteorological Section were earning their wages today as they battled to provide an accurate forecast the planners at the TOC could rely on.

Another three vehicles rolled into view just after midday and I strained to see if any of them contained Abu Saif. Dexter ticked another two commanders on his list, but they contained no-one I recognised.

It had been a long time since I'd attended the Terrorist Recognition Instructor course and worked in the role while deployed to Northern Ireland, but I had revised my fading notes recently and reached into my memory. Rather than needing a Jedi mind trick, I quickly remembered the feature recognition aide-mémoire in my rucksack and dug it out.

It was nothing I didn't know already, but I found it useful to remind myself of the features that didn't change, irrespective of the efforts a person might make to alter their appearance. Shapes and positions on the face for eyes, ears, mouths, and noses; bone structure for cheeks, chin, and head shape. All these were unchangeable without reconstructive surgery and I mentally summoned the features of Abu Saif, trying to imagine him with different hairstyles, completely bald, bearded, clean-shaven, and everything in between.

Efforts could be made to disguise height with a stoop or limp, but Abu Saif was a big guy and that would be tough to conceal. However, for all my earlier positive thinking, it had been so long since I last met him that a surge of doubt flashed through me. Would I definitely recognise him again? Had I already missed his arrival? No, I was certain he hadn't been any of the men we'd seen arrive so far.

An hour later the wind had noticeably dropped, and the sun made an effort to break through the reduced level of dust in the air. I settled behind the eyepiece and slowly ran the optic from right to left and back again. More armed men were present than at any time during the morning. One of them began shouting and pointing, eliciting a burst of energetic activity from the previously lethargic group.

'Dex, something's happening.'

In my peripheral vision, I saw Dexter check the camera and drop his face behind the viewfinder.

'Roger, I see three vehicles approaching.'

I swung my scope back to the left and the lead vehicle filled my view. I couldn't make out the features of anyone in that or the other two Land Cruisers yet. The SUVs pulled to a stop in our line of sight and the front passenger of the lead vehicle jumped out. He looked familiar, but I couldn't place him – probably nothing. Armed men spilled out of the front and rear vehicles as I searched for signs of my target.

A face suddenly filled the display and disappeared just as quickly. Someone had walked across my field of view, much closer to our position than any time before. I reared back and instead scanned the ground with my mark one eyeball. An armed man stood taking a piss about fifty metres in front of us, but I saw no sign anyone was patrolling in our direction. Satisfied, I adopted my position again behind the scope.

The passenger of the second vehicle, a top-of-the-range white Land Cruiser, had disembarked and opened the rear passenger door. Out stepped Abu Saif. He'd hardly changed since I'd last seen him. The same haircut, the same shadow on his jawline, and definitely the same intelligent features. I had no doubt in my mind that the figure in front of me was the man introduced to me the previous year in Baghdad as Abu Saif al-Tikriti. When he turned his head, he seemed to look straight back down the scope at me.

I shook off the unnerving sensation.

'Positive ID Abu Saif, rear passenger vehicle two, now walking past vehicle one.'

I expected Dexter to react as though we'd just scored the winning goal in a cup final, but he was oddly subdued in his response.

'Are you sure? Can you check again that you have PID?'

Abu Saif was now being greeted by the earlier arrivals. As he shook hands, embraced, and kissed his insurgent colleagues on both cheeks, I had a clear view of his face again, and then again.

'Confirm PID Abu Saif.'

'Fuck,' said Dexter quietly, 'I know that guy. I need to speak with the TOC.'

I turned to look at him. 'PID of Abu Saif and your other guys, so we're good to go, yeah? Get this show on the road.'

But he looked like he'd swallowed a turd as he crawled out of the hide to send a secure message to the TOC from Morgan's radio.

CHAPTER 49

Alone in the hide, I focused back on the expansive greetings taking place less than a hundred metres in front of me. I didn't understand what Dexter's problem was; surely we were about to deal AQI and the insurgency a serious body blow. When the main group finally entered the largest building, Dexter still hadn't returned. With the weather brightening up, Team SILVER could be summoned to arrive in less than fifteen minutes.

Dexter reappeared with Greg behind him and slid in next to me.

'Are we going to DISNEYLAND?' I joked.

'That's a negative,' said Dexter. 'The mission has been aborted. The abort code LOCK KNIFE has been issued and we'll be exfiltrating on foot to the north.'

What the hell?

'Why? We have PID. Why is the mission aborted for fuck's sake? We've got them sat here for the taking. We can decimate the al-Qaeda command.'

'John, I'm gutted about this as well. But the man you've identified as Abu Saif is a senior Sunni official in the Iraq government and, far more importantly, has recently been recruited by the Agency. There's no doubt about it. He is the CIA's latest prize asset.'

'What? So, what is he doing here planning terrorist attacks if he's spying for the CIA? And hang on a minute, if he's an asset for the CIA, why the hell didn't you know who he was?'

'My understanding is that no-one on our side knew he was the Shadow Emir. In fact, they're going to find it difficult to accept back at Langley if they didn't know already. The point is that if that man is the Shadow Emir, then his potential use to us is far greater than anyone anticipated. His recruitment is already being touted by Langley as a game changer. If he's the Shadow Emir, then it moves things into a different league.'

I couldn't take it all in. Greg's face screamed frustration; he wasn't loving this turn of events either.

'Put it this way,' said Dexter, 'killing and capturing Abu Saif and the others at this meeting would gain us a short-term success, but extinguish an intelligence opening which could give us a critical long-term advantage in the fight against the insurgency. This was a call made from the very top. And I mean the very top. However much you or I might not like it, sitting here right now with our fingers on the trigger, the Joint Chiefs and the intelligence community, hell most likely the president himself, agree the most effective option right now is to abort the mission. It might feel like losing a battle, but it will help to win the war.'

'But no-one can be sure of that. It's possible Zarqawi himself could be on his way here. After all the months of effort, the sacrifices, to finally get into position to take the shot and… we're just going to let it go.'

I felt drained. I understood the argument and in the grand scheme of things it made little difference to me one way or the other, but this simply seemed wrong.

Whether he really felt it or not, Dexter was full of the positives.

'It may not seem like it to you, but it's a good result. We've now identified the suspected number two to Zarqawi, and he's already a US intelligence asset. Don't underestimate how vital a development this could be. If he's trying to play us, them, or both sides, then it will catch up with him and soon. You've done well here today, and it will help the fight against the insurgency.'

Begrudgingly, I could see this was a compelling argument, even if it still tasted like failure right now. So unsatisfying. I shook my head and sighed.

'Fuck it. So, what happens now?'

Greg took over. 'We remain in situ until nightfall, before moving back about a klick to the forested area to our north-east and going firm. In the quiet hours tonight, we'll make our way north to the ERV with the Kurds across the Diyala River, in coordination with the two GOLF teams. We need to keep our discipline and not switch off. It's vital we don't get compromised on our way out of here. Now the raid's cancelled, let's hope the storm blows up some more.'

Great. At least five hours sat in the dirt before we'd be moving and the urge to take a shit had crept up on me out of nowhere. I hadn't had to Ziploc my shit and carry it with me in a long, long time, but at least I supposed this would be the last time ever.

That afternoon we watched as the insurgents left in the same three groups of vehicles in which they'd arrived. The only difference was the orange dust now coating them from the storm that had diminished to a windy day with occasional gusts of sand and grit. Abu Saif and his three cars left first, just before 15:30, with the other two groups leaving soon afterwards.

By 16:30 the AQI security team appeared to have left, although we couldn't be sure if there might be a small residual presence.

There was no discernible change in the attitude or vigilance of our team. Like me, I'm sure all the others were very much aware the compromise in Mosul had occurred during the extraction phase. It was vital we remained switched on and didn't let complacency set in.

We packed up all the equipment before last light and stood-to as the daylight merged into twilight and then darkness. Soon after 19:00, Greg led the team out of the OP and towards our new harbour position in the forest. Thirty minutes later, we were stood-to again in a hasty ambush position at the new harbour location, watching and listening for any signs of compromise and enemy attack.

Once we'd been stood down, the team began a sentry routine that would last until our planned departure at 23:00. Dexter and I weren't included in the roster, so it was a welcome chance to catch some sleep.

This time I didn't bother with my fleece; too much admin to get it on and off. As I tried to nestle into a comfortable position, I already regretted my decision. When I turned over, something dug into my chest. I reached into a pocket under the body armour and there was the recognisable shape and feel of my taped-up lucky eyeball. An image of Becky's smiling face popped into my head, followed by my other girls, Claire and Natalie. But rather than sadness and longing, it inspired determination. Determination to stay switched on and get home in one piece.

The route to the ERV was longer than our insertion – about twelve kilometres in total. We were heading for a different crossing point over the Diyala River and the ERV itself was at a different location to our drop-off. Whilst the two GOLF teams were also moving north in our vicinity, their pickup locations were a few kilometres further on than ours. The plan called for all the teams to be extracted before first light.

It was after 02:00 when, having given a wide berth to a compound with a generator running and lights blazing, I almost jumped out of my skin as a dog barked viciously nearby to my front left. I couldn't see it in the darkness, but I tensed, expecting a sudden flash of teeth and saliva at any minute. The signal to go firm came from the man ahead. I dropped to one knee and motioned for Dexter behind me to do the same.

The barking escalated as an ominous blur closed on the point man, Greg, before it stopped and issued a low, menacing growl. Sudden movement from Greg, a sickening crunch of bone accompanied by a yelp, then silence. I squinted towards the unclear shapes, Glock in hand in case the dog, its friends, or its owner approached. I looked slightly off-centre for better visibility and saw Greg sheathing a large knife. I assumed the dog had come off second best because it lay unmoving in front of him.

Greg dropped into a kneeling position with the butt of his weapon back in his shoulder. He signalled Neil and Morgan in front of me to grab the dog's body and hide it in the tangle of vegetation to our right. After lifting the body and throwing it into the bushes, they rejoined the team and we prepared to move. Sorry Taz.

A faint glow of light flicked on in the direction the dog had approached from. A door closed, and the low murmur of a man's voice carried on the wind. The signal came down the line to go prone and I slunk down into the grass.

I held my breath at the sound of a bolt being slid back and the clank of a metal gate opening. This guy was in for a bad night if he didn't fuck off back to bed sharpish. The muttering came closer and a man wearing a dishdasha came into view.

He stopped and called out sharply in Arabic. When he shuffled forward again, it was impossible he wouldn't see one or more of the eight men spread in a line in front of him. But as I prepared for the violence that appeared unavoidable, he turned and made his way back out of sight. The gate was closed and the light extinguished. If he saw us, I didn't blame him for pretending he hadn't seen a thing and getting back under the covers. In the following silence, the signal to move was issued and we continued into the night.

After we forded the river, the level of threat diminished as we neared friendly forces poised to embrace us and ready to provide support if required. The call to prayer summoned the faithful in the distance, but it was behind us as we patrolled on towards the ERV. The wind had dropped to a pleasant, cooling breeze.

As one of three special forces teams acting in concert, the idea we could be vulnerable felt absurd. However, it's the time at the end of the mission when men are tired, hungry, and tempted to switch off that can be the most dangerous. I forced myself to concentrate and hoped no-one made the mistake of getting in our way.

The night was lifting as we clambered into the Peshmerga vehicles and set off. Roper shook my hand before indicating I would be in Dara's vehicle again. In the gloom I thought he had a disappointed look on his face. He'd probably been up all night as well so I knew I shouldn't read much into it.

After passing through a Peshmerga checkpoint marking the start of friendly-controlled territory, we stopped at a large, unmarked compound. Inside the gates we were met with plates of breakfast and teapots full of chai. It felt an age since I'd eaten hot food and I stuffed down eggs, bread, and cheese and drank sweet tea, which was becoming a habit again. Roper and Greg were in deep conversation with the General and Nabil; the General looked perplexed and Nabil confused. They couldn't be told what had happened and why. I expect it was explained away as duff intel and another no-show from the bad guys.

There was still a hint of the previous day's dust storm in the air as the Black Hawk's landed at the Kurd's makeshift LZ. I'd hoped to drive back up to Suli with the General and his men, but along with Roper and the team I had to return to Balad for a debriefing. I shook hands with my Kurdish friends and thanked them for their efforts. Despite the juddering and the noise inside the helicopter, I drifted into a welcome sleep as we flew west.

★

The Factory in Balad was a hive of activity; perhaps busier now than before the mission. Katie grabbed Dexter as soon as we arrived and took him into a huddle with people I hadn't met before.

Once Katie and Dexter reappeared twenty minutes later, Roper and I joined them, Joe Holmes, and two American colonels for a debriefing. The vibe from the two officers was one of: *Well done. It didn't go quite as planned, but we had a good result.* The knowledge of what had transpired was limited to some of us from EAGLE 6, elements of the TOC, and the great and the good within intelligence, political, and military circles. With my role here finished, I'd become an interloper. I sensed misgivings that I knew the details of the 'big secret'.

Not from Joe though. When we'd finished, he shook my hand and said, 'You did a great job, John. We couldn't have asked for any more, really. Thanks.'

'I'm glad it worked out. It's not what I expected, but I understand why you guys are pleased about it. That's my bit over and done with anyway.'

Our handshake had morphed into a static grip and Joe squeezed my hand. 'You got that right. It wasn't how any of us expected it to go,' he said, shaking his head. 'But believe me when I say this outcome will lead to many more successes in the future. You can count on it.'

I gripped his hand in return. 'Pass on my thanks to all your people. Everyone's made me feel welcome, and that's come down from the top, from you. All the best for the rest of your tour.' I glanced around the TOC and the determined personnel dealing with the non-stop operations: planning, briefing, missions, debriefing. The cycle never stopped.

'Reckon I'll be touring this place until I retire,' Joe said with a grimace as he followed my glance.

'Well, good luck with everything and thanks.'

As Roper had his own last words with Joe, one of the American full-bird colonels closed on me and leaned in. 'I need to check it has been fully explained to you that any information you now possess as a result of Task Force operations is bound by the highest confidentiality classification.'

He'd fixed me with a flinty stare as he spoke. He reminded me of that twat in Amman and his 'do we have a problem' bollocks.

'Yes colonel, I'm well aware. I'm also vetted and signed up with Official Secrets and the rest. I just want to get out of here and get back on with my business you people dragged me away from.'

Roper cut in and pulled the colonel off to one side. They spoke briefly before he returned and said, 'Right, let's get going before we outstay our welcome.'

Despite the uncomfortable atmosphere emanating from some, as Katie and Dexter walked us out of the TOC, several people came over to shake hands and say goodbye.

'We should definitely meet up for a beer sometime soon,' said Dexter once we'd stepped outside.

'Yeah, I'd be up for that,' I replied. 'Any time you're in London give me a shout. Or up in Kurdistan come to think of it. I'll be back up there soon, probably in Suli again. Even Tom here hangs out there sometimes.'

Katie lifted her hand to shield her eyes from the sun and flashed that heart-melting smile. 'Try to keep yourself out of trouble. I hope we do see you again.'

'Me too,' I said, but we all knew it was unlikely.

After Dexter shook our hands, Katie gave Roper and then me a hug. A hint of delicious perfume and feminine curves reached through my weariness to stir thoughts I shouldn't be having.

'It must be the British accent,' said a familiar voice. 'Put him down, Katherine.'

Greg and the team strolled into view.

Katie fired a scornful look at the newcomers. 'Jealous are we, Gregory?'

'Hell yeah,' Greg fired back with a smirk as he reached out a big hand and grasped my shoulder. 'Now if you've quite finished, you didn't think we'd let you go without saying adios?'

'Thanks mate. You all take care, yeah.' They still had all their kit with them, so I asked, 'Out again soon?'

'We wanted to make sure we caught up with you before you left. We'll get to stand down now, but there's always another one coming up. Good luck, buddy. Stay low and watch your six.'

Roper and I mostly made a mess of bumping fists and exchanging gangland handshakes with Greg, Neil, Russ, Moose, Morgan, and Tex. Morgan said something hilarious I can't recall, but it had everyone in stitches as we parted and went our separate ways.

That afternoon we were back on a helicopter bound for Baghdad's Green Zone. Waiting transport took us from LZ Washington to overnight accommodation in a large villa inside FOB Fernandez, home to elements of US Special Operations Forces and various three-letter agencies.

After a substantial breakfast the following morning, we drove in armoured vehicles to BIAP for an onward flight to Amman. The IDP Summit had finished, after which Ali had flown to Sulaimaniyah. Although I made noises about maybe travelling up to Kurdistan to join him, Roper's insistence I return with him on the British Airways flight to London for a debrief wasn't unappealing. I didn't fancy the debrief one bit but once the thought of seeing my girls again took hold, I was sold on the idea of going home. Especially as Roper was paying for business class.

CHAPTER 50

UK – JULY 2005

For someone unused to travelling business class, the novelty put a spring in my step before, during, and after the flight from Amman to London. On arrival at Heathrow, the experience wasn't diminished as we were taken from the plane to the Hounslow Suite, one of Heathrow's hidden resources used by VIPs for relaxed and speedy arrival and departure. Once our luggage arrived and passports had been checked, a colleague of Roper's directed us to a black Jaguar before whisking us towards Central London.

For some reason I imagined we'd be going to the ostentatious MI6 headquarters next to Vauxhall Bridge. As I'd tried to doze off on the flight, ridiculous images of a champagne reception on the upper floors overlooking the Thames and the nearby Houses of Parliament had sneaked into my head.

After twenty-four hours of reflection since the drama at the farm and subsequent debriefings, I had converted to the view it had all been a roaring success, with all thoughts of failure discarded. If Joe Holmes and the rest of TF145 believed a great result had been achieved, then who was I to argue? I was brought back down to earth a little when we pulled up outside a nondescript building in London's Mayfair.

Chapman was all smiles and excited energy; a man clearly pleased with himself.

'Well done, Pierce. We knew you wouldn't let us down. The Americans are thankful for our help, if a little embarrassed it was due to us that their new star was revealed to be moonlighting as the Shadow Emir.'

There was an uncharacteristic twinkle in his eye and a cold smile at the edge of his lips.

I was a bit nonplussed. 'Of course. I was happy to help.'

'We still need to go through a debriefing, so we have the full picture of course. We may be allies with the Americans, but there's nothing like the words of a man who was there, at the centre of things.' He must have noticed the look on my face because he added, 'Don't worry, we'll get this wrapped up quickly and you can get home to your family.'

It was already late afternoon, so I doubted I'd be home until deep into the evening, but I felt an unexpected reluctance for this adventure to be over. Although I wanted to get back to concentrating on my business efforts, now my involvement in this clandestine world was drawing to a close I realised I'd miss it.

'We also need to bottom off a couple of legal points. Charles here will fill you in with the details. Suffice to say you are now in possession of information that is classified at the highest tier of Top Secret. I don't mean to dampen the mood, but any revealing of this information now or in the future will result in your prosecution. I'm sure I don't need to stress how badly any unfortunate revelations of that type could go for you. Anyway, enough of that. Tea? Coffee?'

I didn't rate it as much of a pep talk. Still, it was almost reassuring that underneath his unnatural bonhomie, there still lurked a ruthless agent of the establishment. It snapped me out of my temporary sense of security and reminded me these people gave no real thought to my personal welfare or wellbeing. I needed to forget any romantic notion of helping Queen and country and make sure they didn't screw me somehow at the last knockings.

It was eight-thirty by the time I signed yet another set of confidentiality papers. The straightforward debriefing about the events in Iraq had been completed twenty minutes earlier and folders were being shut, pens capped, and laptops returned to their bags.

Chapman stood and offered his hand.

'One last thing. Although this concludes your involvement with us, you do appear to operate in countries and regions where information about various situational aspects is valued. This might be goodbye today, but we expect a cordial welcome should we ever need to approach you again.'

I met his gaze. The question that had been on my mind all evening popped out.

'The customs case, the Basra letter, these things are all finished with now, yes? What you're asking is for me to keep an open mind about something that might happen in the future, not a…' – I was cautious to use the word – '…threat hanging over me?'

He answered evenly, as though the question had been expected. 'As I've made clear in previous conversations, there have never been any threats. There are simply actions that you have taken, and which can have consequences. I can't undo those actions you've taken, but I can tell you my understanding is both of those issues have been laid to rest.'

I smiled and shook his hand. It really was all over.

'Thank you, Mr Chapman. If my help is required in the future, then of course I'll be happy to talk to you.' I wasn't sure if I meant it, but I couldn't really tell him to stick his cordial welcome up his arse.

★

Becky was asleep in bed when I got home just after 10.00pm, but Claire and Natalie were awake and watching TV in the living room. Taz whined with joy trying to get my attention as I hugged the girls after setting my bags down. The dog's wet nose on my hand prompted a twinge of guilt. I banished it and concentrated on the moment. I hadn't picked up any wounds this time, so as far as Claire knew I'd simply returned from the Amman conference as planned.

'How did it go?' she asked.

I looked into her smiling eyes and thought of the conference and the mission.

'It was good. A couple of issues needed to be sorted out, but I think we're all set now. Oh, and some interest from a British outfit. I need to call Ali in the morning and check how that's going. Probably arrange to meet with them here in London soon.'

'It sounds hopeful,' said Claire. She then glanced at Natalie, who had returned to watching the TV, smiled and whispered, 'I've got some news for you later.'

She laughed as I frowned.

'Okay. Later it is then.'

★

Claire looked me in the eyes. 'I'm just going to come right out and say it. I'm pregnant.'

There'd been plenty of surprises over the last twelve months, but that topped the lot. Even as I processed the information, a grin broke out on my face.

'That's… amazing. Is it mine?'

'You bastard.'

Claire laughed as she grabbed a pillow and hit me with it. I'd made the same joke when she'd announced her other two pregnancies in years gone by.

It wasn't a complete shock. Natalie had complained regularly about being an only child until Becky had been born. When we'd made up in March after my return from Mosul, Claire and I had agreed to leave it to fate to determine whether we had a third child, a sibling who would be in the same age range as Becky. Fate must have reacted immediately because the new baby was due in December.

★

Three days later, on 7th July, London was struck by a series of bomb attacks by al-Qaeda, quickly dubbed the 7/7 attacks. I was working

341

from home, eating toast and drinking coffee, as the news of the strikes against Tube trains and a London bus filled the TV channels. Despite the carnage, I couldn't help but smile when my phone buzzed with messages from Kurdistan to check I was okay. Before long Ali rang and told me I needed to return to the safety of Sulaimaniyah.

CHAPTER 51

SULAIMANIYAH

LATE DECEMBER 2005

I signed the consultancy contract with the British firm in the autumn, even though they'd baulked at paying upfront fees. Instead, I'd only earn any money if we managed to secure them a deal in Kurdistan. Not the type of contract I preferred by any stretch, and I'd turned all previous similar offers down, but something tangible at least.

A week before Christmas, Claire had reached the final stages of pregnancy – we hadn't thought that through very well. My intention had been to return to the UK in early December for the run-up to the festivities. However, the Asayish (Kurdish security service) scheduled an inspection of our office at the Salim Building late in the month, necessary to complete the branch company registration.

The timing was a pain, but worse I'd run out of cash to furnish and equip the office. Bank transfers to Iraq weren't yet possible and I could hardly ask Claire to waddle up to a Hawallah office in Central London with an envelope full of cash to send over.

Ali got creative though. The company in the suite next door agreed to lend us their office for the morning. We had just finished switching the door numbers and adorning the walls and desks with our company logo and cheap, locally-printed brochures when the Asayish arrived. After a cursory examination and a social chat that lasted three glasses of chai and a discussion about tipping the commander the wink when we had a 'sure thing' investment for his family savings, we finally closed the door and laughed at getting away with it.

'Have we got time to make the flight?'

Ali checked his watch. 'Plenty of time.'

I took that with a pinch of salt, although fortunately the officials at the fledgling Sulaimaniyah Airport were far more relaxed about passengers turning up at the last minute than I'd ever experienced elsewhere.

'Come on, let's get going then. I was there when Natalie and Becky were born, so I need to be there this time.'

We removed our signage, switched the numbers back on the office doors, and flew down the stairs where one of Ali's brothers waited to drive us to the airport. Four days before Christmas and neither of us had tickets booked for the afternoon flight, but we already had our gear in the car and pockets full of dinars and I intended to blag my way onto the flight one way or another. Claire wouldn't make a big deal about it, but I knew she really wanted me there for the birth. Just maybe not as much as I wanted to be there with her.

CHAPTER 52

EPSOM GENERAL HOSPITAL, UK

23 DECEMBER 2005

Claire woke me in the early morning, calmly instructed me to take her to the hospital, and checked the contents of her night bag as I scrambled to get dressed. Pregnancy number three meant we were old hands at this game and we made our way up to the labour ward in good spirits. After a short and sweet labour – no doubt shorter and sweeter for me because I wasn't pushing a baby out of my nether regions – we had a new addition to the Pierce family.

'Congratulations, you have a healthy baby girl,' said the nurse, handing the quiet bundle to Claire after the checks for fingers, toes, and obvious abnormalities.

Claire nuzzled the baby's head then turned to me with a proud smile. 'Say hello to Daisy.'

Together with Natalie, we'd all agreed on provisional names for a boy or girl in advance, depending on how things panned out.

As I held Daisy for the first time, the love surged through me and another unbreakable bond locked into place. She looked serene, almost doll-like, and beautiful.

It took me back seventeen years to when Natalie was born; she too arrived with a quiet beauty. Our more recent experience three years ago saw a bawling, red, and angry-looking Becky arrive in the middle of the night. At the time I'd joked she resembled Winston Churchill, but now Becky had grown into a pretty little girl with long blonde hair and a third birthday looming. Amid the happiness, it weighed on me that I now had three beautiful daughters and a tired wife I needed to provide for.

Twenty minutes later I checked my watch: 08:35. I took a deep breath and stood up.

'I really need to get going to a meeting in London with the clients. I was going to cancel but seeing as everything's okay…'

The nurse shot me a dark look before she turned towards the bed. 'Are you going to let him leave like that?'

Claire glanced up with a tired smile. 'It's fine. He needs to go, and my mum will be here soon.'

The nurse didn't attempt to hide her obvious disapproval as I put my jacket on and then held Claire's hand. We kissed and hugged briefly before I bent down to kiss Daisy's tiny, perfect cheek.

'Good luck,' whispered Claire, before adding with more enthusiasm, 'this time next year, eh…'

'Yep, this time next year.'

I flashed a determined smile, told Claire I loved her, and headed out the door.